NEW DIRECTIONS IN PSYCHOLOGY

ROGER BROWN
HARVARD UNIVERSITY

EUGENE GALANTER
UNIVERSITY OF WASHINGTON

ECKHARD H. HESS
THE UNIVERSITY OF CHICAGO

GEORGE MANDLER
UNIVERSITY OF CALIFORNIA, SAN DIEGO, CALIFORNIA

NEW DIRECTIONS
IN PSYCHOLOGY I

✤ *Models of Attitude Change*

✤ *Contemporary Psychophysics*

✤ *Ethology: An Approach toward the Complete Analysis of Behavior*

✤ *Emotion*

FOREWORD BY THEODORE M. NEWCOMB

Holt, Rinehart and Winston
New York • Chicago • San Francisco
Toronto • London

2114908

FOREWORD

Psychology, as Galileo is said to have remarked about the planet Earth, does move. But its course is less predictable than that of *orbis terrarum;* some of its many fronts move now rapidly, now at a modest, walking pace, while others seem barely to hold their own. The present venture attempts to plot some of the movements.

Professional psychologists have their journals; within the United States alone some dozens of them are family members or close relatives. The American Psychological Association's *Psychological Abstracts* can direct the sophisticated inquirer just where to go to find just what, and its monthly *Contemporary Psychology* reviews most of the important new books. The *Annual Review of Psychology* provides condensed, encylopedic overviews of important developments of the past year in each of a dozen or more areas of psychology. Such are the resources that professional psychologists provide for one another. For our students and apprentices we have no dearth of textbooks, handbooks, and volumes of selected readings, but the informed instructor—and, sometimes, even the alert student—knows about the publication lag that is compounded of multiple delays, first in the journals and then in the textbooks. Occasionally the student-apprentice, along with the scientifically oriented nonpsychologist, can titillate his appetite for "what's news in psychology" from the pages of *The Scientific American.* What none of these sources has yet managed to do is to present to the student or layman an account, fresh and informed but not highly technical, of recent contributions to a few problem-areas that lie somewhere between "the science of psychology" and "the change from trichromatic to dichromatic vision in the human retina."

Four of us—including Mr. Alan Turner, of Holt, Rinehart

and Winston, and Professors Donald Marquis and Roger Brown, of the Massachusetts Institute of Technology—began to plan *New Directions in Psychology* in 1959. The rest of us were able to persuade Dr. Brown, after our planning was well along, to put on his author's hat; with him available, why should we seek elsewhere for a lucid account of recently emerging models of attitude change? And for exactly the same reasons we have asked Professors Eugene Galanter, Eckhard H. Hess, and George Mandler to portray some recently developing themes about old problems that are conventionally known, respectively, by the labels of psychophysics, ethology, and emotion. Each of the four contributions was written in 1961. They are not only still warm; they are authoritative and they are readable. The students for whom they are primarily written might do well to call them to the attention both of their teachers and of their wives.

ANN ARBOR, MICHIGAN   THEODORE M. NEWCOMB
MARCH 1962

⊕ CONTENTS

1 ✣ MODELS OF ATTITUDE CHANGE

ROGER BROWN
HARVARD UNIVERSITY

FOR CRITICAL READING OF THE MANUSCRIPT I AM GRATEFUL TO MY COLLABORATORS IN THIS VOLUME AND ALSO LEON FESTINGER, THEODORE NEWCOMB, CHARLES OSGOOD, AND EDGAR SCHEIN.

In architecture a model is a miniature—reduced in size but preserving certain characteristics of the original. The general advantage of every sort of model is that it can be manipulated more easily than the original objects or events. With a model of a housing development an architect can try out various arrangements—shifting a housing unit from one side of a miniature park to another—and these small-scale experiments indicate to the architect the outcome of large-scale experiments that cannot easily be performed.

A model house, like any sort of model, resembles its original only up to a point; it may preserve the shape and relative size of the elements, but the construction material is likely to be balsa instead of brick, and walls may be joined by glue. In general one undertakes to preserve in a model those characteristics that will make it possible to predict for the original the kinds of outcomes that interest us. For a housing development these outcomes may be the relative amounts of space that different structures will occupy, the shapes of space into which structures will fit, and the façades that will confront one another. It is by not preserving such characteristics as absolute size and weight and construction material that we make the model handier—more manipulable—than the original.

A model of a house usually has no moving parts, but a model of attitude *change* will necessarily have moving parts. For this reason our models will be more like model trains or model planes than like a house. The electric train preserves certain dynamic characteristics of the steam locomotive—the power

of the engine is transmitted to the linked cars in a similar way—
but the source of power is not the same. A successful model
of attitude change will preserve something of the direction and
degree and durability of attitude change in human beings, but
it will not be powered by oxidation and it will not be constructed of protoplasm.

It is the plan of this essay to begin by describing a fairly rich
example of the kind of human behavior for which a model is
to be provided. Then one model—the congruity model—will
be explained in full detail. We will test this model against our
intuition and against experimental results to discover its virtues
and shortcomings. Then we will examine two alternative
models that operate with the same general and powerful principle as the first but at several points make crucially different
assumptions.

THE NORTON-SILVERS PROBLEM

The distinguished drama critic of the *Boston Record*, Mr.
Elliott Norton, conducts a weekly television program during
the theater season on which he interviews stars of shows appearing in Boston. A large number of new productions have
their pre-Broadway tryouts in Boston and one of these, in the
winter of 1960, was the musical *Do Re Mi*, which starred Phil
Silvers. Mr. Norton interviewed Mr. Silvers on one of his programs and the interview generated a quality of personal tension
that is very seldom encountered on television.

Elliott Norton is a forthright critic. He had written a very
unenthusiastic notice of *Do Re Mi* in advance of the television
interview and, at the start of the interview, he said quite un-
mistakably that he did not think much of the show. Mr. Silvers,
on the other hand, thought very highly of the show and, in any
case, was bound to it by contract. A simple disagreement between two persons is not uncommon on television; there are

numerous Sunday afternoon discussions that confront one party-line Democrat with one party-line Republican over one partisan issue. The result is a conflict between persons but not a conflict within persons. And somehow we know that in this situation neither participant will change his opinion nor even feel any strong pressure in the direction of change. The special discomfort produced by the Norton-Silvers conversation is in part derived from the fact that there was internal or intrapersonal conflict for each participant and this sort of conflict creates a force toward attitude change. In addition, however, the participants were prevented from discharging this tension by making the usual kinds of attitude adjustment because they were operating within a set of social constraints that proscribed such adjustments. The result was fifteen minutes of very hard psychological work for the main figures and also for the sympathetic viewer.

The protagonists of our little drama began by expressing great admiration for one another: Phil Silvers was in Elliott Norton's opinion one of our great comedians; Elliott Norton was in Phil Silvers' opinion a dean of the American theater. In these circumstances it was very disagreeable for Mr. Silvers to know that Mr. Norton disliked the show, and it was very disagreeable for Mr. Norton to find Mr. Silvers appearing in such a show. In the more usual Republican vs. Democrat set-to each participant has an advance low opinion of the political position of his opponent and expects to find that opponent espousing views he himself rejects. There is a battle between the two on familiar lines but no serious division of mind within either man.

It seems to be a general law of human thought that we expect people we like and respect to associate themselves with ideas we like and respect and to dissociate themselves or disagree with ideas from which we dissociate ourselves. These latter disapproved ideas we expect to find espoused by the wicked and the stupid—those we do not like or respect. The "goods" in the world in the way of persons, things, and ideas are supposed to clump together and oppose the "bads," who are expected to form their own clump. This is the way the world ought to go, and as long as things work this way nothing much happens to our attitudes. But when a new girl friend dislikes our favorite music or an admired professor ridicules our religious beliefs or an esteemed critic attacks a play in which we are appearing, the mind starts working.

It is time to make a first try at modeling the Norton-Silvers problem. This first try will not be identical with any of the three detailed models which are later to be described, though it will be similar to all of them. The idea is to give ourselves some experience in the game of abstracting from a complicated social interaction what we hope are the essentials.

The first abstraction is an enormous simplification which throws away all sorts of detail from the original; it is like deciding to use a blob of blue ink to represent Lake Superior on a map of the United States. We shall represent the situation in each of the two minds by a simple drawing (Fig. 1) in which

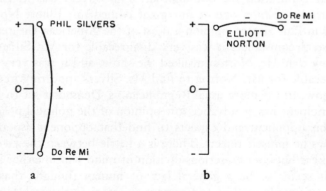

Fig. 1. The Norton-Silvers problem: (a) The mind of Elliot Norton; (b) The mind of Phil Silvers

the names of persons and things appear on vertical lines from + through 0 to −. The idea is that to have an attitude is to be either for or against something; that the essence of attitude is a value scale on which persons, objects, ideas—the contents of a mind—can be placed. For things that can be evaluated we shall use the term *cognitive objects*. We assume that the important objects in Mr. Norton's mind are Phil Silvers and *Do Re Mi;* the former is good (hence at a + position) and the latter bad (hence at a − position). For Mr. Silvers the important cognitive objects are Mr. Norton and *Do Re Mi*, and both are good.

So far our model comprises a generalized attitude scale and cognitive objects placed on such a scale. There is one remaining class of formal element—the bond or link between valued cognitive objects. Bonds are represented in Figure 1 as curved lines linking objects, and labelled either + or −. The + bond in Mr. Norton's mind is intended to represent the fact that Mr. Silvers and *Do Re Mi* are known to be associated; in a way Phil Silvers is contained in *Do Re Mi*. The − bond in Mr. Silvers' mind is intended to represent the fact that Mr. Norton has criticized *Do Re Mi*, has withheld his approval from the show; these two are dissociated. In general, associative or + bonds between objects exist in a mind when the two objects are known to like one another or to be bound together, and dissociative or − bonds exist when there is dislike or withdrawal. At this point the model is a static picture of a situation. It remains to set the parts in motion.

The parts will not move so long as the picture satisfies what we shall regard as an equilibrium condition, and they will move when this condition is not satisfied. This conception of a psychological equilibrium is the great common property of this first trial model and of the three more serious versions that will later be described. We have already suggested its nature. The human mind expects good things to cluster together and to be opposed to the cluster of bad things. In terms of the model this means that positively valued objects should be linked by associative bonds and, similarly, negatively valued objects should be linked by associative bonds. Between positively valued objects and negatively valued objects there should be only dissociative bonds. If these conditions are satisfied, all is well with the world and there is no need to change one's mind about anything.

If you look now at the Norton-Silvers problem of Figure 1, you will see that it does not represent a state of equilibrium. For Elliott Norton there is an associative bond between something good (Phil Silvers) and something bad (*Do Re Mi*). For Phil Silvers there is a dissociative bond between two things that are good (Elliott Norton and *Do Re Mi*). Disequilibrium, we shall assume, sets up a tension or force toward the restoration of equilibrium, and so there must be such a force in both of the minds with which we are concerned. By what means can equilibrium be restored? Primarily by changing the scale positions of objects or the signs of the bonds linking them, and that means—to return from the model to life—changing attitudes between the persons or toward the show.

There are three simple resolutions possible for the Norton-Silvers problem. If Norton would change his mind and like the show, that alone would eliminate the tension; or, alternatively, if Silvers would agree that the show is no good, that would do it; or, finally, the men might give up thinking well of one another and then their disagreement on the show would not represent a disequilibrium. Each of these conceivable changes would alter just one element in each mind: the position of an object or the sign of a bond. Such an alteration of a single element is what we mean by a *simple* resolution. More complicated resolutions, which we shall not describe (though you may find it interesting to work them out), can be attained by shifting more than one element at a time.

Let us look more closely at the simple resolutions to see just how each would serve to restore equilibrium. Figures 2a and 2a′ represent the actual disequilibrium conditions that constitute the problem. Notice that the one figure requires the other. If there is a + bond between Silvers and *Do Re Mi* in Norton's mind, then it follows that *Do Re Mi* must be positively valued in Silvers' mind. Similarly, the dissociative bond in Silvers' mind between Norton and *Do Re Mi* requires that *Do Re Mi* have a

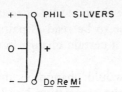

a. The original problem —
    Norton's Mind

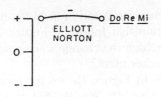

a'. Silvers' mind

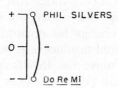

b. Silvers Changes his opinion
of *Do Re Mi*—Norton's mind

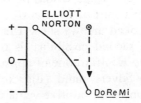

b'. Silvers' mind

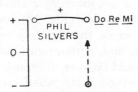

c. Norton changes his opinion
of *Do Re Mi*—Norton's mind

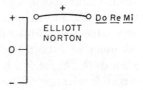

c'. Silver's mind

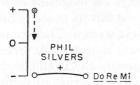

d. Norton and Silvers change
their opinions of one another
—Norton's mind

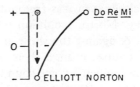

d'. Silvers' mind

Fig. 2. Simple resolutions of the Norton-Silvers problem

negative position in Norton's mind. The three modes of resolution that follow in Figure 2 are likewise to be read as pairs in which the change in one mind requires a certain change in the other mind.

In Figure 2b we see that if Silvers would change his mind about *Do Re Mi* that would change the associative bond in Norton's mind to a dissociative bond and so restore equilibrium. That change would be represented in Silvers' mind (Fig. 2b′) by a shift of *Do Re Mi* to a negative position. Notice that the broken arrows show the paths of change for valued objects. A second possibility is for Norton to change his opinion of *Do Re Mi* to one of approval, which would produce a + bond in Silvers' mind (Fig. 2c′) and would move *Do Re Mi* to a consonant positive value in Norton's mind (Fig. 2c). Thus far we have equilibrium restored by one of the two participants changing his opinion of the show. A third possibility is for the two gentlemen to change their opinions of one another. Elliott Norton could decide that Phil Silvers is not much of a comedian, after all, and drop him to a negative value (Fig. 2d) and, at the same time, Phil Silvers could decide that he does not think much of Elliott Norton as a critic and, without changing the bonds to *Do Re Mi*, both minds would be in equilibrium.

Attitude change of one sort or another is the usual consequence of the kind of disequilibrium we have described, but in the present instance a peculiarly restrictive set of conditions forced the participants to find their way to another solution. Neither man was free publicly to change his judgment of the play. Norton's opinion was in print, and Silvers could hardly speak against the show in which he was starred. They could, of course, change their opinions of one another and, several times, when a voice sounded testy, I thought this would be the outcome. But the two were face-to-face, and so if one turned antagonistic he could expect the other to do the same. Each time this resolution seemed imminent they turned away from it and renewed their vows of mutual esteem. There was a kind of social contract not to use mutual denigration. The constraints all derive from the fact that this was a public encounter. The various attitude changes that could not be revealed on television may have occurred in their secret thoughts. Perhaps one or the other began to think less highly of the other. On the covert level there may well have been a resolution different from the one the viewer saw.

It was Phil Silvers who hit on an acceptable public solution, He recollected that conditions backstage had been hectic during the opening-night performance. During an important scene a sandbag overhead had begun to leak down on him, and he had feared it would fall. This kind of thing had seriously thrown off his own performance, and, in addition, the show had been in fairly rough shape. Numerous scenes and songs had been shuffled or rewritten since opening night. In fact, Phil Silvers

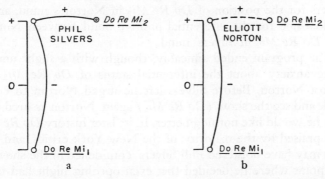

Fig. 3. Resolution of the Norton-Silvers problem by differentiation of *Do Re Mi:* (a) The Mind of Elliot Norton; (b) The mind of Phil Silvers

found that he had to agree with Elliott Norton that the show Norton had seen on opening night was not very good. It deserved to be panned. But the show which Silvers must necessarily praise was *Do Re Mi* as it was now constituted and as it

would be on Broadway. Norton could not very well have a
poor opinion of that *Do Re Mi* because he had not seen it.
There was no disequilibrium in the fact that a great comedian
liked one show and a great critic disliked another show.

This very satisfactory solution can be abstractly described as
an agreement to differentiate the original global *Do Re Mi* into
*Do Re Mi*₁ (opening-night performance) and *Do Re Mi*₂ (the
show at present). Figure 3 shows one of several ways in which
the differentiation answer can be pictured. Elliott Norton sees
the admired Phil Silvers as dissociated from the not-admired
*Do Re Mi*₁. This much is certain: that Silvers is associatively
linked with *Do Re Mi*₂, which Norton has not seen but might
conceivably admire. Norton's opinion of *Do Re Mi*₂ is not
known, but if equilibrium prevails it will be positive. The fact
that *Do Re Mi*₂'s placement in Norton's mind is inferential
is indicated in Figure 3 by using a double circle and italicized
letters for the position of *Do Re Mi*₂ in Norton's mind, and a
broken line for the inferential positive bond between Norton
and *Do Re Mi*₂ in Silvers' mind.

The program ended amicably, though with a slight underlying anxiety about the inferential status of *Do Re Mi*₂ for
Elliott Norton. Before Silvers left he urged Norton to come
back and see the show (*Do Re Mi*₂) again. Norton assured him
that he would like nothing better. In its later history *Do Re Mi*₂
was praised by the majority of the New York critics, and this
fact may have bolstered Phil Silvers' confidence in the show to
the point where he decided that even opening night had been
good. Elliott Norton, he may have concluded, was not much
of a critic; or he may have been more generous and differentiated Mr. Norton into an astute critic of the drama and
a bad judge of musicals. The New York reviews probably
caused Mr. Norton to differentiate among New York re-
viewers; it was not the discerning critics who liked the show.

It has happened more than once that Elliott Norton has disliked the vehicle of an admired star, and I have several times

seen the participants find their way to the differentiation answer. Once, however, it failed. Miriam Hopkins, trying hard to understand how a critic of Elliott Norton's stature could dislike her show, introduced the fact that another admired Boston critic had seen and liked the same opening night performance. Thereby she made things difficult. In order to differentiate, a generic object must be divided into subvarieties along a line that accounts for the inconsistencies of evaluation The chronological line separating the past performance seen by the critic from the future performances in which the star must appear obviously recommends itself. But by bringing into the problem two admired critics, both present on opening night, Miss Hopkins excluded the usual solution.

However, before the fifteen minute program finished, Miss Hopkins hit upon another basis for differentiation. With sudden inspiration she asked, "Which side of the house were you sitting on?" "The right side," answered Mr. Norton. "I thought so. This whole show is played to the left. You were getting my back the whole evening and the other critic, my face." Unluckily, Miss Hopkins had neglected to allow for the fact that what is called the "right" side of the house from in front is the "left" from the stage and, too late, it dawned on the participants that it was Mr. Norton who had been getting the expressive half of Miss Hopkins. As the program ended, two white, strained faces showed what disequilibrium feels like.

The three models of attitude change to be described in the remainder of this essay differ among themselves on numerous points, but are agreed that it is disequilibrium that initiates change and that the change generally operates in the direction of equilibrium restoration. The models have different names for their conditions of equilibrium and disequilibrium. In the first case we have congruity-incongruity (Osgood and Tannenbaum, 1955); in the second case consonance-dissonance (Festinger, 1957); in the third case balance-imbalance (Abelson and Rosenberg, 1958). We shall identify the three models

by the respective titles: congruity, dissonance, and balance, and
this is also the order of description.[1]

 THE CONGRUITY MODEL[2]

We begin with a now-familiar assumption: that attitudes in
a particular mind can be represented by a vertical line from
+ to − with the names of the objects of attitudes ranged along
this line. The drawing of Figure 4 is simpler than previous
drawings because we are dealing with just one mind at a time.
The scale of Figure 4 has, however, quantitative aspirations, and
so there are numbers along the line. I have placed the names of
some attitude objects on this line so that we may operate with
concrete examples. This lineup of valued objects represents
one sort of mind common at the time of the 1960 presidential

[1] The credit for originating the line of thought developed in all three
models unequivocally belongs to Fritz Heider (1944, 1946, 1958). Cartwright and Harary (1956) and Harary (1959) generalized Heider's
balance theory to a greater range of empirical cases and also resolved
several ambiguities in the theory by utilizing as their formal model the
mathematical theory of linear graphs. Newcomb (1953) has made very
fruitful use of Heider's notions of balance in an analysis of communicative acts. The three models described in the present essay were
selected because of the interesting empirical work they have inspired and
because they include all the major variations on the idea of balance.

[2] The congruity model was developed in connection with the work of
Charles Osgood, George Suci, and Percy Tannenbaum on a measure of
connotative meaning (1957). Using factor analytic methods, these
authors have demonstrated that the three major dimensions of meaning
are evaluation, potency, and activity. The first dimension—evaluation—
they have equated with the concept of attitude. The congruity model is
thought to have very general application to problems of cognitive interaction as well as particular application to attitude change. The full
theoretical and empirical context of this model is of great interest, but
it need not be described here since we are focusing on attitude change.

election. The objects valued and their placement are not, of course, a part of the model. Its operations are the same whatever the objects scaled and however they are placed.

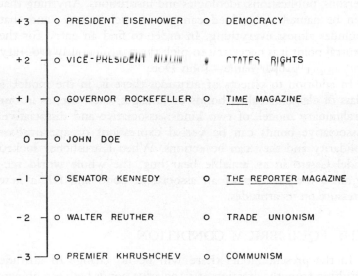

Fig. 4 A congruity scale with illustrative cognitive objects

In social psychology the theory of attitude scaling is a relatively sophisticated development. The standard methods for developing scales—the methods of Thurstone, Guttman, Likert, and Coombs—all begin with concrete statements concerning an attitude object (the Negro, the Church, Communism, and so on) and elaborate techniques for ordering such statements. The congruity model bypasses all this sophistication of measurement and offers a generalized attitude scale that is content-free, a line from −3 to +3, on which any object whatsoever can be placed. In support of their use of a general evaluation scale the authors of the congruity model (Osgood and Tannenbaum, 1955) report that scores on such a scale correlate with scores on Thurstone attitude scales toward The Church, The Negro, and Capital Punishment with the values .74, .82, and .81.

The illustrative objects of Figure 4 are a mixed lot, including persons, publications, ideologies and institutions. Anything that can be named and valued can go on such a scale, and that includes almost everything. In order to find an entry for the neutral point it is necessary to pick the conspicuously arbitrary and empty proper name—John Doe.

In addition to objects of attitudes there is, in the model, a class of elements called bonds or linkages; these are, as in our preliminary model, of two kinds: associative and dissociative. Associative bonds can be verbal expressions of approval or solidarity and they can be actions. When Khrushchev locked Fidel Castro in an amiable bear hug, the whole world recognized the creation of an associative bond and felt a new pressure on its attitudes.

THE EQUILIBRIUM CONDITION

In the present model there will be no change of attitude resulting from the creation of associative bonds between objects at the same scale position. If Eisenhower praises democracy, nothing happens; if Khrushchev praises Communism, nothing happens. There will also be no change of attitude resulting from dissociative bonds between objects occupying mirror-image positions, i.e., in positions tagged with the same number but with opposite signs. If Khrushchev (−3) denounces Eisenhower (+3), or if Eisenhower (+3) attacks Communism (−3), nothing changes in the mind we are describing. Pairs of this kind can be unambiguously described as occupying positions that are equally polarized (i.e., having numerical positions equally remote from zero) but of opposite sign.

The equilibrium conditions for this model are more narrowly defined than in our provisional model. In the latter case we called it an equilibrium if there were associative bonds between two positive objects or two negative objects—without regard to the degree of polarization—and it was also an equilibrium if any positive was dissociatively linked with any negative. The congruity model says that some associations between positives (such as Eisenhower [+3] with States Rights [+2]), some associations between negatives (such as Senator Kennedy [−1] and Mr. Reuther [−2]), and some dissociations between objects of unlike sign (Mr. Nixon [+2] and Mr. Kennedy [−1]) do not constitute equilibria and will produce attitude change. We cannot now say which of these assumptions is the better reflection of reality, but it is worth noting that making a model compels us to make some explicit assumption and to raise an empirical question of general significance.

CHANGE FROM ASSOCIATIVE BONDS

The occurrence of any associative and dissociative bonds other than those defining equilibria creates forces toward attitude change. Let us consider first an associative bond between Mr. Nixon and Mr. Rockefeller: Suppose the two gentlemen were to have a friendly private talk. This is not an equilibrium bond since the objects have different values. It would be an equilibrium bond under either of two hypothetical conditions: If Mr. Nixon were to stay where he is and Mr. Rockefeller were to be moved to that same +2 position or if Mr. Rockefeller were to stay where he is and Mr. Nixon were to be moved to that same +1 position. These hypothetical positions of equilibrium are indicated on Figure 5 by double circles and italicized letters. In the present model the forces of attitude change are always toward re-establishment of equilibrium. This would seem to mean movement toward the hypothetical positions. But how much and by which object?

In this model we assume that the total force toward change, the total scale distance to be traveled, is equal to the difference between the actual scale position of either object and its hypothetical position of equilibrium. This value is necessarily always the same for the two objects and, in the present case,

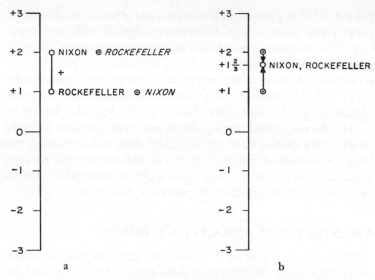

Fig. 5. The effect of a slightly incongruous association bond:
(a) Original positions and hypothetical positions-of-
equilibrium; (b) The new equilibrium

is one unit. Which object will travel the distance? At this point
the congruity model makes some assumptions which intuition
says are sound and yet, we think, are not obvious. The assumption is that both objects associated will be subjected to forces
of change, but the more extremely polarized object (the one
having the higher number and so farther from zero) will feel
the lesser force. In general, it is assumed that the total scale
distance to be traveled (one unit in our example) will be
divided between the objects in inverse proportion to their
respective polarizations.

Think of the one unit to be traveled in our example as
divided into thirds. Mr. Nixon is more polarized than Mr.
Rockefeller; they are at the positions +2 and +1 respectively.
Mr. Rockefeller, who will absorb the greater force, must move
two of the three thirds of a unit to be covered and Mr. Nixon,

just one of the three thirds. This brings the two men to the same position, $+1\frac{2}{3}$, where the associative bond that links them is congruous and so equilibrium is restored and the mind comes to rest.

It seems to us that in everyday "folk psychology" we think of the effect of an associative verbal bond (for example, one man speaks well of another) as the setting up of a single force— a force on the person spoken about. The object of the assertion is usually assumed to absorb the full force of the change. However, in extreme cases, we recognize that a verbal bond can also affect the speaker. If, for instance, Mr. Kennedy had, in his presidential campaign, spoken favorably of either Castro or Khrushchev, the recoil force of the bond would have been very great. Castro or Khrushchev would have improved his standing somewhat in some American minds, but Mr. Kennedy would have damaged his own standing greatly.

In calculating the persuasive effects of various assertions we make, most of us reckon with a single force: the one we intend to create, the one that acts on the object spoken about. The congruity model makes a different assumption, a less obvious but probably superior assumption that bonds affect both participants in the bond.

In assuming that the amount of change in the value of an object is inversely proportional to the extremity of its initial value, the model incorporates a principle that is backed by some research (Birch, 1945; Klapper, 1949) as well as intuition. Extreme attitudes are less easily changed than moderate attitudes. There is in this simple mechanical model an inertia factor which increases as you move out on the scale. In the special case where one object is at the neutral point (John Doe in Figure 4), the model assumes that this least polarized object will absorb the full force of the pressures to change, and so if Mr. Nixon were to praise John Doe, the latter would move all the way up to $+2$. This may seem to predict a stronger effect than one would find in fact, but that is a question of the adequacy with which the model represents reality, and we had best suspend this kind of question until we are more thoroughly familiar with the formal machinery itself.

In order to acquire some facility in handling the model, here are a few additional examples of change. If *Time* magazine were to praise Mr. Reuther, then the two would move towards one another across the three scale units that separate them. *Time*, being less polarized, would move two of those units (2 being the value of Mr. Reuther), and Mr. Reuther would move one unit (1 being the position of *Time*), and the two would reach equilibrium at -1. If, as in a previous example, Mr. Kennedy were to praise Mr. Khrushchev, then Kennedy would move three parts of the distance (3 being Khrushchev's scale position), and Khrushchev would move one part of the distance (1 being Kennedy's scale position). Since there are two scale units separating the objects, it is handy to think of these units as four halves, and then Kennedy would fall three halves to $-2\frac{1}{2}$ and Khrushchev would rise one half to the same position, thus restoring equilibrium. If a great national hero such as President Eisenhower ($+3$) were to associate himself with anything less ideal than peace and democracy (both $+3$), his value would be diminished in the mind we are imagining. Mr. Khrushchev, on the other hand, can associate very freely as far as this mind is concerned, since most objects are more highly valued than is he. Mr. Eisenhower does seem to have taken a rather "gingerly" approach to association as compared with Premier Khrushchev's "nothing-to-lose" expressiveness during his visit in America.

CHANGE FROM DISSOCIATIVE BONDS

The general principles governing change from dissociation are the same as those governing change from association, but it takes some practice to see how they are applied. As a working example let us suppose that Mr. Reuther has criticized ($-$) Mr. Rockefeller. It is easiest to begin by locating hypothetical positions of congruity. Since dissociative bonds are in equilibrium when they link objects of equal polarization and opposite sign, it follows that there would be an equilibrium if Rockefeller were at +2 with Reuther steady at −2, or if Reuther were at −1 with Rockefeller steady at +1. Movement will be towards equilibrium, which means the dissociation will elevate Rockefeller (for this mind) and also elevate Reuther. There is considerable surprise in this prediction, but let us hold off considering whether the prediction is sensible until the mechanics are clear.

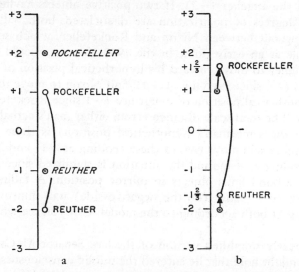

Fig. 6. The effect of a slightly incongruous dissociative bond: (a) Original positions and hypothetical positions-of-equilibrium; (b) The new equilibrium

With dissociation as with association both objects will be subjected to forces of change, and the strength of the force will be inversely proportional to the polarization. In the present case, then, Rockefeller should move more than Reuther. The scale distance to be traversed is, as with an associative bond, the difference between either object's actual position and its hypothetical equilibrium position—in this example one unit. That unit will be divided in the ratio of two parts to Rockefeller (Reuther's position is 2) and one part to Reuther (Rockefeller's position is 1). This brings Rockefeller to $+1\frac{2}{3}$ and Reuther to $-1\frac{2}{3}$; in which positions the dissociative bond is congruous.

Again let us acquire facility. When one object to the bond is at the neutral position (John Doe) and the other object is polarized (such as Mr. Nixon), the neutral object absorbs the full force of the attack and moves to the mirror-image position of the attacker (-2). If two positive objects having different degrees of polarization are dissociated, both will lose. A falling-out between Nixon and Rockefeller, which seemed probable at an early point in the 1960 election, would cause Rockefeller to move toward his hypothetical position of equilibrium (-2 since Nixon is at $+2$), and Nixon to move toward his hypothetical position of congruity (-1 since Rockefeller is at $+1$). The total scale distance (from either man's actual position to the same man's hypothetical position) is three units. Rockefeller will move two of these (ending at -1) and Nixon one (ending at $+1$), and the situation is stabilized since a dissociative bond links objects in mirror position. A falling out between two "bads" (on the negative side) will improve the standing of both according to the model. Can you see why this is so?

A greatly simplified version of the late Senator McCarthy's career might hold that he entered the public consciousness near the neutral position, and by persistently and fiercely dissociating himself from the -3 of Communists-in-Government, boosted himself to a positively valued mirror-image position. Once there, his dissociative bonds were greatly feared by figures not so popular as he, since they would tend to reflect these men into negative positions—until, of course, Senator McCarthy attacked persons and institutions more positively valued than himself—General George Marshall and the U. S. Army. These dissociations started him on a descending course, and as he passed others it became expedient for them to join the attack.

We have now reviewed the basic operations of the model. The parts begin to move when there is an associative bond between objects not identically valued or a dissociative bond between objects not in mirror-image positions. Both members of the bond experience forces toward change, but the size of the individual force is inversely proportional to the extremity of the object's polarization. The parts stop moving when the objects arrive at new positions of equilibrium. To these basic assumptions the authors add a pair of special corrections, and these are next to be described.

THE CORRECTION FOR INCREDULITY

Probably the most widely known technique of persuasion (or of propaganda) is prestige suggestion. The idea is that someone's attitude toward an object can be made more favorable by telling him that a person or institution of high prestige thinks favorably of the critical object. Prestige suggestion appears in the congruity model as the case in which an object of lesser value is positively linked with an object of greater value. There have been many experimental demonstrations of prestige suggestion and one of these (Helen Block Lewis, 1941) turned up a result that illustrates the need for an incredulity correction in the congruity model.

Dr. Lewis worked with a set of ten political slogans ("America First," "Balance the Budget," "Share the Wealth," and so on) and with the names of three politically prominent men: Franklin D. Roosevelt, Herbert Hoover, and the then General Secretary of the Communist Party of the U.S.A., Earl Browder. Some of the subjects in the experiments were Republicans, some Democrats, and some Communists. One set of subjects evaluated the slogans themselves in terms of such variables as "social significance," "approval," "author's intelligence," and the like.

Another set of subjects (matched with the first in terms of political affiliations) evaluated the slogans after having been told how the same slogans had been evaluated by Roosevelt, Hoover, or Browder. The latter evaluations were made up on various patterns of probability and improbability. A Communist reading that Earl Browder had a high opinion of the slogan "Workers of the World, Unite!" would not be disturbed in his views, but a Communist (or a Republican for that matter) who was told that Herbert Hoover had approved the same slogan might experience some surprise. For our present purpose the important point about the results of the experiment is that some subjects—not a great many—refused to believe that such unlikely endorsements were genuine. Presented with a very improbable picture of Earl Browder's judgments, one girl said indignantly, "Do you really expect me to believe that these are Browder's rankings?"

This reaction of incredulity supports our general assumption that people expect associative bonds (such as endorsement) between objects of like value. When such bonds link objects of unlike value the congruity model predicts attitude change. Where the discrepancy is very great (Earl Browder at -3 and "America First!" at $+3$), an associative bond should bring both objects to the neutral point. In fact, however, the model as described blows a fuse. The subject refuses to believe in the associative bond and there is no attitude change. In terms of our illustrative array of valued objects in Figure 4 it is as if we were told that Eisenhower had come out in favor of Communism. Our reaction might very well be, "Who are you trying to kid?"

Osgood and Tannenbaum incorporate in their model a correction for incredulity that serves to "damp" or reduce the change that would be predicted by the unmodified basic rules. As the authors have arranged things, this damping effect reaches its maximum when the departure from equilibrium is at a maximum, in other words, an associative bond between a $+3$ and a -3 or a dissociative bond between either two $+3$'s or two −3's. The corrected model says in fact that people will not shift their attitudes if you tell them that Eisenhower favors Communism, or that Hoover applauds the sentiment, "Workers of the World, Unite," or that Eisenhower disapproves of democracy. They will not change because they will not believe you. At maximal incongruity, then, disbelief is supposed to wash out attitude change. What will it do when incongruity is less extreme?

Since congruity represents the expected way of the world, it seems reasonable to suppose that disbelief or incredulity will increase as incongruity increases, but Osgood and Tannenbaum confess that their notion of the exact form of this function is a pure hunch. They propose that there will be no incredulity so long as both objects in an associative bond are of the same sign; no incredulity for Nixon favoring Rockefeller or Rockefeller favoring Nixon even though these various positives have different scale values. For dissociative bonds there will be no incredulity if the two objects are of unlike sign; any + can attack any − without raising suspicions. There will also be no incredulity if either object in a bond is a neutral one. In all the remaining cases—associations between objects of unlike sign, dissociations between objects of like sign—there will be some incredulity. The incredulity correction is always subtracted from the change that would otherwise be predicted. It is a positively accelerated function, that is to say it grows larger at an increasing rate as the incongruity rises, and ultimately, as we have seen, equals and so cancels out the force toward change.

THE ASSERTION CONSTANT

In describing the basic rules of operation, we counted it a special virtue that the model represents associative and dissociative bonds as forces changing attitudes toward both members of the bond, and not simply as a force on the object talked about. It seemed to us that this representation was

superior to the everyday assumption that only the thing talked
about, the thing approved or condemned, is affected. But
perhaps we were too quick to reject everyday opinion, or perhaps I was alone in rejecting it and you disagreed with me at
this point.

Suppose that Kennedy praises Reuther or that Reuther
praises Kennedy. What would really happen here? The model,
as far as we have described it, says that these events are the
same and that the changes would be identical. But would they
be? Does it make no difference whether an object is the source
of the praise or the object of the praise? Common sense says
that it does make a difference. The everyday view is right, we
think, in suggesting that the object of the bond will be *more*
affected than the source of the bond. However, the model as
we have described it seems to us to be right in suggesting that
both will be somewhat affected. Probably the best position to
take is a compromise one: there will be forces on both participants in the bond, but there will be, other things equal, a
somewhat greater force on the object. If Reuther is praised by
Kennedy, Reuther should experience more change of value
than if he (Reuther) praises Kennedy.

Once again Osgood and Tannenbaum are ahead of us. The
full model incorporates a correction along the lines suggested
above. The assertion constant is a value added to the change
that would otherwise be predicted for the object of praise or
blame. The constant is of the same sign as the predicted change
and the authors set it at ±.17 of a scale unit on the 7-point value
scale. This figure was suggested by some results obtained in
the authors' major empirical test of their model (Tannenbaum,
1953).

EVALUATION OF THE CONGRUITY MODEL

There are three dimensions to the quality of a model. The
first of these is the clarity and economy of the formal structure
in itself and without reference to the external world. Is it clear

what causes the parts of the model to move, how much and in what direction they move, and when they stop moving? Is it possible to predict many different outcomes by means of a few general principles? The model we are considering handles both associative and dissociative events with the same principles of incongruity and relative polarization, and the operations are unambiguous, so we think the formal properties are clear and impressively economical.

Since a model is intended to represent something outside itself, it must tell us how its parts and operations correspond to parts and operations in the real world. The rules for moving back and forth between a model and reality are called rules of correspondence. The formal elements of the present model are objects that can be evaluated and bonds (of two sorts) between objects. The objects of the model can apparently correspond to persons, groups, offices, countries, ideologies, or concepts—any nameable mental content. Associative bonds are statements or actions which suggest that one object approves of another or is associated with another. Either of the statements "Catholics favor John Kennedy" or "John Kennedy is a Catholic" constitutes an associative bond, as would also a photograph of John Kennedy shaking hands with Cardinal Cushing or a photograph of John Kennedy attending Holy Mass. Dissociative bonds are statements or actions implying disapproval or detachment.

The rules of correspondence in the congruity model are usually adequate, we find, for mapping empirical events into the model, but since the rules are not completely explicit, cases of doubt do sometimes arise. One might wonder, for instance, whether the handshake described above links Kennedy with Cushing alone or, more broadly, Kennedy with the Church of which Cushing is a representative. Or suppose that when Mr. Eisenhower was President some reporter had asked him in a press conference what he thought about John Kennedy and he answered, "No comment." Are these technically neutral words not a bond of any sort or are they a dissociation? Given the full context we would usually know; but not invariably.

There is a third aspect to the evaluation of a model, and this is usually the critical one. Once the formal elements and operations are coordinated with empirical counterparts, one can use the handy model to generate any number of predictions about the course of events in the world. These predictions must be checked against real outcomes, and if the predictions are regularly confirmed, our confidence in the model will increase; we will begin to believe that it can really be used as a kind of paper and pencil substitute for the complicated operations of influence and persuasion. The goodness of fit between a model and reality can be estimated from ordinary observation or from controlled experiments. The latter is the superior procedure, and we will review a major experimental test of the model. But first a few remarks based on unsystematic observation.

Change in the model depends on whether a bond is associative or dissociative, on the relative polarization of the members, on the credibility of the linkage, and is greater for the object of an assertion than it is for the source. What else is likely to matter? There is no provision for variation of intensity in a bond. A denunciation is the same as a mild disapproval; adulation is no different from a slightly favorable remark. Probably the amount of change resulting from a bond is responsive to the intensity of the bond, but the model does not say so.

With the small correction of the Assertion Constant, the model recognizes that it makes a difference which of the two members of a bond is the source. However, in certain cases our intuition says that this is insufficient recognition. Imagine the effect in a Republican mind of an associative bond between Mr. Eisenhower at +3 and John Doe at neutrality. It seems obvious that it will make a great difference whether Eisenhower lauds Doe or Doe lauds Eisenhower. Without the Assertion Constant the model treats these events as identical and predicts that Doe, being least polarized, will move up to +3, whereas Eisenhower will stay where he is. It is certainly right in saying that Doe will be the one chiefly affected, and if

Eisenhower is the source of the approval, perhaps Doe will move very high. But can the model be correct when it says that if Doe praises Eisenhower he can, at one stroke, make himself into a hero of comparable stature in this Republican mind?[3] Obviously not. Great popularity is not so easily won.

The Assertion Constant does say that Doe will not rise quite so high when he is the source of the bond as when he is the object and Eisenhower the source. However, a difference of .17 scale unit is far too small and probably the effect is due to something other than the difference between being an object and a subject. Intuitively it would seem that the difference has something to do with the fact that many people express approval of Eisenhower whereas Eisenhower expresses approval of relatively few people. The improbability of being singled out for praise from above seems to account for the power of the bond in one direction, and the probability of praise from below for its weakness in the other direction.

The changes predicted by the present model are all movements toward congruity. This means that the model does not allow for the actual resolution of the Norton-Silvers problem which took the form of differentiating *Do Re Mi* into "opening night performance" and "the show as now constituted." Of course there were some fairly special constraints in the Norton-Silvers problem: a public appearance, a previously published review, a contract to star in the show. These constraints were of the sort to prevent resolutions by change toward congruity, in which one of the participants would revise his opinion of *Do Re Mi* or both would revise their opinions of one another. However, differentiation is a common response to pressures of incongruity even when no special constraints operate.

At M.I.T., for example, there are a good many seriously

---

[3] In a private communication Osgood has suggested to me that exposure to a combination of this kind would have to be thought of as a single trial not producing the full effect, but with additional trials there would be increments in attitude change following some negatively accelerated function.

religious students. Their scientific education eventually teaches them some things that do not accord with Bible accounts. The student may find that the theory of natural selection and of the evolution of species makes very good sense of an enormous array of facts, and so he may value highly this scientific generalization. However, it appears to be in flat contradiction (dissociation) with the account given in Genesis of the simultaneous creation of the species. The differentiation resolution of this and a large number of related dilemmas is to distinguish between a "literal" Bible and a "figurative" Bible (Abelson, 1959). Science conflicts with the literal Bible, but an educated religious man does not take the Bible literally; he acknowledges that the literal reading is untenable and that it is the figurative, interpreted Bible that a man reveres.

There are other widely shared differentiations. We may like the whole population of the United States in its political voting role but dislike it for the sort of entertainment it supports on television and radio, and so we differentiate the "people" who are the electorate from the "masses" who are TV-viewers. America has "popular government" but "mass media." Another example results from the fact that many people have found it necessary and even desirable to tell some lies while disapproving of lying. We have, therefore, the phrase "little white lies" or the word "fibbing" to distinguish what we do from what we disapprove.

The congruity model makes no provision for differentiation as a reaction to incongruity nor, indeed, for any reaction except attitude change that re-establishes congruity. Ordinary observation suggests that the possibilities are more numerous than this.

A TEST OF THE CONGRUITY MODEL

For his doctoral dissertation Tannenbaum (1953) carried out a test of the congruity model. He used an experimental design that has long been popular in the field of attitude change: the Before-After design. There is an initial assessment of attitudes, subsequent communications for experimental subjects, and no communication for control subjects, with a second assessment of attitudes for all subjects. In general, this design has been used to determine the relative effectiveness for changing attitudes of different kinds of communications, for example, an "emotional" appeal, a "reasoned" appeal, and no communication at all. The congruity model predicts that the effect of communications that make evaluative assertions will vary with initial attitudes toward the sources of the assertions and toward the concepts evaluated.

The experiment was concerned with six cognitive objects: Labor Leaders, *Chicago Tribune*, Senator Robert Taft, Legalized Gambling, Abstract Art, and Accelerated College Programs. The first three functioned as sources of opinions and the last three as objects of opinions. Subjects first evaluated all six objects on 7-point scales,[4] then were exposed to communications linking some of the sources and concepts, and finally evaluated the six objects once again.

Only three source-concept pairs were used in constructing communications: Labor Leaders-Legalized Gambling; *Chicago Tribune*-Abstract Art; Senator Robert Taft-Accelerated College Programs. These pairs were selected because preliminary testing showed that people had no clear advance opinion as to whether bonds between these pairs would be associative (approval) or dissociative (disapproval). It was desirable that there be no established bonds between the critical pairs because the experimenter wanted to devise communications making both sorts of bond for all pairs.

[4] There is a complication about the method by which Tannenbaum measured evaluation. The objects were not simply placed on a single 7-point Good-Bad scale, but rather the evaluation procedure required the subject to scale an object on each of six scales labeled with such evaluative terms (in addition to Good-Bad) as: Fair-Unfair, Worthless-Valuable, Pleasant-Unpleasant. The evaluation score for an object was actually the sum of a subject's six ratings. The use of six scales to represent the evaluative dimension is founded in the work of Osgood, Suci, and Tannenbaum (1957) with the Semantic Differential.

Five weeks after the initial assessment of attitudes toward unbonded sources and concepts, subjects were exposed to "highly realistic newspaper stories" which included assertions linking the members of the three pairs. There were 405 subjects, students of elementary psychology participating in small classroom groups. Each group read a favorable newspaper story for one of the three pairs, an unfavorable story for a second pair; and, for the final pair, had no story at all. Immediately after reading the stories, subjects were asked to rate, for a second time, the six individual sources and concepts.

Tannenbaum does not analyze his data in such a way as to check the model's quantitative prediction for each individual subject and attitude. The analysis is in terms of large groups of subjects, and it permits only a very general test of the major assumptions of the model. The method for grouping subjects follows; it is applicable to any source-concept pair. Subjects had various numerical evaluations of the source, but these quantitative variations were collapsed into three categories: subjects favoring the source (S^+); subjects feeling neutral toward the source (S^0); and subjects antagonistic to the source (S^-). The same sort of categorization was made with respect to attitudes toward the concept. Since each subject would necessarily have attitudes toward both source and concept, there was a final set of nine categories, formed by making all (3×3) combinations of source and concept attitudes $(S^+C^+, S^+C^0, S^+C^-, S^0C^+,$ and so on).

When such a nine-way categorization of subjects was made for each source-concept pair, the investigator found that the results did not change from one pair to another, and so he combined the data across all three. The problem then was to work out the interacting effects of prior attitudes to source and concept and of associative and dissociative assertions on attitude change.

The baseline condition is that in which no news stories were presented—the neutral or control cases. In these cases there was a period of five weeks between the first and second assessments with no interpolated relevant communication. Whatever the subjects' initial attitudes to sources and concepts, there was, under these conditions, no significant change.

The congruity model predicts, in a general way, that evaluation of concepts will rise when associative bonds are created with highly valued sources, whereas the evaluation should fall when associative bonds are created with disliked sources. Dissociative bonds, on the other hand, should result in a rise for the concept when the source is disliked and a fall when the source is admired. The general directions of change were in accordance with these predictions.

Since both source and concept are objects of evaluation in the congruity model, the predictions for change of attitude toward sources with favorable and unfavorable assertions are the same as the predictions for concepts. In this case, too, the prevailing directions of change agreed with the model. The distinction between source and concept has only one consequence in the model: other things equal, the concept is expected to undergo more change. In Tannenbaum's results this was almost invariably the case, and the size of the Assertion Constant was actually fixed on the basis of these results.

The congruity model also holds that susceptibility to attitude change should be inversely proportional to the polarization or extremity of the attitude. With a few minor exceptions it is true of Tannenbaum's results that the amount of attitude change falls off with the degree of polarization in the original attitude.

The Before-After design always threatens to give away the experimenter's purpose, and knowledge of this purpose can affect the subjects' behavior in some way that will make it unrepresentative of usual human behavior. For this reason the experimenter usually provides some kind of "cover story" to disguise his purpose, and this was done by Tannenbaum. He writes: "There is good reason to assume that this attempt to 'cloak' the aim of the study was successful. There were no cases of suspicion noted among the subjects, and even the class

instructors seemed convinced" (1953, p. 417). Despite this re-
assurance, we do not feel great confidence in such "cloaks"
and at a later point we will consider alternative research
strategies.

The general assumptions of the congruity model have been
confirmed by experiment, but the arithmetical details have not.
The general rules, without the numbers, seem to have a very
wide range of application. They form the sort of productive
intellectual system that causes anyone to reconstrue large portions of his experience and may cause a psychologist to reconstrue some of his own findings. Before undertaking the study
of a second model, let us savor a little of this theoretical
productivity.

CONGRUITY IN ADVERTISING AND SALESMANSHIP

Efforts to sell a product are sometimes messages in the mass
media and sometimes messages in face-to-face conversation.
The fact that a potential buyer can send messages to his would-
be persuader in the second case but cannot in the first case
makes a difference to the strategy of persuasion. Both strategies,
however, fall within the domain of congruity theory.

In advertising—a sales message delivered by a mass medium
—the most general principle is to link the product with some
person or thing highly valued by the consumer and by this
means to cause the consumer to think highly enough of the
product to buy it. Prestige suggestion is simply a subvariety
of the more general technique of value association. In an
earlier, more innocent era advertisers paid ballplayers to en-
dorse Wheaties, or aristocratic beauties to credit their com-
plexions to Pond's face cream. The associative bond, in terms
of the model, had to be paid for. After a time the word got
round among consumers that money was changing hands and
a certain amount of incredulity set in. This is an incredulity

which the model does not predict since it does not arise from extreme incongruity.

Nowadays advertisers do not often trouble to suborn real nobility or real athletes since their goal can be more effectively accomplished by using anonymous models—who are incidentally not very expensive—and bonds of physical association rather than verbal endorsement. There are models who look more like English lords and ladies than do real lords and ladies, and if the advertiser poses them with his product in rich surroundings, some positive value will accrue to the product. Since the advertisement uses no real names and makes no explicit assertions, it disarms our incredulity and accomplishes its effect.

When people are living well above the subsistence level—when food, drink, transportation and shelter are all adequate—they begin to be interested in buying expressive symbols. A desirable symbol is any product that will suggest that its owner is the kind of person he wants to be—rich, virile, devil-may-care, thoughtful, youthful, cultivated or what-you-will. One can make a product into a desirable symbol by placing the product in an appropriately suggestive setting and spending a lot of money to expose the result to a lot of people.

Consider the famous series of *New Yorker* ads for Hathaway shirts. The medium guarantees a sizeable readership with a taste for elegance and sophistication. Each advertisement pictures the same very distinguished looking chap wearing a distinctive black eye patch and occupied with spending conspicuous leisure—yachting, playing polo, sipping sherry in the library. And wearing a Hathaway shirt. The implicit premise may be teased out as *any man who wears a Hathaway shirt is rich, glamorous, cultivated, and distinguished*. Presumably it can be taken for granted that the reader would like to feel that these adjectives apply to himself, and they will apply if he will buy. There is a small difficulty in that Hathaway shirts are not readily recognizable if you cannot read the label. For this reason Countess Mara puts her name on her expensive neckties. Probably, however, a man can enjoy sending himself a symoblic message and feeling enhanced in value as he puts on his Hathaway. Of course, a really smart consumer would leave the expensive Hathaways in the store and buy a black eye patch.

We have never been convinced that there is anything immoral about this kind of selling. Outraged parties sometimes point out that the greater part of the cost of producing such products as perfumes and face creams—and maybe Hathaways—is the advertising cost. But then it is the advertising that creates the symbol, and it is the symbol, not the chemicals or cotton, that the consumer is buying. It seems to us that he gets what he pays for, and we should not expect a symbol-using animal to be interested in nothing but food and drink.

Quite recently the Viceroy Cigarette campaign called *The Man Who Thinks for Himself* has provided a *reductio ad absurdum* of the value-association technique. The many ads trying to get people to buy a product in order "to project an attractive image" have generated a certain revulsion against this sort of external orientation. This fact, in conjunction with a lively contemporary literature attacking conformism and "other direction" have combined to make independence of mind once again a positive value for Americans. Even among businessmen it is common to hear, "X is a little offbeat, but that's all in his favor." And so an advertiser undertook to persuade people that his product would enable them to project the value which has become important as a reaction against the appeals of advertising.

A characteristic ad pictures a man with firm jaws and steady gaze smoking a Viceroy. This is coupled with a text that reads in part, "This man thinks for himself. Knows the difference between fact and fancy. Trusts judgment, not opinion." The implicit logic *if the reader doesn't want to appear to be the sort of weak-minded dupe who is taken in by Other-Directed advertising, let him smoke the cigarette smoked by people who are not susceptible to such advertising (according to such an advertisment*). I have heard that this was not a very successful advertising campaign, and I like to believe that it is so.

The whole path from simple endorsement to buying what others buy in order to feel independent stays within the range of the congruity model. There have been changes in what people value and changes in the credibility of different sorts of bond which the model does not predict and was not designed to predict. Behind the changes is the enduring law that associative bonds which are believed, linking object A to an object of higher value, will enhance the value of A.

In face-to-face salesmanship there is two-way communication, and this makes possible a persuasion technique that is not possible in the mass media. Suppose that a young woman comes into a furniture store intending to buy a sofa and is captured by salesman John Doe who appears on her evaluative scale at zero. A blundering salesman might immediately express strongly favorable judgments of various high-priced sofas. These sofas, by virtue of their prices and perhaps also their appearances, are likely to have negative values for the customer, and weightless John Doe (since the zero position has no inertia) would by his associative bonds move himself down to join the sofas on the negative side.

A more skillful salesman will not at once reveal his own preferences but will allow his customer to look over the possibilities and to express her taste. When she likes something, he will hasten to agree, and the positive bond will draw him toward the valued sofa; when she criticizes, he will hasten to agree, and the dissociation from the ugly sofa will boost him to a mirror-image position. When he has established himself as a man of good taste (when he is safely perched high on the positive side), he can venture some esteem capital by speaking out for a sofa whose costliness renders it mildly negative for the customer and hope to draw that sofa sufficiently high on the value scale to bring it across the purchase threshold.

Of course, there is more to the salesman's technique than the model indicates. Probably his expressions of agreement with a customer's taste, after that taste has been expressed, are somewhat suspect because of their obvious instrumentality. If he has an alert mind and if his customer's enthusiasms follow some rule, he will abstract the dimensions governing her approval-reaction and project ahead to a sofa just around the corner. A woman who favors warm primary colors, lavish ornament, and rich materials is sure to admire "a beautiful red velvet love seat I'd like you to see." Such advance associative bonds probably should be credited with more power than after-the-fact bonds if a model were to be designed for this particular problem.

The salesmanship technique described above can be generalized as a technique of persuasion by reaction. One person (the persuader) expresses an attitude toward some object, and that object is therefore placed on the familiar vertical scale. The persuader is himself an evaluated object in the mind of the one to be persuaded. Bonds of association, then, are reactions of agreement or approval from the persuader that follow the other person's expressions of attitude, and bonds of dissociation are reactions of disagreement. With these rules of correspondence we see that a neutral persuader (John Doe) can, indeed, enhance his own value by agreeing with the judgments of the other person, but this is only one of many possible effects. If the persuader occupies a positive position, he may be able to raise the other person's evaluation of something by selective reaction to evaluative assertions. If the persuader occupies a more negative position than the attitude object, his endorsement of favorable statements will only further depress the object.

Although there are no experiments that collect all the data the model calls for, there are several that illustrate a part of it. Hildum and Brown (1956) administered in Cambridge a lengthy questionnaire concerning attitudes toward the general education program at Harvard. The questions were asked and the answers were given on the telephone. The experimenters found that by selectively interpolating the reaction "Good" they could cause respondents to shift the direction of their answers, in the course of the interview, toward either a more favorable or a more unfavorable opinion. If we assume that the interviewer had a little more positive value than the distinctly indifferent topic of general education, then this was attitude change (on the verbal level at least) produced by an associative bond. Ekman (1958) has accomplished a similar effect with attitudes toward capital punishment.

Both the study of Hildum and Brown and that of Ekman have been considered experiments demonstrating operant conditioning of a verbal response. The studies in this tradition (and there are more than 100 of them) have heretofore been conceptualized by analogy with the training of an animal to emit some response by causing food or, more generally, "reinforcement" to be delivered to the animal following the response. Most of the published studies report successful conditioning, and we suspect that this may be because most of the experimenters in these studies have been faculty members, whereas the subjects who endured them were generally students. This would suggest that the experimenter usually had enough value in the student's mind for his associative bonds to increase the value and frequency of the kind of assertion approved. It is important to note that several investigators (Mausner, 1955; Verplanck, 1955) have found that the more admired of their experimenters were more effective in changing behavior. In some of the unpublished experiments of which we have heard, where the operant response either did not increase or even decreased, the reacting person may have occupied a less favorable position than the assertions he approved. Mandler and Kaplan (1956) have obtained results which show that the effect of an experimenter's selective reaction depends on whether the reaction is thought to be approving (associative) or disapproving (dissociative). Each subject was asked, as a test of the "total available vocabulary of college students," to say all the words he could think of without repeating any.

In the "reinforcing" period the experimenter said "Mm-hmm" after each plural noun response and only after such a response. Afterwards subjects were asked what they had thought about this "Mm-hmm." Those subjects who thought that the interjection meant they were doing all right produced more plural nouns than those subjects who thought the "Mm-hmm" expressed disapproval. This difference in outcome is to be expected if the experimenter's approval reaction is taken to be an associative bond and his disapproval a dissociative bond. It would be very worthwhile in the "verbal conditioning" work to forget about the analogy with animal training and collect the sort of data that an animal cannot provide—before and after evaluations of the reacting person, the meanings of his reactions, and the kinds of assertions that will elicit reactions. We suspect that the verbal operant experiment would open out to reveal the full range of effects predicted by congruity theory.

CONGRUITY IN SOCIAL RELATIONSHIPS

The persuasive efforts of advertisers and salesmen are the kind of things the congruity model was designed to cover. However, the model is also helpful in some areas of social psychology that are remote from the situations of attitude change Osgood and Tannenbaum had in mind. One of these areas is the psychology of two-person groups or social dyads.

A dyad is created whenever one person is introduced to another. In time the members of a dyad become increasingly close or intimate. From such formal address as *Mr. X* and *Mr. Y* they may advance to the use of first names and later perhaps to very familiar nicknames. From the infrequent and accidental contacts of a nodding acquaintance they may progress to invitations to dinner, willingness to lend one another money, and the heart-to-heart talks of firm friends. Advances in intimacy—more familiar address, invitations, frank personal talk—can be coordinated with the associative bonds of the congruity model, and lapses from intimacy—a distant formal tone, refusing an invitation, failing to telephone—can be coordinated with dissociative bonds.

In every society a major determinant of the intimacy of interaction in a dyad is the relative status of the two members. Status is something one possesses in the degree that he is characterized by attributes valued by a given society. Some characteristics that are valued in a great many societies are being of adult age, being male, being a member of some dominant racial or religious group, being of royal, noble, or distinguished lineage, being wealthy, belonging to an honored profession, holding high office. It seems usually to be the case that members of a society can agree fairly well in ranking one another in terms of several different kinds of status, and also in terms of a generalized status which seems to be a position derived in some complex fashion from individual status components. This generalized status can be coordinated with the generalized value scale of the congruity model, and persons become the evaluated objects of the model.

The congruity model is a model of individual cognition, and so it must be asked whose mind we are representing when we map social status and social actions. We could map in this way any one person's conception of the relative status positions of the members of a dyad and the consequences for these positions of any interaction involving the members. The mind being mapped could belong to someone who is himself a member of the dyad, but it need not. Because there is a high degree of consensus on many status rankings and also on the effect of certain kinds of interaction, a representation for one mind may very possibly hold true for all minds in a given society that have knowledge of the persons and events in question. Matters on which there is a very high degree of consensus are often thought of as real or objective, and so there may be a tendency to think that we are now describing a reality outside of anybody's cognition. However, this is not the case. Social value and meanings of intimacy and withdrawal are psychological. In the present case we are describing psychological meanings that are very widely shared within a society—in fact are a part of that society's culture—but they remain psychological meanings, not objective facts.

When relative status is coordinated with value positions, acts of intimacy with associative bonds, and acts of withdrawal with dissociative bonds, the model yields a set of predictions about dyadic behavior that seem to work out very well. An associative bond (such as an invitation to dinner) between objects of unequal value (such as myself and the President of M.I.T.) should cause the two objects to move toward positions of congruity, the less polarized (me) moving more. This is to say, I would experience a large gain in status from such an experience, and the President, a small loss. It suggests very generally that the member of a dyad who has less status should be motivated to increase the intimacy of interaction, since he stands to gain, whereas the person of higher status should be motivated to resist such intimacy.

The prediction is obviously sound as far as the lesser member is concerned. One can see these forces in pure form at large gatherings of professional groups. Professional standing is the major component of generalized status in America and in all large industrial Western societies. If we look about us at a convention of the American Medical Association, or even the American Psychoanalytic Society, we will see our model working. Wherever there is a conversational dyad of unbalanced status, note the intense interest and absorption of the lesser member and the slightly abstracted air and wandering gaze of the greater member. The greater man scans the throng in quest of an acquaintance whose status is still greater than his own. The lesser does what he can to hold attention.

The other half of the model's prediction—that a person of higher status will lose something by association with an inferior—is not clearly correct. Does the President of M.I.T. lose anything by having dinner with a young faculty member? Probably not. Would President Kennedy lose anything by doing a kindness to a person of humble station? Probably not. Still there are circumstances in which the prediction seems to be right. Dinner with James Hoffa, for example, could damage the standing of a popular figure. Perhaps the model should be modified for this problem so that the more polarized positive figure suffers no loss from association with less polarized positive figures, but does lose from association with figures across the neutral line and into negative territory. In other words, lesser degrees of positive status in an associate are not damaging, but any amount of ill fame is.

The large professional convention displays the rather ugly psychology of status parasitism in bold form because it provides occasions (such as "Social Hours") when persons of unequal status are expected to mix freely and where it is quite acceptable for a man of lower status to initiate conversation with a man of higher status. In ordinary life, however, members of different social strata maintain a certain distance, and the initiation of associative bonds across strata follows a definite protocol. The protocol says that it is the person of higher status who has the right to make the first move in the direction of increased intimacy. The employer calls his employee by first name before the latter has the right to reciprocate; the employer can more easily suggest that he and his wife attend the theater with the employee and wife; the employer can more easily borrow a lawn mower, or five dollars, or a pocket comb. By studying the rules of address in the languages of Europe and India and in Japanese, Brown and Gilman (1960) have found evidence suggesting that intimacy initiated from above is everywhere considered to be correct social behavior. This (possibly universal) norm is surprising in view of our analysis in terms of the congruity model, since the norm requires that the person having nothing to gain from an association be the one to initiate it if it is to be initiated.

We must grudgingly acknowledge at this point that there are more reasons for establishing friendships than pure status parasitism. Shared interests, propinquity, common friends, re-

mote ties of kinship, and Christmas cheer may provide reasons
for the establishment of some intimacy across status levels.
When such a reason exists, the initiative can be very confidently
taken by the superior for the reason that the subordinate is unlikely ever to reject the advance. For the subordinate there is
added to whatever other motives may exist the possibility of
status enhancement. He should always be the more willing of
the two to become friendly and so, if the less willing is prepared
to initiate, the compliance of the subordinate can be taken for
granted. The general practice of initiation from above will
serve to minimize social rebuffs or dissociative bonds in interaction across status levels. What may this mean in terms of the
model?

Dissociative bonds between positively valued objects will,
the model says, invariably cause both objects to decline in
value. Going all the way back to Figure 4, note that a social
rebuff between Eisenhower and Rockefeller would (if there
were complete credulity) move Eisenhower down one step to
+2 and Rockefeller down three steps to −2. There is nothing
in it for either of them. Dissociations are a peculiarly unrewarding sort of bond. It can be argued then that the courtesy norms
of societies are nicely designed to prevent the occurrence of
this most unrewarding outcome. At large gatherings where
different statuses are supposed to mix, a society foregoes its
usual precaution and runs the risk of rebuffs in order to gain
the excitement of free initiation. This may be why gatherings
of this kind are particularly exciting but also particularly disturbing to men in junior positions.

 THE DISSONANCE MODEL

Both the congruity model and dissonance theory (Festinger,
1957) describe conditions which cause the human organism to
think or take overt action, and so both are in the general
sphere of motivational processes. The vital needs for nutrients,

water, and oxygen, which are the motivational processes that have been most thoroughly studied, produce two kinds of effect in the animal organism. They set off automatic and internal restorative actions called homeostatic processes, and they create drive states that cause the organism to take goal-directed action in the external world. Perhaps the most fundamental difference between the congruity model and dissonance theory is the fact that the former is essentially a homeostatic mechanism and the latter essentially a drive state.

The great concept of physiological homeostasis (Cannon, 1932) reveals the systematic nature of the body's internal regulative actions. Our living cells exist in an internal fluid environment that is fed and drained by the circulating blood. In order to sustain life, this environment must maintain a "steady state" (homeostasis) with regard to temperature, oxygen and carbon dioxide concentration, blood sugar, and so on. The living cells are very nicely adapted to this steady state, and marked departures from it would cause them to die. When the environment starts to fall off from its steady state— for example, when the concentration of blood sugar declines— there are automatic internal processes that operate to restore the proper level. In the case of blood sugar, glycogen stored in the liver is released; if it is temperature that falls off, the blood vessels near the surface of the body constrict so as to reduce heat loss to the atmosphere. If the concentration in the blood of carbon dioxide becomes too great, then nerve endings in the carotid sinus stimulate the musculature so as to produce more vigorous breathing, which causes the concentration of carbon dioxide to fall. Restorative actions of this kind are turned on by a departure from equilibrium and turned off by a return to equilibrium.

A manufactured homeostatic mechanism, familiar to every-one, is the room thermostat. If the desired temperature is 70° and the thermostat is set to maintain this temperature, then the heat goes on when the room cools below this level and it goes off when the heat has raised the temperature to 70°.

The modern high-speed digital computer follows programs

that involve testing for a particular critical condition, and, if that condition does not maintain, processes are initiated which will bring it about. The machine advances to a next stage when the condition is satisfied. Miller, Galanter, and Pribram (1960) have suggested that this sort of homeostatic mechanism is the general model for goal-directed behavior and for purposive thinking.

The congruity model is a homeostatic mechanism. Departure from the steady state of congruity initiates a completely determined and automatic value change. If we leave out the corrections for incredulity and the Assertion Constant, then the basic rules prescribe that the value change will continue until congruity is restored. The two corrections modify this conclusion, but the basic model is clearly homeostatic.

The vital biological needs create drive states that lead to action in the external world, as well as the completely internal homeostatic adjustments. A drive such as hunger causes an animal to engage in food-seeking behavior that, if it is successful, will result in the ingestion of nutrients. The form of this food-seeking behavior is not completely determined by the drive, but depends on past learning and accidental circumstances. Nor does the behavior necessarily result in reduction of the drive; there may be no food to be found. Drives lead to a variety of actions that are bound together by the fact that they have a common direction. Festinger's dissonance theory (1957), we shall see, is a theory of drive rather than of homeostasis. Festinger's human animal seeks to reduce cognitive dissonance by one or another of a varied set of instrumental actions; neither the elimination nor even the reduction of dissonance is guaranteed.

The elements in Festinger's theory are items of knowledge—beliefs, information, opinions, and attitudes. Items frequently used in Festinger's examples are the pair "Smoking is harmful" and "I smoke" and the pair "I like my new car" and "My new car gets very bad mileage to the gallon." In general, his elements seem to be propositions or assertions rather than, as in congruity theory, objects that can be evaluated. When a Festinger element is a simple pro-or-con assertion ("Smoking is harmful") it translates most naturally into the congruity model as a single evaluated object (smoking placed at -2). When the assertion links two objects with evaluations easily guessed ("My new car gets very low mileage to the gallon"), it translates most naturally as two evaluated objects with a bond between them ("My new car" at $+3$ and "low mileage" at -3 with an associative bond between them). These translations are best guesses, but they serve to show that the two theories are working in the same general sphere.

The conditions of equilibrium (consonance) and departure from equilibrium (dissonance) are defined more broadly and more loosely than in the congruity model. Any two cognitive elements in a single mind may be irrelevant to one another or consonant with one another or dissonant with one another. Irrelevance and consonance are equilibrium conditions while dissonance, like incongruity, produces change. If we define dissonance first, the definitions of the other two will then be very easily made.

In the most general terms, one item A is dissonant with another item B when A implies not-B. In some cases the implication is said to be logical: someone believes that man will in the near future reach the moon (A) and also that man will not be able to build a device than can leave the earth's atmosphere (B). In some cases A implies not-B because A is a general cultural prescription (Do not pick up pieces of chicken at a formal dinner) while B is an action that would violate the prescription (picking up a drumstick). In some cases B is merely very unlikely to be true if A is true: someone who is a registered Democrat (A) is not likely to vote for the Republican candidate for president (B). In some cases B is an action that does not accord with a belief A: someone believes that smoking tends to cause lung cancer (A) and yet smokes (B). In all of the above examples the combination of elements is dissonant since A and B exist together in a mind when A tends to imply that B would not be true. Consonant combinations, of course, are pairs such that A implies B (I believe smoking is dangerous [A] and I do not smoke [B]). Irrelevant combinations are pairs such that A implies nothing whatever about B (someone believes smoking is dangerous [A] and is a registered Democrat [B]).

Apparently we all have an intuitive understanding of dissonance which is clear enough so that a set of examples and some fairly loose statements serve to communicate. That the definition is loose can be demonstrated with any of the examples that are said to involve a logical dissonance such that A strictly implies not-B. This is not strictly true of any of the examples. Even the fellow who believes that man will soon reach the moon and at the same time believes that man will be unable to build a device that can leave the earth's atmosphere is not necessarily guilty of logical contradiction. The apparent contradiction stems from the fact that we are supplying certain very plausible additional premises, for example, man can only reach the moon in a device that can leave the earth's atmosphere. Let us imagine that this premise is violated and someone gets us to the moon by moving the earth near enough so that we can step across without leaving our familiar atmosphere. Now it is clear that the original two propositions did not alone constitute a strict contradiction. Indeed, the only way in which two propositions can be in strict logical contradiction is for one to negate the other: A and not-A—"Man will travel to the moon" and "Man will not travel to the moon." Probably such pairs are not often simultaneously entertained by the same mind.

Perhaps it seems pointless to cavil at the fact that a contradiction is not strictly logical when it would be so if one supplied any of the more probable missing premises. The point is made because it is important to know that the explicit definition of dissonance is not completely precise, and so there is no real guarantee that those who work with the theory will be able to agree about when a situation involves dissonance and when it does not. In addition, it is worth noting that strictly logical dissonance is probably very uncommon.

Cognitive dissonance can be seen as an antecedent condition which leads to activity oriented toward dissonance reduction just as hunger leads to activity oriented toward hunger reduction. We can illustrate some of the possible modes of dissonance reduction by referring to the man who believes smoking is dangerous but who nevertheless smokes. There are two simple changes, either of which would eliminate dissonance: give up smoking or give up the belief that smoking is harmful. However, there are considerations that make these changes difficult: tobacco addiction on the one hand and publicized correlations with lung cancer on the other.

The unhappy smoker may be unable completely to eliminate dissonance, but may succeed in reducing it. He may, for instance, begin to select his reading so as to take in as little as possible of the evidence and expert opinion that suggests smoking is dangerous. At the same time he may begin to seek out criticisms of the evidence that links lung cancer with smoking. These are efforts more closely analogous to food-seeking behavior than to the automatic release of stored blood sugar; they are efforts made in the external world (not merely in one's mind) that may reduce the drive without eliminating it.

There are several ways in which the dissonance between the smoking habit and the dread of its effects could be represented in the congruity model. In Figure 7a, smoking, valued at −3 because of the belief in its deleterious effects, is linked associatively with the highly valued self. The associative link is the person's knowledge that he himself has the habit of smoking. The link must be knowledge and not the habit itself, because the congruity model represents cognition. Now let us see how we can represent Festinger's techniques of dissonance reduction or elimination.

If the smoking habit is given up, then the knowledge of it could be given up and the associative bond erased. It is not really the technique of giving up smoking that can be repre-

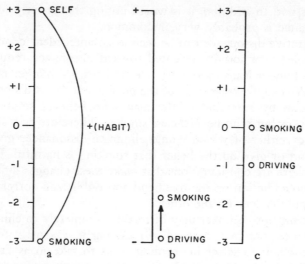

Fig. 7. The technique of "worse peril": (a) The original dissonance; (b) Driving as "worse peril"; (c) Final positions

sented, but rather the effect of this change on cognition. The outcome for the congruity picture would be exactly the same if the subject were incredulous (as the degree of incongruity requires) and simply refused to believe that he himself could be a smoker while continuing to smoke. Relinquishing the belief that smoking is dangerous and seeking out evidence that undermines that belief are, also, only representable in terms of their ultimate effects on attitudes—specifically the evaluation of smoking. The congruity representation will be the same if the subject comes to believe that smoking is not dangerous as if he comes to wish for an early death from lung cancer—a rise in the value of smoking.

The congruity model itself, of course, makes a definite prediction—incredulity. If we set this aside on the ground that one must believe in the existence of so obvious a habit, then the model predicts that both the self and smoking will move to neutrality. The smoker thinks less highly of himself for being a smoker but more highly of smoking for being one of his own habits.

Neither Festinger nor Osgood provides rules for translating between models, and the translation we have provided in the present case is only one of several that are plausible. It serves very well, however, to illustrate the general relation between the two models. Cases of cognitive dissonance are also generally cases of cognitive incongruity. Dissonance theory offers a variety of techniques for dissonance reduction or elimination, but, unless many variables other than dissonance are specified, the theory does not predict one particular technique. Congruity predicts a particular cognitive change, but does not differentiate among the techniques by which this change might be accomplished.

The modes of dissonance reduction so far described are all rather obvious ones, and Festinger is not an investigator who lingers over the obvious. Most of his work on dissonance is concerned with nonobvious techniques of reduction. There is, for instance, the interesting tendency for smokers in a state of dissonance to mull over the horrible statistics that show how dangerous it is to drive an automobile. Dwelling on these statistics seems to make smoking more bearable. How on earth does this work? The smoker-driver ought to plunge himself into another acute dissonance crisis, since he has to drive an automobile in spite of the danger. Still there is no doubt that people take comfort in this kind of rehearsal of perils more serious than the one they have been contemplating. We find that the real enthusiasts for automobile-accident statistics are people who fly a great deal. They are forever going over the fact that driving is still more dangerous than flying. But how is this helpful, since if we smoke and drive and fly we are just multiplying our peril?

Festinger suggests that what we shall call the technique of "worse peril" is helpful because it makes the smoking dissonance seem relatively unimportant. This is not a very satisfactory explanation, since whatever relief is gained from smoker's dissonance would seem to be made up by driver's dissonance. I have a rather fantastic explanation in terms of the congruity model. Suppose the basic problem is, as pictured in Figure 7a, a link of habit between Self and the dangerous and stupid smoking practice. To think about the greater danger of driving is to realize that, wherever smoking ought to fall on a scale, it cannot be as bad as driving; therefore driving ousts smoking from the most unfavorable position (Fig. 7b). The question then is: Where shall we put driving? Well, practically everyone drives nowadays, and driving is an absolute necessity. If everyone does it and it has to be done anyway, then the danger cannot be so extreme, and in any case life compels us to run some risks. So driving is not so bad (perhaps —1) and since driving is relatively worse than smoking, why, smoking must be an innocuous neutral habit (Fig. 7c).

Festinger shows that there is a rough sort of fit between his dissonance theory and numerous past experimental results, as well as new results from studies of his own design. The concentration on not obvious effects makes his work extremely interesting. He argues, for instance, that a decision following on consideration of two or more alternatives necessarily leaves some dissonance. The man who has just bought a Thunderbird still has in mind the attractions of the rejected alternatives—a Corvette and a Mercedes-Benz. However, the decision is one not easily reversed, and so he will strive to bolster it with consonant information. Festinger predicts that after buying a car the new owner will seek out advertisements extolling the advantages of the car he has purchased and avoid advertisements for cars he considered buying but did not buy. This prediction is partly supported by the data collected, and partly not supported.

Festinger considers situations in which someone is induced to some sort of public compliance either by reward or by the threat of punishment, and examines the impact of such behavioral compliance on related beliefs. He makes the extremely interesting point that if a man can be induced to take some action that does not "follow from" his beliefs, then the accomplished action will exert a force on his beliefs in the direction of a change to rationalize what has been done. In experimental situations (Brehm, 1960), this prediction has been confirmed.

In connection with Festinger's ideas about the effect of compliant behavior, one thinks of the American prisoners of war who cooperated with their captors (Schein, 1958). These acts of cooperation implied certain favorable views of Korea, China, and Communism, and unfavorable views of the United States. It is likely that while the collaborators were in prison camp they resolved the dissonance between thought and action by making some changes in what they thought and said. Once the war ended, however, and the POW's were released, their changed views would have been seriously dissonant with the views of their American rescuers with whom they would have been bound to identify. It seems likely that the dissonance between collaboration and beliefs about Communism and democracy was, at this point, handled by excusing the collaboration as having been elicited under duress. A POW could even plead that he had been "brainwashed."

Festinger makes a very interesting prediction in this general connection. He argues that if techniques of coercion are extremely severe, then they provide a good consonant explanation of collaboration. One does what has to be done. The maximal pressure for attitude change will be exerted when coercion is mild, since the coercion itself then provides a very poor explanation for the collaboration and one seeks to justify it by changing attitudes. The precise recommendation to the "brainwasher" who wants to change attitudes by inducing collaborative action is to use the mildest coercion that will produce the action. We do not have the comparison conditions to say whether the POW coercion was severe or mild, but the lasting ideological change accomplished seems to have been slight. Only twenty-one American POW's chose not to be repatriated, and even in these cases there are data suggesting that they remained behind for reasons other than a change of ideology. On the other hand, the re-education techniques used by the Chinese on certain Western civilians (Lifton, 1956; Schein, 1961) do seem to have accomplished in a few cases some genuine, enduring ideological change. If these techniques (more properly called "brainwashing" than the indoctrination techniques used with POW's) were more severe than those employed in Korea, then Festinger's theory would predict less ideological change from brainwashing than from POW indoctrination. The available data do not permit a test of this hypothesis; the assessment of the incidence of genuine ideological change and of the severity of change techniques is too uncertain a business. One authority (Schein, 1961) thinks that the essence of the matter does not lie with simple severity of coercion but rather with matters of group identification.

DISSONANCE AND SOCIAL SUPPORT

The foregoing materials illustrate the power of Festinger's imagination as well as the flexibility of his theory. For a more detailed description we have chosen the single extraordinary study he reported in *When Prophecy Fails* (1956). Several years ago in Lake City (to use the name given in the research report) a Mrs. Marian Keech was receiving messages from Outer Space which she recorded in automatic writing. Late in September there came to her from the planet Clarion a prediction that on December 21 Lake City would be destroyed by a great flood. The newspaper report of this prophecy was read by Festinger and his collaborators, Riecken and Schachter, at the University of Minnesota. They made an interesting prediction from dissonance theory about what ought to happen when a clear prophecy of this kind was clearly disconfirmed by events (as they felt sure it would be). The investigators flew to Chicago and infiltrated the group of followers collected about Mrs. Keech so as to be present on

December 21. It would be fun to report that they were drowned while taking notes on that date, but in fact Lake City was not flooded on that December 21.

Judicious prophets do not make predictions that are subject to unequivocal disconfirmation, but a very sincere novice like Mrs. Keech may do so. For Mrs. Keech and for some members of the circle of believers that she acquired, there was a deep commitment to the prophecy. Some of her followers even quit their jobs and freely spent their money, so firm was their expectation of the end. What happens when Lake City is still there on December 22? The obvious thing to do to resolve the dissonance is to lose faith in the prophet. However, where the commitment to the belief is so great that reversal would involve severe hardship and embarrassment, and where there are others with you who are in the same position, Festinger predicts a different outcome. The followers will become very active proselytizers, trying to win others to their cause—to bolster the endangered belief by additional social support. This demonstrates the same principle as does the smoker who seeks out elements consonant with his obstinate habit, except that in the case of the apocalyptic social movement the members seek to create consonant elements in the form of new believers.

There have been several historical instances of the disconfirmation of a prophecy followed by a heightened proselytizing, and one can even argue that primitive Christianity is such a case. Some of the disciples of Jesus seem to have believed that He was destined to become King of the Jews in His lifetime and on earth, though Jesus Himself seems not to have said anything of the kind. For the disciples with this secular view the ignominious fate of crucifixion must have constituted a clear disconfirmation. The subsequent apostolic zeal was of course one of the great forces of history.

Mrs. Keech's movement was divided between the Lake City group that met at her home and a group at the nearby town, Collegeville, centering around one Dr. Armstrong who worked in the university health center. The date of the prophecy,

December 21, fell during the Christmas vacation, and so the Collegeville followers, mostly students, were dispersed to their homes and had to meet disconfirmation without social support. The Lake City group met the disconfirmation all gathered together at Mrs. Keech's home, and so could supply one another with support. Festinger's prediction was that those without support would relinquish their faith, and those with support would increase their proselytizing.

The collection of ideas that emerged from Mrs. Keech's many automatic writing sessions was a wonderful mélange of mysticism, science fiction, and Christianity. The Guardians who spoke to her from Outer Space told the group that they, the Seekers, would be spared in the great flood. They were to stand by on the 21st, prepared to be picked up by flying saucers. If one reads Mrs. Keech's teachings with a skeptical eye, one suspects that she was having delusions of grandeur. Not the least interesting aspect of this study is the example it provides of a deluded person playing an influential role that might have become of historic importance. Mrs. Keech was fortunate in having a well-protected social position. She did not hold a job, and so her delusions did not get her in trouble with employers and fellow workers. Furthermore, she had an extraordinarily indulgent husband who did not believe in her Voices and yet let her have her meetings while he went about his business. He slept soundly through the night of December 21.

Attempting an experimental study in this setting created some very special methodological problems. In order to keep full records, the false members frequently had to hide in the bathroom or on the porch, where they frenziedly scribbled notes. It is always a problem in psychological work for the experimenter to avoid influencing the process he studies, but in the present instance this problem was exceptionally difficult. If the false members were too enthusiastic in their role as followers, they might intensify the convictions of others; if they were too cool, they might dampen enthusiasm. The effort to avoid a too direct participation reached a droll climax when one of the false members was asked to act as medium and receive messages from the Guardians. He kept a long silence and finally Mrs. Keech said with some irritation, "What do you see?" "Nothing," he replied. "That's not nothing," he was told, "that's the Void."

Late in the morning of December 20 Mrs. Keech received a message instructing her group to be prepared to be picked up at midnight. They would be escorted to a parked flying saucer and whisked away to safety in Outer Space. The day and early evening were spent in preparation—rehearsing passwords, removing metal from their clothing (as they were told that metallic objects would be dangerous on the saucer). As the clock hand approached midnight the group of ten believers sat in strained expectation of an other-worldly knock at the door. The clock ticked past the hour and for a few minutes there was discussion of who had the right time and whose watch was fast. But it became clear that—by anyone's timepiece—the hour had passed without the prophesied delivery. At first there was no visible reaction—just frozen, expressionless faces. Gradually and painfully, feelings of despair engulfed them. They reexamined the prophetic messages in search of some explanation. Near 4:00 A.M. Mrs. Keech began to cry and to say bitterly that she knew some in the group were beginning to doubt her. At 4:45 Mrs. Keech summoned the group together to hear a message; with radiant face she announced: "For this day it is established that there is but one God of Earth, and He is in thy midst, and from His hand thou hast written these words. And mighty is the word of God—and by His word have ye been saved—for from the mouth of death have ye been delivered and at no time has there been such a force loosed upon the Earth." (Festinger, Riecken, and Schacter, p. 169) More followed in this same high solemn style, which apes the King James version even to the archaic pronouns *thou* and *ye*. The gist of the message was that the world had been spared a cataclysm because of the impressive faith of the small group of believers. This elegant explanation was received with high enthusiasm.

In the aftermath of the disconfirmation the members of the Lake City group took turns telephoning newspapers and wire services to publicize their explanation of the failure of the prophecy. Before the disconfirmation the group had avoided publicity but afterwards they were very active proselytizers. The Collegeville members, on the other hand, who passed the prophetic midnight waiting for their individual rescue saucers in isolation from the group, responded to disconfirmation by relinquishing their faith or by having greatly diminished confidence in the prophet. The prediction of the social psychologist prophets (Festinger, Riecken, and Schachter) was confirmed, and the importance of social support was rather well demonstrated. Even so, these prophets wrote a book to proselytize for dissonance theory.

There is one aspect of the theoretical prediction that is not made clear in *When Prophecy Fails* and that shows why the logical character of a dissonant relation needs to be made clear. Much of what the authors say sounds as if they were predicting that it is the disconfirmed belief for which the believers will proselytize. The specifically disconfirmed belief is *There will be a great flood on December 21 and the believers will be picked up by flying saucers.* This belief is unequivocally dissonant with the events of December 21, since if those events are expressed in a verbal proposition they assert the negative of the prediction. This is dissonance in the sense of strict logical contradiction.

If the believers had gone on to proselytize for the disconfirmed belief they would have had to assert that the flood and the delivery therefrom had in fact occurred on schedule. To have done so would have been to deny the clear evidence of their senses. To have met dissonance with denial in this case would have been psychotic. Nothing of the sort happened.

The prophet's prediction exists in a deductive matrix; it is rather like an empirical prediction deduced from premises in a scientific theory. If it had been confirmed it would have reflected credit back upon such a premise as: Marian Keech receives true messages and is a trustworthy prophet. Its disconfirmation threatens to discredit such a premise, but the disconfirmation can be disarmed by creating additional after-the-fact premises that predict what happened. It is such a premise that Marian Keech invented. In full context what we have is: Mrs. Keech receives messages that are true when received, but any prediction can be suspended by the Omnipotent Guardians, who in the present case were moved to compassion by the faith of a small group; Mrs. Keech remains a trustworthy prophet but she is relaying the messages of a personal God, not a mechanical principle.

The reason why it is necessary to eliminate ambiguities in the definition of dissonance is that, unless it is done, we cannot be sure just what the theory predicts. Had we understood the authors to be saying that there would be proselytizing for the specifically disconfirmed belief, we should have had to conclude that the theory was not verified. If we understand them to be concerned with a more general faith in Marian Keech, then the theory works. It must be recognized, however, that it is not the strictly dissonant expectation of a flood for which the group proselytizes, but the not so strictly dissonant faith in the prophet.

This is caviling indeed; to criticize a theory that works even roughly on so complex a problem is to set an absurdly high standard for social psychology. But it does no harm to keep high standards in view if it is clear that we are full of admiration for the experimental inventiveness of the authors and their effort to be systematic.

THE BALANCE MODEL

This third model of attitude change, devised by Abelson and Rosenberg (1958), is very like the congruity model, but, at several crucial points, different assumptions are made. We begin with the now familiar notion that the mind contains cognitive elements which are such things as persons, concepts, institutions, and groups, and that such elements can be named. As in the congruity model, though not in Festinger's dissonance model, it is assumed that cognitive elements toward which people have attitudes can be assigned positive (+), neutral (0), and negative (−) signs.[5]

In addition to elements, the mind contains relations, and these may be positive (p), as in *"x* likes *y"* or *"x* causes *y"*; negative (n), as in *"x* dislikes *y"* or *"x* prevents *y"*; or null (0), as in *"x* is indifferent to *y"* or *"x* is unconnected with *y."* The positive and negative relations are exactly equivalent to the associative and dissociative bonds of the congruity model. The null relation is simply the case in which no bond exists in the

[5] In their first published presentation of the balance model, Abelson and Rosenberg (1958) do not provide their cognitive elements with the +, 0, and − signs and do not define the condition of balance in terms of such signs. A later presentation (Rosenberg, Hovland, McGuire, Abelson, and Brehm, 1960) describes the model as it is described here. The change in the model is not, however, so great as it might appear; for many problems the analyses provided by the two models are essentially the same. This is true because, in the first version but not in the second, the list of cognitive elements ordinarily includes the Ego and Ego's relations (+, 0, or −) with all other relevant elements taken into account. If Ego as an element has a + relation with another element, e.g., "getting good grades at Yale," this is the same thing, really, as assigning a + value to that element. So long as Ego is an element in the analysis of a problem in terms of the first model, it turns out that elements are being assigned +, 0, and − values, though this is accomplished in terms of a relation between Ego and something else rather than simply in terms of single valued elements—which is the method of the second version.

congruity model. In terms of its elements and relations, then, the balance model is identical with the congruity model and, as we have seen, closely similar to dissonance theory. There are, however, important novelties in the definition of a state of equilibrium, in the statement of conditions disturbing equilibrium, and in predicted outcomes.

Elements in the balance model have signs (+, 0, −), but they are not necessarily assigned numerical values (as in the −3 to +3 of congruity), and equilibrium is defined without reference to numbers. There is equilibrium so long as elements of identical sign are linked by positive relations or by null relations (not linked at all), and so long as elements of opposite sign are linked by negative relations or by null relations. This is the same as the definition of congruity except that numerical values are not involved.

The authors take as an example the issue of whether Yale should admit coeds or not. For some Yale students the principal elements in this attitudinal arena are Having Coeds at Yale (C) and Getting Good Grades (G). Suppose a student was for Getting Good Grades (G+) and also for Having Coeds at Yale (C+). If he believed that the presence of coeds would make it easier for him to get good grades, than he would be in a state of mental equilibrium on this issue, since he believes that G is positively related to C or that there is a + p + link. If, however, he believed that the presence of coeds would interfere with his getting good grades, then he has a + n + bond and is not in equilibrium. Figure 8 shows how one might diagram a bond that is balanced because the objects linked positively are both positively valued. Note that for balance theory, relative standing within the positive region means nothing. If now we imagine the congruity scale from −3 to +3 and suppose that Having Coeds at Yale has the lower value of the two positive elements, it is clear that what is an equilibrium in the balance model need not be but may be an equilibrium in congruity. In general terms it may be said that the conditions of congruity are more exacting than the conditions of balance—

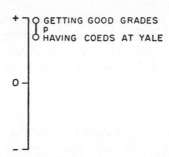

Fig. 8. A bond that is balanced but not necessarily congruous

congruity requires matched values as well as matched signs. It follows that there will be more balanced situations than congruous situations, that balanced conditions include and extend beyond congruous conditions. Since congruity is more narrowly defined, there will be a larger residual class of incongruous situations that of unbalanced situations, and, in fact, cases of incongruity will include and extend beyond cases of imbalance.

At this point congruity and balance theories differ only in that one aspires to the power that numbers can give and the other does not aspire so high. We come now to a more fundamental difference between the two. A condition of imbalance is not alone sufficient to generate change in the present case. Putting it another way, we may say that while incongruity is identical with disequilibrium, imbalance is not. In the balance model a person must think about the elements and relations in question before he will be motivated to change. Undiscovered unbalanced bonds are not sufficient to produce change. In effect, one must notice his unbalanced relations before being concerned about changing them. The congruity model makes no such stipulation.

If we turn from these models to experimental efforts made to test them, we shall find that the formal difference in conditions prerequisite to change has not so far made any difference. All of the experiments that have been done require subjects to report on their cognitive elements and the relations between them, and so presumably subjects are forced to think about the attitudes in question. In order to give real substance to its novel assumption, the balance model should tell us how to obtain evaluated elements and relations in two ways: (1) so that the subject will not think about them and (2) so that the subject will think about them. Until operations corresponding to the formal distinction are specified, the formal distinction, in spite of its great plausibility, cannot be tested.

The present model allows for three general outcomes of thought about such unbalanced bonds as Coeds at Yale (C+) would interfere with (n) Getting Good Grades (G+). The first sort of outcome is to change the signs of one or more elements or to change the sign of the relation between them. If one can believe that coeds will not interfere with or will even facilitate getting good grades, then there is the balanced bond C+ p G+. If one can decide that one does not want Coeds at Yale under any circumstances, then there is a balanced C− n G+. Finally, for these minimal balancing changes, there is the possibility of preferring not to get good grades (C+ n G−). In addition to these adjustments, which change only one thing at a time, balance can be brought about by a variety of more complex changes in the signs of elements and the relations between them.

The second general outcome, and one for which the initial Norton-Silvers problem demonstrated the need, is to redefine or "differentiate" one of the elements. It would be possible, for example, for the "unbalanced" Yale student to make a distinction between good grades in the sense of a satisfactory passing C and good grades in the sense of all A's. He could go on to realize that coeds probably would make it difficult for him to get A's, but would not interfere at all with getting C's. And, luckily, C's are all he really wants; he has never cared about getting A's. The result is a happy, though possibly precarious, balance.

The final sort of outcome is made possible by the provision

that thinking is necessary to make imbalance into disequilibrium. One can, therefore, restore equilibrium by ceasing to think about the matter in question. There may even develop some clever strategies for keeping away from areas of potential internal contradiction.

I count it an advantage of the balance model (and also of dissonance theory) that it allows for more kinds of outcome—particularly such very plausible outcomes as differentiation and stopping thinking—than does the congruity model. However, the gain in flexibility is at the cost of a loss in precision or power. The balance model, as far as it has been specified, does not predict which of the three major outcomes will occur in a given case of disequilibrium, nor does it choose among the various changes of sign that could produce balance. The congruity model predicts a completely determinate quantitative change from its assumptions about congruity, inertia due to polarization, incredulity, and the Assertion Constant. The balance model says that any one of a number of rather general things may happen as a consequence of disequilibrium. The congruity model says that one very particular thing will result from any given disequilibrium, though, it must be added, there is not yet any experimental work that tests the individual quantitative predictions of congruity.

Of course, precision in the model does us no good if the outcomes so well specified do not correspond with outcomes in the real world. It surely would be the position of Festinger and of Abelson and Rosenberg that it is better to sacrifice precision than to win it by making a set of unjustifiable assumptions. The authors of the looser models would contend, I think, that this looseness is a realistic representation of the state of scientific knowledge concerning attitude change.

The exasperating difficulty with testing a theory of attitude change is the necessity of collecting fairly elaborate data before and after the introduction of some change factor without causing your subjects to produce artificial reactions not representative of the life situation. It is common to assume that reactions will be artificial if subjects are wise to the experimenter's intent.

By this assumption the social psychologist is committed to deception. In Tannenbaum's test of congruity theory, mocked-up news stories were represented as the real thing, though we may suspect that not all subjects were deceived. Festinger, Riecken, and Schachter did not create an apocalyptic social movement (that would be more intervention than society would approve) but rather seized on the first appropriate one they heard about. These investigators had to conceal their true purpose in joining the movement, and did not risk paper and pencil measures of individual commitment to the prophecy as a tight experimental design might have suggested. The proponents of balance theory have still a third research style. They do not try to conceal their manipulations, but rely instead on two techniques for inducing subjects to behave in a natural and fully involved way. The more extreme technique is hypnotism; the less extreme, role-playing.

IMBALANCE FROM HYPNOTIC SUGGESTION

Rosenberg and Gardner (1958) have made very imaginative use of hypnotism as a research tool. Only a small percentage of subjects can go into a deep hypnotic trance, but for those who have this ability very extraordinary phenomena are possible. To mention a single example, it has been known for more than a century that a deeply hypnotized person may be able to have a limb amputated without anesthesia without showing evidence of pain. Hypnotic phenomena are fascinating to the beginning student of psychology because they challenge his fundamental notions of how the mind works. A great many professional psychologists and medical men for a great many years would not permit themselves to be interested in hypnotism—presumably because they did not want their fundamental notions to be challenged. But the student is right; hypnotic phenomena are genuine and startling and should be studied in their own right, and also, as in the present instance, utilized in research.

We shall not do justice to the systematic detail of Rosenberg's hypnotism studies because it would make too long a story, and we want to conserve the reader's remaining tolerance for long stories to carry him through an account of a role-playing experiment that is more crucial to balance theory. Here we shall take the liberty of plucking from Rosenberg and Gardner's case studies (1958) of cognitive change under hypnotic suggestion those fragments that are especially interesting and illustrative.

Eleven subjects were selected for their demonstrated ability to be deeply hypnotized. Each subject was rehearsed in hypnosis to the point where he could carry out posthypnotic suggestion with amnesia for the suggestions. The posthypnotic suggestion is probably the most familiar phenomenon of hypnosis—it is the one that students usually try to produce in dormitory experiments on hypnosis. The subject, while in a trance, is told that after he has emerged from the trance he will experience something or perform some action, but will not remember that he had been ordered to do so, and will not recognize the hypnotist's suggestion as the cause of the experience or action. A subject has, for example, been told that at a certain time he would see a cat come into the room, walk over to his chair and settle down beside him. Such a subject may at the specified time look toward the door and follow with his eyes the slow progress of an hallucinated cat until it reaches his chair—when he reaches down to scratch its imaginary ears. This whole performance can be very persuasive indeed. In the present case each subject was to be given the suggestion that he had reversed his position on some strongly held attitude, and the experimenter would then see how this change in the value of a single cognitive element affected a cluster of related elements.

In advance of the hypnotic intervention subjects were tested by questionnaire on their attitudes toward various matters, such as permitting Negroes to live in white neighborhoods, comprehensive federal medical insurance, the city manager plan, and moving to Los Angeles. For each subject the posthypnotic suggestion would reverse his stand on one such issue. In order to explore the relations between the critical attitude and related matters, subjects ran through a "cognitive structure test." In this test each subject works with a set of thirty-one cards on each of which is printed a statement of some goal that most people feel strongly about, such as "all human beings having equal rights," "people being well educated," "making one's own decisions," "complying with the wishes of people in authority." To each such statement the subject assigned a positive or negative number indicating its value to him. In addition, he was asked to reveal the bonds he perceived between each goal and the critical attitude object. For example, would "comprehensive federal medical insurance" promote (p) or hinder (n) the goal of "making one's own decisions"? In this way the initial bonds between a certain valued element and thirty-one other valued elements were mapped. These procedures, carried out before the posthypnotic suggestion, were repeated after the suggestion. The suggestion itself applied to a single valued element only. The question is, Does changing one element cause changes in related elements that are such as to preserve balance among cognitive bonds? The general result was highly confirmatory. There was much more cognitive reorganization in the direction of balanced structure for the experimental subjects than for a control group of subjects given no hypnotic suggestion. For four experimental subjects it was possible to conduct numerous interviews along psychiatric lines, and the report of these interviews gives some life to the abstract operations of the model.

Subject R was a young, single graduate student with rather severe moral standards, who expressed great disgust at the licentiousness, filth, and sensuality of city life. He contrasted this sort of life with the cleanliness, simplicity, and piety of his childhood rural home. On the attitude questionnaire he was strongly opposed to living in Los Angeles, and on the "cognitive structure test" revealed that this city seemed to

him to be associated with loose living and antagonistic to
strict moral standards. The hypnotist's suggestion was "When
you awake you will feel very much in favor of living in the
city of Los Angeles. The mere idea of living in Los Angeles
makes you feel happy and exhilarated." The reverse attitude
was incorporated into his cognitive structure by changing
the relations between living in Los Angeles and various moral
values from negative to null. He came to think of living in
this city as unrelated to his important ethical concerns.

Two subjects handled the hypnotically induced imbalance
by differentiation rather than by attitude change. One young
woman set great value on personal autonomy and indeed could
only accept hypnosis by thinking of it as a largely self-in-
duced rather than imposed state (which, to be sure, it is).
She was initially opposed to the "city manager plan," which
she thought would lead to "complying with the wishes of
persons in authority"—a negative value for her. When it was
suggested that she become favorable to the city manager plan,
she accepted the suggestion and made the acceptance balance
by differentiating "city manager plan." In an interview she
said that she had assumed "It was a thing that restricted you—
more or less enforcing all sorts of things." But, she explained
after the suggestion, "I think I changed my assumption a
little bit—it seems as though it all kind of reversed—I think
really I feel the same way about it—only I have just stressed
the . . . another angle of it." The plan now seemed to be "something voluntary which the people themselves would want to do
for the city—and have everybody represented." Another subject who was induced to adopt a less favorable attitude toward
federal medical insurance accomplished a differentiation that
is the contrary of the preceding example. He came to believe that such medical insurance was a threat to individual
rights.

There was finally a subject whose balancing operation may
be reasonably described as "stopping thinking." He was a
student in divinity school who had initially indicated a strong
positive reaction to "Negroes being allowed to move into

white neighborhoods." After the contrary suggestion he expressed violent anti-Negro sentiment, but "the card-sorting test of cognitive structure, which he had taken and fully understood before the experimental hypnotic session, now seemed to confuse and overwhelm him. He completed it only by throwing the cards into categories in an almost haphazard fashion, all the while voicing the complaint that the test was confusing, senseless, and boring." It should be added, after this example, that each subject was relieved of his amnesia and restored to his former attitudes.

FENWICK'S ART DISPLAY

While not every one can achieve deep hypnosis, most people can do a satisfactory job of playing the part (or role) of someone else if that part is well described and not completely outside his experience. In the present experiment subjects were to play a role defined in terms of certain feelings and beliefs which taken together constituted a cognitive structure with a built-in dilemma. Would role-playing subjects resolve their dilemmas in accordance with the predictions of balance theory?

All subjects were Yale undergraduates. Each man was given a pamphlet which on its first page told him that he was to try to put himself into another person's position and exhorted him to "try to *be* this man." The assigned role was that of "the owner of a large department store in a middle-sized, Midwestern city." As part of the content of the role each subject was told to adopt a specific attitude on each of three matters. In the first place all subjects were, in the role of department store manager, to set high positive value on "keeping sales at the highest possible volume in all departments of your store." This is the unchanging aspect of the role—a store manager could not credibly set low value on sales—but the other two attitudes were varied among subjects so as to create three different versions of the role.

One group of subjects was also instructed to feel positively toward modern art and toward Fenwick, the manager of the rug department. In a second group the assigned role required that the subject feel negatively toward modern art and positively toward Fenwick. For a third group both modern art and Fenwick were to be negatively valued. In summary, one attitude—setting positive value on sales—was an invariant part of the manager role but favorable and unfavorable attitudes toward two other objects (modern art and Fenwick) were varied to yield the three roles diagrammed in Figure 9.

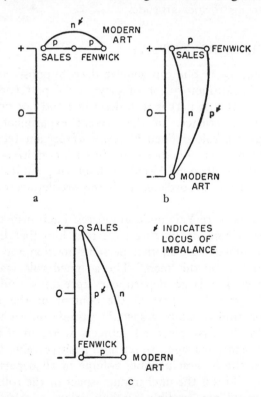

Fig. 9. Three versions of the store manager's role: (a) Role 1; (b) Role 2; (c) Role 3

The assigned role also involved beliefs about the relations among the three concepts, and the beliefs were identical for the three roles. They were (1) Displays of modern art in department stores *reduce* (n) sales volume; (2) Fenwick *plans to mount* (p) such a display in the rug department; (3) Fenwick in his tenure as rug department manager has *increased* (p) the volume of sales. These three beliefs were persuasively backed with paragraphs of alleged facts. Belief (1) above, for instance, was supported by the following:

"One year ago a report by the Merchandising Institute appeared in a leading market research journal. It warned against modern art exhibits in stores merchandising popular household products to lower and middle-class customers. The conclusions were based on a thorough and well-conducted research study which found that 55% of a representative sample of American consumers did not like modern art. Probably it was this basic attitude which underlay the further finding that 46% were offended or distracted by modern art displays and thus tended to spend less time and money in stores featuring such displays." (Rosenberg, Hovland, McGuire, Abelson, and Brehm, p. 126.)

Each subject then has a role defined by a set of three elements bound in pairs by three relations. The three relations are identical for all subjects, but the attitudes toward Fenwick and toward modern art are varied. The result is that each of the three roles of Figure 9 involves an imbalance, but the locus of the imbalance shifts as indicated in the Figure by small arrows. For Role 1, with all elements positively valued, a state of balance requires that all relations be positive, and it is the single negative bond between Sales and Modern Art that is the locus of imbalance. For Role 2 the negatively valued Modern Art ought to be negatively related to both positive elements, and the fact that Modern Art is positively related to Fenwick is inconsistent. For Role 3 the single positively valued element —Sales—ought to be negatively related to both negatively valued items, and so the positive bond with Fenwick is inconsistent.

A subject in any one of the three roles can achieve peace

of mind, can balance his cognitive structure, in a number of different ways. However, the simplest solution is, in each case, to change the sign of the single unbalanced relation. Consider Role 1, where a change of sign for the negative relations between Sales and Modern Art (i.e., believing that a display of Modern Art is likely to increase Sales rather than to decrease them) would resolve the dilemma. The problem could also be solved by leaving the negative relation intact, setting a negative value on Modern Art, and changing the relation between Fenwick and Modern Art to a negative one. In other words, if the store manager can decide that he actually dislikes Modern Art and can believe that Fenwick really has no intention of mounting a Modern Art display, he can comfortably continue to think well of Fenwick, to want high sales, and to believe that a Modern Art display would lower sales volume. This is a more complicated resolution because it entails changing two aspects of the original structure. For each role there are numerous possible resolutions that require changes in two or more aspects of the structure. The specific hypothesis of the experiment is: *The order of preference for paths toward restoring an unbalanced structure to balance will correspond to an ordering of the paths according to the number of sign changes required, from the least to the most.*

The first phase of the experiment involved training some ninety-nine subjects (distributed about evenly among the three roles) in the attitudes and beliefs constituting a particular initial cognitive structure. In order to see whether subjects had fully grasped the structure, had successfully internalized it, the experimenters required them, after training, to rate the elements and state the relations between them. It is an interesting incidental fact that for each role a small number of subjects brought about premature balancing, i.e., they did not grasp the role correctly and in fact distorted it so as to eliminate the imbalance. For Role 1 a total of twelve subjects somehow understood that displays of Modern Art would *promote* Sales in spite of the perfectly clear paragraph saying that such displays *lower* sales. The otherwise balanced set of elements and relations seems to have implied a favorable relation so strongly that some subjects thought that relation actually existed.

For the remainder of the experiment only those subjects who had correctly learned their roles were used. These subjects went on to read three communications that were represented as issuing from three different store officers; each communication had something to say that was relevant to the general dilemma involving Fenwick and the rug department. One communication (hereafter called the Art-Sales communication) contended that displays of Modern Art actually *increase* Sales volume; i.e., it reversed the unbalanced bond of Role 1. A second communication (hereafter called the Fenwick-Art communication) argued that Fenwick really *does not plan* to put up a display of Modern Art in his department; i.e., it reversed the unbalanced bond of Role 2. A third communication (hereafter called the Fenwick Sales communication) argued that Fenwick has actually *failed* to maintain Sales volume in his department; i.e., it reversed the unbalanced bond of Role 3. In effect, then, there was for each role a communication designed to balance the role structure in the simplest possible way.

All subjects in each role read all three communications and then rated each communication in terms of how much it pleased him, how much it persuaded him, and how accurate it appeared to him to be. The general prediction was that subjects in each role would find most acceptable the communication tailored to the imbalance in that role. In addition, however, it is possible to work out the implications for each role of accepting the other two communications; if a communication were to be accepted, how complicated would be the changes necessary in order to achieve balance? In the case of Role 1 the Art-Sales communication would directly correct the inconsistent bond, and so should be most acceptable to subjects in this role. The Fenwick-Art communication establishes a negative bond (Fenwick will not set up a Modern

Art display) which requires one additional change: Modern Art must assume a negative value if balance is to be attained. The Fenwick-Sales communication (which holds that Fenwick has *failed* [n] to maintain sales volume) requires two additional changes for balance: Fenwick and Modern Art would both have to assume negative values. The order of acceptability for the messages to persons in Role 1 ought then to be Art-Sales (1 change), Fenwick-Art (2 changes), Fenwick-Sales (3 changes). In similar fashion detailed predictions can be worked out for Role 2 and Role 3.

The data provide very strong confirmation of the hypothesis. The simplest resolution is indeed the preferred one, and the less simple resolutions are preferred in the order of their simplicity. Imbalance reduction within a structure of attitudinal cognitions will tend to follow a least effortful path. In a second experiment, which reproduced the essential features of the first, this result was replicated. The role-playing design does seem to permit the testing of detailed implications in a model of attitude change without relying on elaborate techniques of deception. We believe that a role-playing subject will behave in a way that corresponds more closely to the life situation than a hoodwinked subject will.

MODELS OF ATTITUDE CHANGE AND GENERAL PSYCHOLOGICAL THEORY

Social psychology has in the past seemed to be short on real intellectual interest. One took to it becauses of this or that interesting fragmentary fact, and there are a great many such facts, but on further study the field disappointed us because the facts did not fall into any general compelling pattern. With the theory of congruity-consonance-balance we think this pattern has at last appeared.

The good idea that is central to all three models is the

notion that human nature abhors incongruity-dissonance-imbalance (Zajonc, 1960) and continually strives to eliminate it. So good an idea is never invented. The antecedents of the authors we have discussed also have their antecedents, and in the end we find the idea seems always to have existed. What has changed is the precision of its statement and the detail with which its implications are developed.

The observations that follow, relating models of attitude change to general psychological theory, apply equally well to all three models. Rather than continue to write *incongruity-dissonance-imbalance* we have used *imbalance* as the generic term for all three. In addition, the examples are all composed in terms of the balance model, though translations can be made in every case to the other models.

Fritz Heider's papers in the 1940's unquestionably anticipated and, in some cases, directly inspired the current formulations of attitude change. In the 1930's, however, we have extremely cogent analyses of psychological conflict developed by Kurt Lewin (1935) for human behavior and by Neal Miller (1944) for the laboratory animal, which, though they do not mention attitude, remind us of the recent work. Lewin first and Neal Miller after him distinguished three major varieties of conflict: the Approach-Avoidance Conflict; the Approach-Approach Conflict; and the Avoidance-Avoidance Conflict. An Approach-Avoidance Conflict for the laboratory rat can be created by feeding him at a certain point in a maze and also subjecting him to electric shock at a point just before he reaches the food. If the hungry animal is then placed some distance away from the food, he may be said to be in an Approach-Avoidance Conflict, since he will wish to approach the food but cannot do so without moving toward the shock which he would prefer to avoid. If we describe the rat's state of mind in terms of the balance model, it is clear that the food is positively valued and the shock negatively valued. In addition, there is a positive bond between the two cognitive objects, since an approach to one is also an approach to the other

—they go together. A positive bond between objects of unlike sign is a condition of imbalance (Figure 10a).

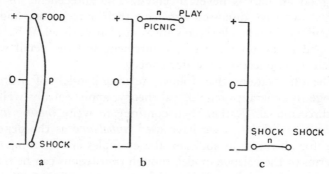

Fig. 10. Conflict theory in terms of the balance model: (a) Approach-avoidance conflict; (b) Approach-approach conflict; (c) Avoidance-avoidance conflict

An Approach-Approach Conflict would exist for a child who, for example, had to choose between going on a picnic and playing with his pals in the neighborhood. It is a situation of conflict because the one desire cannot be gratified without giving up gratification of the other. In Figure 10b this situation is represented as one in which two positively valued objects are linked by a negative bond. The bond is dissociative because if one is attained the other cannot be—they do not go together. A negative bond between objects of positive sign constitutes imbalance.

An Avoidance-Avoidance Conflict can be created for a laboratory rat by first training it to escape an electric shock by running away from whichever end of an alley is distinguished by a light and then placing the trained animal between the two ends and turning on the lights in both. He cannot avoid one without approaching the other. In Figure 10c this situation is represented as one in which two negatively valued objects are linked by a negative bond, and is again a condition of imbalance.

The three basic kinds of behavioral conflict correspond exactly to the three basic situations of imbalance. Translations from conflict to dissonance or incongruity can be made as easily as translations to imbalance. It appears, then, as if the new formulations are very similar indeed to the old. Is this, then, another one of those embarrassing cases in which psychology has freshened up some familiar truisms with a new vocabulary and mistaken them for new insights?

Imbalance is not just conflict theory in a new guise. Lewin and Miller were mainly concerned with detailed predictions about the gross actions of moving toward or away from objects. They worked out the way in which forces to approach or avoid would fall off with distance from the object. From this analysis it followed that in the case of an Approach-Avoidance Conflict there would be a point short of the object where the two sets of forces would exactly balance one another and the organism in conflict would stop there. Approach-Approach Conflicts, it developed, should be easily resolved, since locomotion towards one goal would cause the forces in that direction to increase and opposing forces to decrease. The Avoidance-Avoidance Conflict should set up a field of forces such as to make the most attractive action moving out of the field away from both objects; thus the rat between two points where shock threatens will make frantic efforts to claw his way out of the box. Conflict theory, in short, is focused on the direction of gross actions of approach and avoidance, whereas balance theory is concerned with cognitive adjustments.

Starting with an identical set of disequilibrium conditions the two theories have explored completely different sets of implications. The one theory has not made the other superfluous. Rather, there is here a rich opportunity for theoretical integration. One immediate gain for balance theory from the identification with conflict theory is that we are enabled to understand why human nature abhors imbalance. A situation of imbalance is one that calls for mutually incompatible actions—to smoke and not to smoke, to criticize Fenwick and not to criticize Fenwick, to approach food and not to approach it. Imbalance in the mind threatens to paralyze action.

The conflict theory of Lewin and Miller owes something to the more general notion of conflict of impulse developed by Sigmund Freud. Classical psychoanalytic theory is an intricate structure which was often changed and is full of ambiguities, but the general line on which Freud thought is very clear. The early writings on neurosis, on dreams, and on slips of the tongue all argue in the same way. Freud begins with some item of behavior that appears to be unmotivated—a paralysis of the hand that has no organic cause, a dream of murder, a slip of the tongue in which a man announces that a meeting is adjourned when it was supposed to have been opened. In each case the behaving person insists that he has not wished to act as he has acted and indeed has wished to act in just the contrary way. The insistence is vehement. Freud then proceeds to adduce evidence that while the person is right in reporting that he wished to act in one way, it is also the case that he has wished to act in a directly contrary way. In fact, there is a necessity to divide the psyche into contending forces such as to allow for simultaneous directly opposed wishes. However, the executive agency in the mind abhors this untidy conflict of impulse and commonly admits into consciousness only one impulse at a time. The other impulse is suppressed or repressed or denied, but finds expression in one or another disguised form. In psychoanalytic theory there is a central assumption of imbalance and also of a drive to balance.

Consider Freud's beautiful case study called *The Analysis of a Phobia in a Five Year Old Boy* (1909). Little Hans, the five-year-old, in classical Oedipal fashion hated his father and wished to be rid of him but also loved him and wished him to be close by. Most of the time only the loving impulse was in consciousness and the hatred and fear were "displaced" to horses. It was the boy's exaggerated fear (or phobia) that a horse would bite him that caused Hans's father to ask Freud's advice.

Hans's mother had been accustomed to take the little boy into bed with her when they awakened in the morning. She had done this particularly often during a summer in the country when father was away most of the time. Later on, however, father had interfered with this cosy practice and ordered Hans out of bed. Hans's father was a physician and through an unlucky chain of associations it had been suggested to Hans that physicians sometimes punished sexual naughtiness in small boys with castration. There was a link in Hans's mind between his beloved father and the feared and hated castrator who was his rival in love.

The conflict in Hans's mind can be diagrammed as an un-balanced positive bond linking a beloved father and a hated castrator. It is also, of course, a situation of Approach-Avoid-ance Conflict, since Hans cannot move toward his beloved father without moving toward the feared and hated castrator. There is a third way of describing such a situation, the de-scription that Freud favored. Hans might be said to have ambivalent feelings, feelings of love and hate toward the same person—his father.

It is very generally true that cognitive imbalance amounts to ambivalence. The man who enjoys smoking but believes that it may cause cancer is surely ambivalent about smoking. The department store manager who likes Fenwick and detests modern art but believes that Fenwick will mount an exhibit of modern art is ambivalent toward both Fenwick and modern art (Rosenberg *et al.*, 1960). If objects of unlike sign are bound together positively, one may think of the charge on either object as flowing toward the other and creating ambivalence. If objects of like sign are bound together negatively, one may think of a contrary charge flowing toward each object and generating ambivalence.

In the case of young Hans the ambivalence or imbalance would be extreme and the abhorrence of the ambivalence extraordinarily intense. In such cases the human being may resort to modes of resolution that are more exotic than attitude change or differentiation or stopping thinking.

Freud suggested to Hans's father some questions concerning the sort of horse that the little boy expected to bite him. It turned out to be horses wearing blinders and having a piece of black harness about the mouth that were especially feared. When we learn that Hans's father wore spectacles and had a black moustache about the mouth and, like most fathers of small boys, had often played "horsie" with his son, it seems certain that the feared horse was some kind of substitute for the father and that biting was connected with castrating.

Freud said that the fear and hate inspired by the father were "displaced" to the horse so as to have in consciousness unalloyed affection for a parent. At the same time the boy's phobia worried his father and interfered with his father's routine, and provided a reason for Hans to stay close to home and mother; in short, the phobia served some of the purposes of the repressed hatred and yet kept the conscious mind free of imbalance. This is a resolution reminiscent of differentiation: in its elaborate effort to deny any tie between the good and bad. The bad father becomes something quite different—a biting horse—which can only be traced back to the parent by way of a set of trivial and easily overlooked points of resemblance.

The Freudian theory of personality is often called a "dynamic" theory because it deals in conflict of impulse and the continuing effort to resolve such conflict. A great deal of Freud's more abstract theorizing is concerned with classifying the impulses that conflict. The notion that there are three principal constituents of personality—Id, Ego, and Superego—seems to us to say, in essence, that there are two classes of conflicting forces, the pleasure-bent urges of the Id and the moral imperatives of the Superego; what one values positively the other values negatively. The Ego would be a third force, an executive agency that works at resolving conflict or producing balance by adopting intermediate values, repressing, and differentiating.

In Freudian theory, as in Lewin's and in Miller's conflict theories, we have a clear antecedent of the present concern with imbalance, but again the antecedent does not make the contemporary development superfluous. Balance theory explores cognitive adjustments and especially attitude change; conflict theory explores actions of approach and avoidance in both animals and man; Freudian theory explores a range of extreme and sometimes pathological adjustments in both mind and body which occur as reactions to intense imbalance. There is encouragement in this overlap of ideas. There is the promise that psychology will produce something more satisfying than a collection of models for particular problems, that it will find a truly general theory.

It is, finally, to be expected that a psychological notion as good as the one we have discussed will have been often expressed in literature and philosophy. I do not doubt that it can be found in quite explicit and striking form in Plato, and I am sure there is no Shakespearean drama that cannot be analyzed as a problem in reduction of imbalance. However, I have not been reading either Plato or Shakespeare recently. Among the things I have been reading is the novel *Steppenwolf* by the Nobel prize novelist Hermann Hesse, and *Steppenwolf* is all about imbalance, or ambivalence.

The protagonist of Hesse's novel conceives of himself as half-man and half-wolf-of-the-steppes, or Steppenwolf. He is humane and cultivated, but also a vicious and isolated animal. He differs from most men in that he can acknowledge the division in his nature, though even the Steppenwolf greatly oversimplifies this division by thinking of it as a dichotomy. I do not know a more powerful statement of the essence of dissonance than the words that follow by Hermann Hesse.[6]

[6] Reprinted by permission from *Steppenwolf* by Herman Hesse. Translated by Basil Creighton. New York: Holt, Rinehart and Winston, Inc., 1929.

...For it appears to be an inborn and imperative need of all men to regard the self as a unit. However often and however grievously this illusion is shattered, it always mends again. The judge who sits over the murderer and looks into his face, and at one moment recognises all the emotions and potentialities and possibilities of the murderer in his own soul and hears the murderer's voice as his own is at the next moment one and indivisible as the judge, and scuttles back into the shell of his cultivated self and does his duty and condemns the murderer to death. And if ever the suspicion of their manifold being dawns upon men of unusual powers and of unusually delicate perceptions, so that, as all genius must, they break through the illusion of the unity of the personality and perceive that the self is made up of a bundle of selves, they have only to say so and at once the majority puts them under lock and key, calls science to aid, establishes schizomania and protects humanity from the necessity of hearing the cry of truth from the lips of these unfortunate persons. Why then waste words, why utter a thing that every thinking man accepts as self-evident, when the mere utterance of it is a breach of taste? A man, therefore, who gets so far as making the supposed unity of the self two-fold is already almost a genius, in any case a most exceptional and interesting person. In reality, however, every ego, so far from being a unity is in the highest degree a manifold world, a constellated heaven, a chaos of forms, of states and stages, of inheritances and potentialities. It appears to be a necessity as imperative as eating and breathing for everyone to be forced to regard this chaos as a unity and to speak of his ego as though it were a one-fold and clearly detached and fixed phenomenon. Even the best of us share the delusion. (Hesse, pp. 78-9.)

 **REFERENCES**

Abelson, R. P. Modes of resolution of belief dilemmas. *Conflict resolution*, 1959, *3*, 343-52.

Abelson, R. P., & M. J. Rosenberg. Symbolic psychologic: A model of attitudinal cognition. *Behav. Sci.*, 1958, *3*, 1-13.

Birch, H. G. The effect of socially disapproved labelling upon well-structured attitudes. *J. abnorm. soc. Psychol.*, 1945, *40*, 301-310.

Brehm, J. A dissonance analysis of attitude-discrepant behavior. In M. J. Rosenberg, C. I. Hovland, W. J. McGuire, R. P. Abelson, and J. W. Brehm *Attitude organization and change.* New Haven: Yale Univer. Press, 1960.

Brown, R., and A. Gilman. The pronouns of power and solidarity. In T. A. Sebeok (Ed.) *Style in language.* New York: Wiley, 1960.

Cannon, W. B. *The wisdom of the body.* New York: Norton, 1932.

Cartwright, D., and F. Harary. Structural balance: A generalization of Heider's theory. *Psychol. Rev.,* 1956, *63,* 277-293.

Ekman, P. A comparison of verbal and nonverbal behavior as reinforcing stimuli of opinion responses. Unpublished doctoral dissertation, Adelphi College, 1958.

Festinger, L. *A theory of cognitive dissonance.* New York: Row, Peterson, 1957.

Festinger, L., H. W. Riecken, Jr., and S. Schachter. *When prophecy fails.* Minneapolis: Univer. Minn. Press, 1956.

Freud, S. *The Complete Psychological Works of Sigmund Freud,* Volume X (1909). London: The Hogarth Press, 1955.

Harary, F. On the measurement of structural balance. *Behav. Sci.,* 1959, *4,* 316-323.

Heider, F. Social perception and phenomenal causality. *Psychol. Rev.,* 1944, *51,* 358-374.

Heider, F. Attitudes and cognitive organization. *J. Psychol.,* 1946, *21,* 107-112.

Heider, F. *The psychology of interpersonal relations.* New York: Wiley, 1958.

Hesse, H. *Steppenwolf.* New York: Holt, 1929.

Hildum, D. C., and R. W. Brown. Verbal reinforcement and interviewer bias. *J. abnorm. soc. Psychol.,* 1956, *53,* 108-111.

Kerrick, J. S. The weekly newspaper as a source: Prediction of an editorial's effectiveness. Unpublished paper, 1959.

Kerrick, J. S. News pictures, captions and the point of resolution. *Journalism Quart.,* 1959, *36,* 183-188.

Klapper, J. T. The effects of mass media. Mimeographed manuscript, Bureau of Applied Social Research, Columbia Univer., 1949.

Lewin, K. *Dynamic theory of personality.* New York: McGraw-Hill, 1935.

Lewis, Helen Block Studies in the principles of judgments and attitudes: IV. The operation of prestige suggestion. *J. abnorm. soc. Psychol.*, 1941, *45*, 229-256.

Lifton, R. J. "Thought reform" of Western civilians in Chinese Communist prisons. *Psychiatry*, 1956, *19*, 173-195.

Mandler, G., and W. K. Kaplan. Subjective evaluation and reinforcing effect of a verbal stimulus. *Science*, 1956, *124*, 582-583.

Mausner, B. Studies in social interaction: I. A conceptual scheme. *J. soc. Psychol.*, 1955, *41*, 259-270.

Miller, N. E. Experimental studies of conflict. In J. McV. Hunt (Ed.), *Personality and the behavior disorders*, Vol. I. New York: Ronald, 1944.

Miller, G. A., E. Galanter, and K. H. Pribram. *Plans and the structure of behavior.* New York: Holt, 1960.

Newcomb, T. M. An aproach to the study of communicative acts. *Psychol. Rev.*, 1953, *60*, 393-404.

Osgood, C. E., and P. H. Tannenbaum. The principle of congruity in the prediction of attitude change. *Psychol. Rev.*, 1955, *62*, 42-55.

Osgood, C. E., G. J. Suci, and P. H. Tannenbaum. *The measurement of meaning.* Urbana: Univer. Illinois Press, 1957.

Rosenberg, M. J., C. I. Hovland, W. J. McGuire, R. P. Abelson, and J. W. Brehm. *Attitude organization and change.* New Haven: Yale Univer. Press, 1960.

Rosenberg, M. J., and C. W. Gardner. Case report: Some dynamic aspects of posthypnotic compliance. *J. abnorm. soc. Psychol.*, 1958, *57*, 351-366.

Schein, E. H. The Chinese indoctrination program for prisoners of war: A study of attempted "brainwashing." In Maccoby, Eleanor E., T. M. Newcomb, and E. L. Hartley

(Eds.) *Readings in social psychology*, 3rd ed. New York: Holt, 1958.

Schein, E. H. *Coercive persuasion.* New York: Norton, 1961.

Tannenbaum, P. H. Attitudes toward source and concept as factors in attitude change through communications. Unpublished doctoral dissertation, Univer. of Illinois, 1953.

Verplanck, W. S. The operant, from rat to man: An introduction to some recent experiments on human behavior. *Trans. N. Y. Acad. Sci.,* 1955, *17,* 594-601.

Weitzenhoffer, A. M. *Hypnotism: An objective study in suggestibility.* New York: Wiley, 1953.

Zajonc, R. B. Balance, congruity, and dissonance. *Publ. Opin. Quart.,* 1960, *24,* 280-296.

✦ SELECTED READINGS

Festinger, L. *A theory of cognitive dissonance.* New York: Row, Peterson, 1957.

Osgood, C. E., and P. H. Tannenbaum. The principle of congruity in the prediction of attitude change. *Psychol. Rev.,* 1955, *62,* 42-55.

Rosenberg, M. J., C. I. Hovland, W. J. McGuire, R. P. Abelson, and J. W. Brehm. *Attitude organization and change.* New Haven: Yale Univer. Press, 1960.

2 ✦ CONTEMPORARY PSYCHOPHYSICS

EUGENE GALANTER
UNIVERSITY OF WASHINGTON

THIS MANUSCRIPT WAS PREPARED WITH THE SUPPORT OF THE OFFICE OF NAVAL RESEARCH CONTRACT NONR-551(37) AND THE UNIVERSITY OF PENNSYLVANIA. REPRODUCTION IN WHOLE OR PART IS PERMITTED FOR ANY PURPOSE OF THE UNITED STATES GOVERNMENT.

A jet transport comes thundering down the sky to land at a field unseen by the captain . . . somewhere in northern Canada, a soldier, his eyes fixed unwaveringly on the screen of a radar 'scope, reaches for the red button that will launch rocket interceptors to meet a potential enemy . . . a doctor removes his stethoscope from the chest of a patient, glances over a medical history, and proceeds to write out a prescription . . . a geologist looks over the wavy lines of a seismic record and directs a team of well drillers to expend time, effort, and money sinking an oil well at a particular point on the earth's surface. All these people are displaying behavior that is under the most marvelous and subtle control of their sensory systems. They are all engaged in evaluating, judging, expecting, and deciding. The consequences of their actions can entail profound alterations in the economy of the nation, the saving or loss of life, or the beginning of a catastrophic war. In each case, their actions have been subserved, not by the direct apprehension of things, but rather by their ability to detect and discriminate small differences that signaled large effects.

This ability to discriminate, in the nonpejorative sense of that term, constitutes a major field of study for the experimental psychologist. What is it that people do when they discriminate, how do they do it, how can we understand it, what are its limits, and so on? These are the questions we shall examine in this chapter.

Let us consider first the airline captain and the problems he faces. In the passenger cabin of a modern jet airliner people are chatting amiably. Perhaps it is cocktail time somewhere over the Atlantic on a flight from Paris to New York. In the cockpit of the plane, however, things are not quite so calm. It would be romantic to describe the interior of the cockpit as dark and lashed with rain, with only the jagged streaks of lightning breaking the impenetrable blackness on the outside. But today's jet planes fly so high that most of the weather is beneath them. This weather, of course, is of no small concern to the pilot, because he must eventually descend through it, even though most of the trip is conducted in the clear air of the stratosphere at altitudes of perhaps 35,000 feet. Fifteen thousand feet below him are the tops of the clouds. The world looks the same in all directions. This is the substance of the problem he faces. He must find New York City. Specifically, he must find the two square miles of New York City called Idlewild International Airport. Electronic ingenuity makes this feasible, but it is the discriminative capacities of the man that make it possible.

Idlewild International has a radio that transmits signals in all directions. In the airliner is a radio receiver that, when properly tuned to sufficiently strong signals, actuates a radio compass to point in the direction of the station. Once this compass is pointing in the appropriate direction, finding the airport is easy. But the first step is to tune in the radio. At a distance of five hundred miles from the transmitter all that is heard is the clash and sputter of static. The dial of the set must be tuned to the frequency of the Idlewild Radio. The station can be identified because it emits a series of high-pitched tones that spell out in Morse Code the letters IDL. With his earphones on, the pilot rocks the dial in the vicinity of the frequency that he knows Idlewild is using. Through the static he searches for the code signal that marks the correct frequency. These signals can be heard long before the radio compass begins to operate, and it is important that the pilot tune correctly in order to be sure the compass points to New York rather than, say, Miami. He wants to reach New York as quickly as possible, because once down in the clouds he may have to spend time and valuable fuel waiting for permission to land.

Now he thinks he detects, through the noise, the Idlewild call letters. He leaves the dial set, removes the earphones, and returns to his flying. Eventually, if he was right, the radio compass will become activated and point in the appropriate direction. If he was wrong, valuable time and fuel will have been lost.

Here we see some typical problems that the sensory systems of man are called upon to perform. We call the first of these the *detection problem*. The question that is asked is, "Is there anything there?" The second problem we shall call the *recognition problem*. This problem can be phrased as, "What is it?" or "Is it Idlewild?" Detection and recognition are two of the most fundamental things that man does. Normally, we do them quite cavalierly, because the objects that we detect and recognize are so strong in their appearances we rarely fail. Only when we are placed in a difficult perceptual situation can we comprehend the truly complex roles played by the sensory systems. For this reason, these apparently mundane acts are often studied when the perceptual task is overtly simple and impoverished.

Once the plane is headed directly toward New York the flying becomes relatively routine. But when the descent is started, and the windshield suddenly becomes a film of gray fog, new problems arise. The plane is now close enough to Idlewild to pick up all the radio signals that the airport is transmitting. And a new kind of signal is brought into play. Special radios at the airport transmit very narrow beams that are designed to guide the pilot down an invisible path through the clouds to the runway. These beams, called "localizers," are of two kinds. The first actuates a pointer either left or right to indicate that the plane is either left or right of an imaginary line extending the center line of the runway. The second beam, the Glide Slope, actuates a horizontal pointer to indicate whether the plane is above or below the elevation required to arrive at the runway at the proper height. These two needles, one suspended vertically and the other horizontally, are encased in the same gauge. The task of the pilot is to keep both of them centered. This must be done while the plane is undergoing all the perturbations that the atmosphere can arrange. The pilot must therefore make movements to pursue the changes in the needle positions in order to guide the plane safely to a landing. Has the glide slope needle drifted slightly below center? If so, the air speed must be increased slightly. Has the localizer needle drifted slightly to the left? If so, the plane must be turned slightly to the left to bring it back on course. Tasks like these constitute a third set of perceptual issues we shall call the *discrimination problem*. The question that is posed by this class of problems is, "Is this different from that?"

But the landing is not yet complete. Now, as the plane descends below three hundred feet, the windshield clears, and the pilot sees the runway ahead of him. The instrument landing system and his own discriminative capacity have placed him neatly in line with the runway. The remainder of the landing is accomplished by the pilot's direct appreciation of the environment. But judgments are still called for. At a precise distance above the ground, a distance smaller than the error of the altimeters in the airplane, the pilot must decide that the time has come to ease back the nose of the plane in order to dissipate the remaining air speed. This judgment of the distance left before the wheels touch is extremely critical and difficult. It is the judgment that keeps most student pilots sweating for the first hundred hours of their flying time. This problem, the problem of "How high am I?" we call the *scaling problem*. In its general form, the scaling problem deals with questions like, "How much of x is there?"

These four problems, detection, recognition, discrimination, and scaling, constitute the core of a segment of experimental psychology called psychophysics. The name psychophysics derives from the classical question about the relation between the physical environment and the mind. Today, modern psychophysicists are not professionally concerned with this philosophical issue of the mind-body relation, but rather with the constraints that are placed upon the behavior of a person in his judgments, actions, and so on, by the sea of physical energies that surround him. We shall study these problems in the order we have listed them. Our task will be to see how the modern psychologist formulates the issues that he studies. It is toward this goal of problem formulation that we will direct most of our attention. The immediate and apparent problems will be replaced by more subtle and probing issues. Basically, the direction of our inquiry will turn not on the connection between stimuli and responses or reactions, but rather on the constraints on responses that the stimuli impose. We shall study the ways in which the response structure of the person remains constant under the flux of physical events. We shall see that there are underlying laws of behavior which transcend the variations in the impinging stimulation. We shall not concern ourselves with the difference, for example, between the detection of sounds and of lights, but rather with the act of detection. The question of whether we change our ways of detecting things when the signal is auditory or visual is an important one, but we shall see that we can ask questions that are independent of whether the eyes or the ears are the appropriate receiving device. For this reason, we will not be concerned with the specific physiological properties of the receptors. This is not to say that the study of the receptor mechanisms and their physiological bases is uninteresting or irrelevant. Rather it is that there does exist a class of well-formulated problems that are independent of the particular structure of the receptor system. These problems constitute the source of the basic psychological issues of perception.

THE DETECTION PROBLEM

Classically, detection was viewed as the question of how much sound (light, odor, or pressure) was needed in order for a person to be able to say, "I heard (saw, smelled, or felt) something." The reason that such a question exists at all is because people are not infinitely sensitive. There are measurable amounts of energy that simply do not have an effect on people's behavior. The old name for this limit or lower bound of sensitivity is the "absolute threshold." The reason for calling it a "threshold" is that it was thought that as the energy impinging on a person is reduced, there comes a point at which his report that something is present changes abruptly to a report that nothing is present. This change-over point then defines the absolute threshold. Observe that the absolute threshold is a value on the energy scale *defined by the behavior* of the subject. The units in which the threshold is measured, therefore, are units of energy. But although the measure of the threshold is given in energy units, the determination of the threshold is by psychological techniques.

The form of behavior that might be expected if we measured the absolute threshold is shown in Figure 1. Along the abscissa (the horizonal axis) is the measure of the physical energy. Along the ordinate (the vertical axis) is the percentage or proportion of times that the person reports that a signal is present. Observe that below an energy level equal to five units the person never reports a signal present, whereas above five units, he always reports something is there. Unfortunately, this anticipation—theory—turns out to be wrong. A standard method to determine the absolute threshold requires a person to judge whether or not a signal is presented on each of a large number of trials. From trial to trial the signal energy is varied, and a record is kept of what the person says. An example of the result of an experiment of this kind is shown

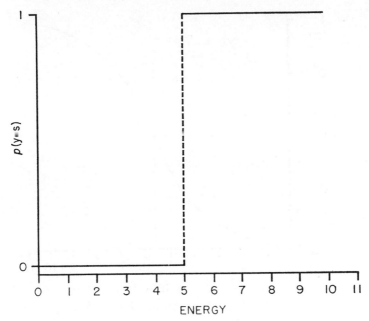

Fig. 1. A possible threshold function

in Figure 2. Here we again plot the signal energy impinging on the subject along the abscissa. The relative frequency of "Yes" responses that the subject makes is plotted along the ordinate. What we see in Figure 2 is that as the signal energy increases, the relative frequency of reporting the signal goes up gradually, not in a single jump as anticipated in Figure 1.

A digression is in order about this relative-frequency measure. A fundamental assumption made by psychophysicists is that the behavior of a person (such as saying "Yes") has some "strength." This strength is presumed to be a magnitude that can be represented by a number. But what kind of number is it? The answer that has been almost universally adopted is that the strength of a particular bit of behavior, a particular response, is given by a numerical estimate of the likelihood that

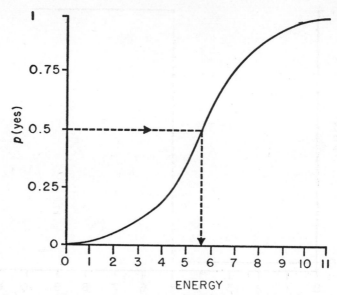

Fig. 2. An actual threshold function

the response will occur. The standard method for estimating this likelihood or, as it is called, *response probability*, is to count the number of times the response in question occurred under given conditions and divide it by the number of times that the response in question could have occurred under the same conditions. Thus, we have the formula: p (Yes) = number of "Yes" responses / (number of "Yes" responses + number of "No" responses). In general, if there are N opportunities to respond, of which N_i are occurrences of the response i, whose strength we wish to measure, then the estimate of the probability of i occurring is

$$p(i) = N_i/N.$$

Observe that $p(i)$ is an *estimate* of a theoretical value that we can never know unless N becomes infinitely large. Thus, there will always be some error in the estimate of the strength of the response. The larger the size of N, the smaller on the average will be the error of our estimate. The trouble is that the error decreases only as the square root of N. Thus, we must make N four times as large to reduce the error by a factor of 2. This becomes extremely costly. But, regardless of the empirical difficulties in collecting enough data, if we obtain estimates of the probability of saying "Yes" as a function of the intensity of the stimuli that we use, we obtain results like those shown in Figure 2. The probability of detection is not an all-or-none affair, as Figure 1 suggests, but rather it changes slowly as the signal strength increases.

Where then is the absolute threshold? There is no obvious answer to this question. What people have done is to select some arbitrary value of the response strength and define the stimulus associated with this arbitrary value as the absolute threshold. The arbitrary value usually selected for the absolute threshold is the value at which the probability of saying "Yes" equals the probability of saying "No"; that is, where they both equal 0.50. For the data displayed in Figure 2 the value

TABLE 1. SOME APPROXIMATE DETECTION THRESHOLD VALUES

Sense modality	Detection threshold
Light	A candle flame seen at 30 miles on a dark clear night (ca. 10 quanta).
Sound	The tick of a watch under quiet conditions at twenty feet (ca. 0.0002 dynes/cm²).
Taste	One teaspoon of sugar in 2 gallons of water.
Smell	One drop of perfume diffused into the entire volume of a 3 room apartment.
Touch	The wing of a bee falling on your cheek from a distance of 1 cm.

of the absolute threshold is therefore 5.6 units of energy. Can you see how we found this number?

The absolute threshold can be determined for any of the various modes of perception, and for each of these a particular value can be found that represents the weakest stimulus that can still be detected 50 percent of the time. Table 1 shows some representative values of the absolute threshold.

Today, the absolute threshold is often called the detection threshold. The reason for this change of name is that there is a serious question as to whether the detection threshold is in any sense absolute. The fact of the matter is obviously that the probability of detection below 50 percent shows the same regularity as it does above 50 percent. This suggests that on some of those trials the subject was detecting something and therefore the 50 percent point is not an "absolute" bound on his detection capacities.

But where then is the problem, if we have a method to determine an arbitrary stimulus value that we can call the detection threshold? To see whether there is any problem let us examine in more detail exactly what is done on an experimental trial. On each one of the hundreds of experimental trials in which a detection threshold is being measured, some stimulus value, say, energy level 4, is presented to the subject and he responds with the word "Yes" or "No," indicating whether or not he was able to detect it. On each trial, then, the same stimulus is presented to him, and his response is presumed to indicate something about his sensory capacities. But if the subject knows that a stimulus is being presented on every trial, what is to stop him from saying "Yes" on every trial? Obviously nothing but his inherent honesty. However, the inherent honesty of an informant is not the kind of guarantee that a scientist likes as far as his data are concerned. We want to have some way to find out if the subject is being honest. This is not to impugn the moral integrity of the subject, but rather to suggest that he himself may not know whether he detects a signal or not, and he may report "Yes" because he would rather have a higher score than a lower one. This is certainly a reasonable motive.

But what have we said? Presumably, we are studying the sensory capacities of the subject and not his motives. However, if we suspect that his motives are affecting what he says, then certainly we will have to find some way either to eliminate them or to bring them under our control. Thus, we see that with the introduction of the term "motivation" and its concomitant implications, something other than the signal may be affecting whether the subject says "Yes" or "No."

Experimenters have been aware of this difficulty for a long time. At first they inserted special trials in the course of an experiment in which no signal was presented at all. These so-called catch-trials should have been answered "No" by any subject who was being honest in reporting what he heard. If the subject said "Yes" to many of these catch-trials, he was warned by the experimenter, or his data were disregarded. If only a few out of the many thousand experimental trials were catch-trials, it could have been the case that the subject would, by chance, say "No" on those trials even though he was often reporting the presence of signals which he could not in fact detect. So the catch-trials have to become part of the experimental procedure itself if we are to make any sense out of the behavior that the subject exhibits. The impressive regularity of the observed results suggest that the subject is doing something sensible, that he is not trying to fool anyone, but it is not clear exactly what it is that he is doing.

Suppose we redesign the classical absolute threshold experiment. The new design will be simpler because we are concerned now mainly with whether or not the observer reports hearing stimuli when in fact none are present. Reports of the presence of the stimulus when there is none are called *false-alarms*. Our concern is with the chance that a false-alarm will occur, and if so, why. So our problem has shifted from an interest in a "threshold" to an interest in a relation between two kinds of responses: correct detection and false-alarms.

Surely the relation between these two kinds of responses depends on the signal, but the signal only sets the stage, as it were, for the response relation to reveal itself. The law relating the responses is in some sense completely contained in the person, and in this sense is a true psychological law rather than a psychophysical law. Psychophysical laws will be discussed later.

It should be clear that there are two kinds of errors that can be made. These are failures to detect a signal when it is there, and reports of a signal when it is not there. Each of these errors can be grievous depending upon the task at hand, but, as we shall see, we cannot eliminate both at the same time. We therefore direct our attention to the relation between them, with the expectation that the nature of this relation will tell us something about the person. Let us then design an experiment in which there are two kinds of experimental trials. On one, the experimenter presents no signal, and on the other he presents a signal. The signal that is presented is weak enough so that on some occasions the observer is unable to detect its presence. That is, it will be weak enough so that the probability of saying "Yes" is less than 1. If in fact the observer is being perfectly "honest," then on those trials on which no signal is presented, the probability of saying "Yes" should equal 0, while on those trials on which a signal is presented, the

TABLE 2. A POSSIBLE DETECTION THRESHOLD RESULT

RESPONSE

		Yes	No
S I G N A L	*On*	0.86	0.14
	Off	0	1.00

probability of saying "Yes" should be something large, but not quite 1. That value should depend only on the signal strength. The ideal result of this simple detection experiment should look like Table 2. When the experiment is performed, the results are more like those shown in Table 3. The observer

TABLE 3.   AN ACTUAL DETECTION THRESHOLD RESULT

RESPONSE

		Yes	No
S	On	0.86	0.14
I			
G			
N			
A	Off	0.08	0.92
L			

occasionally says there is a signal when in fact it is not presented, and occasionally says there is no signal when in fact it is presented.

Now, what kinds of things could have produced the report of a signal when none is presented? One is the expectations that the subject has or develops during the experiment. If, for example, for ten trials in a row he hears nothing and so reports "No" every time, he may become concerned that he is saying "No" too often. The result is that he will be strongly tempted to say "Yes," even though he hears no signal. If the subject's expectations can alter his responses we should be able to observe this by changing the basis on which his expectations are founded. If, for example, we present a signal on almost all trials and only rarely fail to present it, then the subject will come to expect a signal almost always, and the probability of a false-alarm should be higher than it would be if he did not expect signals so frequently. On the other hand, if signals are rare, then we would anticipate that he would tend to assume that no signal was present. The result of this expectation would be to raise the number of "no" responses to the relatively rare occurrences of the signal. Tables 4 and 5 show the results that we obtain when, for Table 4, the signal

TABLE 4.   RESPONSE PROBABILITIES FOR A SIGNAL PRESENTATION PROBABILITY OF 0.90

RESPONSE

		Yes	*No*
S I G N A L	*On*	0.97	0.03
	Off	0.62	0.38

TABLE 5.   RESPONSE PROBABILITIES FOR A SIGNAL PRESENTATION PROBABILITY OF 0.10

RESPONSE

		Yes	*No*
S I G N A L	*On*	0.28	0.72
	Off	0.04	0.96

is presented on 90 percent of the trials and no signal is presented on 10 percent, and for Table 5, when no signal is presented on 90 percent of the trials, and a signal is presented on 10 percent. Thus, if we vary the (signal) presentation probabilities and, consequently, the expectations of the subject, we cause a systematic change in the percentage of false-alarms that the subject makes, as well as in the percentage of "correct" detections. Therefore, we can alter the apparent value of the detection threshold without making any change in the signal energy. The detection threshold, although it appeared to be a reasonable issue to study, turns out to be highly dependent on things other than the stimulus, specifically, upon the expectations that the subject has as to whether a stimulus will be present or not.

If we explore this phenomenon systematically by holding the stimulus strength fixed and looking at a number of differ-

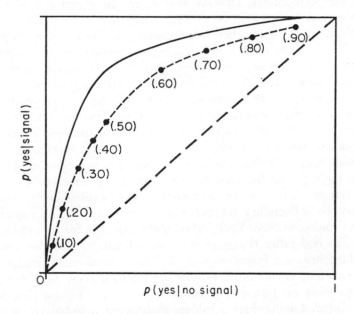

Fig. 3. Iso-sensitivity curves. The solid line is the curve for a strong signal. The dashed line is the curve for an undetectable signal. The points represent a medium signal presented at various probabilities

ent presentation probabilities, then we can see how the probability that the subject will say "Yes" given that the signal is present depends on the probability that he will say "Yes" given that no signal is present. This function, called an *iso-sensitivity contour*, or a *response-operating characteristic*, is shown in Figure 3. Here, along the abscissa, we plot the probability that the subject will say "Yes" given that *no* signal is presented. On the ordinate is the probability that the subject says "Yes" given that the signal *is* presented. The points that make up this curve represent different proportions of times that the signal was presented. The percentages in parentheses next to the points indicate how often a signal was presented in that experiment. Observe that when the signal is rare the subject does not say "Yes" very frequently even when it is presented, whereas when it is frequent, the subject says "Yes" quite often even when the signal is not presented. The points that are plotted are for a fixed signal value. When a stronger signal is used, the iso-sensitivity curve arches higher, as shown by the solid line above the set of points. If the signal is weaker, the iso-sensitivity curve is closer to the 45° line, like the dashed line below the data points. We can argue on the basis of these data that there is no simply observed detection threshold, but rather that the subject adjusts his responses to both the signal strength and to his expectations concerning the signals.

But we have not yet exhausted all the possible factors that may be influencing his behavior. When our airline captain was tuning in New York radio, it was valuable for him to find it. He had other things to do besides fiddle with radio dials. Therefore, we might expect that he would make mistakes concerning the identification or detection of New York radio, depending on how important it was at that moment that he found it. Or consider a soldier monitoring a radar 'scope to detect enemy aircraft. The probability of a signal is very low, and therefore in terms of the iso-sensitivity curves that we have seen, the probability that he will correctly detect the signal when it is present is also very low. But the value of correctly detecting a signal is extremely high, whereas the cost of not detecting a signal may be catastrophic. Therefore, even though his expectation that a signal will be present is very small, the cost to him of not detecting one that is there is very large. This certainly must induce a certain conflict in his willingness to report the occurrence of an ambiguous sensory event. He must choose what kinds of mistakes he is willing to make.

The following experiment simply exaggerates the kind of conflict that occurs in life. Suppose the signal is presented 50 percent of the time, and therefore, from Figure 3, the probability of reporting it when it is present is 0.60 and the probability of reporting it when in fact it is absent is 0.20. Now suppose we offer the observer a bonus of ten cents for each correct detection of a signal. What will happen? If we do not penalize false-alarms—reports of a signal when it is not there—it is clear that he will tend to say "Yes" more often than he did previously. This is because whenever he says "Yes" and the signal is there he receives a dime, yet when he says "Yes" and the signal is not there he loses nothing. On these grounds an observer could rationally argue that he should say "Yes" all the time.

So if we are going to pay him for saying "Yes" under some conditions we had better introduce some penalty for saying "Yes" at the wrong time. We must introduce a new set of constraints into the experiment—constraints which affect his motives and which take into account that the subject may have reasons quite independent of the signal or of his expectation for saying "Yes" or "No." These new conditions are technically called the *outcome structure* of the experiment.

The outcome structure of a psychophysical experiment is often communicated to the observer by giving him what is called a *payoff* function. This is a list of the prizes and penalties that he receives depending on what he does under the various stimulus conditions. An example of a payoff function coupled with our previous signal detection experiment looks like Table 6. Here we see that if he says "Yes" when a signal is present, he receives ten cents; if he says "Yes" when a signal is not present, he loses five cents; when he says "No" and a signal is present, he loses five cents; and when he says "No" and a signal is not present, he gains ten cents. For this payoff function it is obviously to the observer's advantage to be "right" as often as possible. The term "right" is defined here by the experimental condition and not by other intrinsic

TABLE 6. A PAYOFF FUNCTION FOR A SIGNAL DETECTION EXPERIMENT

RESPONSE

		Yes	*No*
S I G	*On*	10¢	−5¢
N A L	*Off*	−5¢	10¢

For this payoff function false alarms are not as heavily penalized as correct responses are rewarded.

characteristics. Specifically, the observer is right under two conditions: when he says "Yes" and the experimenter has turned on the signal, and when he says "No" and the experimenter has not turned on the signal. The effects of the payoff function on the observer's behavior show us how these specific motives also influence the reports he makes about these simple signals.

Beginning with the assumption that behavior in a simple detection experiment is contingent only upon the stimuli that occur in the course of that experiment, we have discovered that the behavioral measures are influenced by at least two other factors: the expectation that the subject has, which is contingent upon the signal probability, and the motives induced by the payoff function.

If we keep the signal probability and the signal strength fixed, and vary only the relative value of saying "Yes" and "No" by appropriate variations of the payoff function, we can trace out iso-sensitivity curves analogous to the kind we observe when we vary the signal probability. As a result, we can find points where a particular payoff function has the same effect as a particular change in signal probability. Therefore, we can map out the trading relations between expectations and values for a particular subject in a detection experiment. An increase in the presentation probability of 10 percent may, for example, be exactly offset by a reduction in value of a "Yes" response of 20 percent, and so on. Even though the experimenter can change the signal probabilities and the payoffs separately, the two variables have an equivalent effect only on how the subject biases his reports. The existence of this trading relation suggests that the effects of both variables can be summarized by a single quantity, which we shall call a response bias. In these terms then, both expectations and motives affect the response bias of the observer.

Although response biases reflect the effects upon behavior of both expectations and values, there is some hope that the two effects can be decomposed. What one would like to do is propose a theory that lets us calculate a numerical representation of the effect of the payoff function, and, independently, the effect of the presentation probability, and then gives the combinatorial principle that will yield a number that represents the total response bias effect. The result of theory of this kind will be not only to illuminate the effects of stimuli upon judgments, but also to give us new insights into the nature of motivation itself. If we are able to find numerical representations for the degree of effect of a payoff matrix, then we can reasonably assert that we have discovered something about the nature of the motivating factors that the payoff matrix presumably induces. A psychophysical experiment, therefore, is more than just a study of the effects of sensory events upon behavior, it is composed of the effects of prior experience (learning) and of motivation upon that same behavior.

In all the experiments that have been described so far, we have presumed that the only stimuli impinging upon the subject were the stimuli about which he was to make his judgments. This, of course, is empirically false. A tremendous amount of "background" stimulation was also present. In fact, in many experiments, an endeavor is made to eliminate this background stimulation by imposing a controlled background upon the stimuli. Thus, for example, in an experiment on the detection of acoustic stimuli, the subject may be listening for a tone that does not appear out of a silent background, but rather comes out of a noisy background. The idea here is that the introduction of experimentally controlled noise gives greater

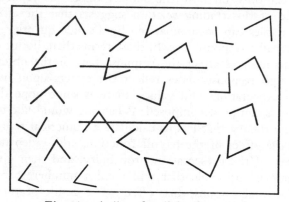

Fig. 4. A "random" background

reliability to the experiment than does the uncontrolled existence of extraneous factors that also constitute what could be called "noise." In an experiment on hearing, the notion that the background is "noisy" is a reasonable one. In other sense modalities, the notion of noise is less appropriate, unless the term "noise" is generalized to include more kinds of things than simply acoustic noise. This is what we do. The term "noise" in its technical sense refers to any background stimulation that is not systematically associated with the events that are the primary judgmental concern.

If the stimuli that constitute the background are systematically associated (in some intuitive sense) with the stimuli that are to be judged, then we are dealing with phenomena that have been classically called "perceptual" judgments. That is to say, if we are asked to judge the difference in lengths of two lines shown in Figure 4 against a background of randomly scattered "V's," the effect of the "noise" does not normally introduce any bias into the judgment. Most people are willing to agree that the two lines appear to be of equal length. On the other hand, if the "V's" are scattered in a systematic way with respect to the lines, as in Figure 5, then the judgment

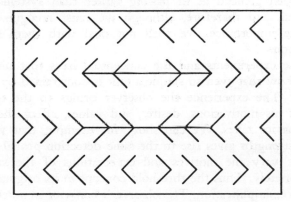

Fig. 5. A "systematic" background

about the relative lengths of the lines is seriously biased. This kind of display is often called an illusion, because the measured lengths of the lines do not agree with the impressions that a person has. But obviously these impressions are not contingent upon the lines alone. Rather, they depend upon a systematic orientation of background effects that interact very strongly with the stimuli to be judged. These interactive effects of backgrounds that are systematically related to the stimuli exist even though the subject is instructed to make judgments without regard to these "extraneous" events.

The study of the interactive effects of backgrounds with stimulation has been a province of research on perception. Unhappily, little more than simple empirical generalizations have resulted from this research. However, recent psychophysical work has been directed toward the nature of these background effects as they interact with the subject's expectations and his motives. The amount of this research has been slight. For example, it has been found that the illusion of unequal lengths seen in Figure 5 cannot be entirely nullified by appropriate payoffs that reward accurate reports and penalize inaccurate ones. But these background variables have only been glanced at in passing rather than systematically explored, and therefore, although we must recognize their ultimate importance, we shall not deal with them in our discussion.

These experiments and the conceptual basis that underlies them show that even so simple a task is constrained by many factors. The experience the observer brings to the task, as well as his motivations, desires, and values, affect the form his behavior takes. We can show, for example, that varying signal strengths gives rise to the same detection probability if we but vary the motives and expectations of the subjects appropriately. Thus the threshold concept in its original form is an oversimplification. The observer's behavior in a detection task is ambiguous. The solution for the observer is some compromise between his values, his expectations, and the sensory limits of his eyes or ears.

Our study of detection has led to a consideration of the constellation of variables that are relevant to this task. Psychophysicists used to argue that responses of a person are a function of the stimulus; today, it is clear that they are dependent also upon the stimulus probability and the observer's motives. The effects of these response bias factors appear to be independent of the stimulus effects. Discovery of the nature of the dependence of responses upon these two independent factors is a major result of the study of detection. These experiments have decomposed the behavior of the subject into two presumably independent components. On the one hand, the behavior is surely dependent upon the stimulus strength, just as had been thought in the past. On the other hand, however, the person can bias the responses that he chooses to select, independently of the stimulating conditions. The response bias itself is not a simple variable, but rather is the result of the interplay of the observer's motives, his expectations, and background effects. Figure 6 is a graphical conception of the factors

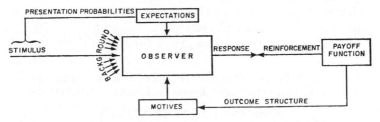

Fig. 6. The conceptual form of a psychophysical experiment

that enter into the response of a subject to the presentation of a simple stimulus. As a result, the subject's behavior is analyzable into several parts. One would like to be able to show that this analysis is tenable and extends over more than the simple detection experiment. This has been done by extending the detection experiment to several more complex forms.

We have considered only the simplest case of detection, the so-called "yes-no" design. What now if we complicate the detection task slightly into what has come to be called the "forced-choice" design? Let us assume, in order to understand this experiment, that an observer is sitting before a radar screen. He knows for certain that a target is present somewhere in the environment. The question we ask him is whether the target is on the left side of the screen or on the right side. Whether something is present or not is not at issue. The only question is "Where is it?" If we abstract the essential structure of this experiment we see that the subject is told on each trial that a signal will be presented in one of two places or times (it could just as well be three, four, five, or any fixed number). His task is to report where the signal is located. One line of analysis that psychologists have adopted for the forced-choice experiment is to treat it as two (or three, or four, or five, or n) simultaneous, correlated, yes-no experiments. Thus, on each trial, the observer can be thought of as first looking at one place, and deciding whether the stimulus is present or not, and then looking at the other place(s), and deciding similarly, subject to the a priori constraint that it must be in only one of the various places.

By coupling the appropriate payoff function (Table 7) with

TABLE 7. A PAYOFF FUNCTION FOR A FOUR-ALTERNATIVE FORCED-CHOICE EXPERIMENT WITH EQUALLY LIKELY PRESENTATIONS

RESPONSE ALTERNATIVES

		1	2	3	4
	1	10¢	−2¢	−3¢	−4¢
	2	−2¢	10¢	−2¢	−3¢
	3	−3¢	−2¢	10¢	10¢
	4	−4¢	−3¢	−2¢	−2¢

SIGNAL LOCUS

this design, one obtains as a table of responses something like that shown in Table 8. Because we can vary the probability

TABLE 8. Hypothetical Response Data from a Four-Alternative Forced-Choice Experiment with Payoff as in Table 7

RESPONSE ALTERNATIVES

		1	2	3	4
S I G N A L	L O C U S				
	1	0.91	0.04	0.03	0.02
	2	0.09	0.83	0.06	0.02
	3	0.08	0.13	0.74	0.05
	4	0.02	0.03	0.17	0.88

of the stimulus occurring in each of the four places, we can again induce response bias via the subject's expectation. In addition, with appropriate payoff functions, we can vary the preference that the subject has for saying the signal is in one rather than another place. The signal strength is of course kept fixed in the experiment. Experiments like this show that although the response probabilities are quite different from what they are for a simple yes-no experiment, the theoretical decomposition of the behavior leaves the signal strength contribution the same as it was for the yes-no experiment. The component contributed by the response bias is the only thing that is altered. Thus, we have evidence that indeed there is independence between the effects of the signal on the subject's behavior and the effects of other biasing factors such as his motives and his expectations.

The utility of the forced-choice experiment resides in the fact that we are able to anticipate behavior in complex situations by an analysis of the constraints on the behavior in a simple task such as the yes-no experiment. We still have to estimate independently for the two experiments the effect of the response biases, but the direction of current research, both theoretical and empirical, is to find some way to predict what the response bias will be from an analysis of the payoff matrix and the stimulus probabilities. When this can be done we will have a theory that is capable of describing in detail the behavior of a subject in detection tasks of a variety of kinds and complexities from an analysis of the signal strength, the signal probability, and the particular payoff function.

This predictive power will help in the design of appropriate displays to maximize the effectiveness of people who have to detect ambiguous signals. One can argue, for example, that because the detection probability is increased when the probability of a signal is high, it might be worthwhile to train people who watch for targets on radar screens with a large number of simulated false targets. In addition, one would expect that appropriate payoff functions which reward correct detection and punish false-alarms would help keep the behavior within bounds.

But detection alone is not the be-all and end-all of human sensory activity. In point of fact it is only the first step on the more complex road to the recognition of what the signal is. Detection and recognition are almost always conjoined in normal human activity. We have pulled them apart here in order to analyze detection. We turn now to the recognition problem that presumably follows upon the detection of a signal.

THE RECOGNITION PROBLEM

The pathologist lifts his head from the microscope . . . are the cells on the slide malignant or normal? The doctor removes his stethoscope from the patient's chest . . . was the sound the slurring of a diseased heart or the normal pulsings of the healthy? The radar operator sees a target on the screen . . . is it foe or friend? Many of the perceptual tasks that we perform are dependent upon stimulus presentations that are clearly above the detection threshold, but that can take a variety of forms. Our problem in these cases is to "recognize" which of the various possibilities has occurred. Moreover, when signals are difficult to detect it is rare not to have to recognize which of several possibilties occurred, assuming any did. If the stimulus display is weak or ambiguous, we may not even be sure that we have detected the stimulus, and yet we may be called upon to make a response indicating which of several possible stimuli it could be if one had been there.

We shall distinguish these two cases in our discussion. In the first case, we assume that the stimuli are sufficiently detectable for there to be no question whether or not a stimulus is present. The only task is to decide which of the several possibilities it happens to be. In the second case, we shall be concerned with the problem of simultaneous detection and recognition. That is to say, not only are we asked to tell whether a stimulus is present or not, but regardless of our answer to this question, we are to tell which it is.

Consider first the case of stimuli clearly above the detection threshold, and ask simply what determines recognition. Let us begin by asking what behavior we would expect of a person who is unable to recognize anything, but who knows that one of two different stimuli is present. Suppose, for example, that he is presented with a paper cup containing either *x*-cola or *y*-cola. What is the likelihood that he will be correct in deciding that the cup contains *x*-cola, even if he is unable to recognize the difference between the two drinks? The answer is that he will be correct about half the time. On any single occasion, then, we would not consider it remarkable if a person happened to be correct in identifying the cola, even though he was unable to distinguish between *x*- and *y*-cola. If there are only two alternatives, the chance of being correct (neglecting biases) is 50 percent, even though you have no information upon which to base a choice.

Now let us extend the set of possible alternatives from two to four. How likely is it that our insensitive subject will be correct when asked to recognize which of the four cola drinks he is tasting? Assuming no response biases, the chances are exactly $\frac{1}{4}$, when the stimuli provide no information whatsoever. If a person is correct on a single trial when the number of possibilities is four, we can again reasonably attribute the result to chance. Consider now a set of ten alternatives. The a priori likelihood that a person would be correct given that he had no information whatsoever is now $\frac{1}{10}$ or 0.10. And this time if the person chose correctly, we would be hard pressed to attribute it to chance alone. We would suspect more strongly that the person is able to distinguish among the variety. These considerations imply that we are more surprised when an insensitive person is able to identify correctly from a large set of alternatives than from a small set.

This degree of surprise or newsworthiness is called the *selective information* in the stimulus display. For example, you get very little information when you answer the telephone and someone says, "Hello." But if you answer the telephone and someone says, "The arms will be shipped in crates marked 'farm machinery,'" a tremendous amount of information has been transmitted, especially if the number of possible alternatives is large.

The amount of information in a stimulus display is related to the number of alternatives that could possibly appear. A measure of the amount of information in a set of stimuli is based on how many questions a person would have to ask to find out which member of the set had been presented.

Consider the case of two alternatives. If you know that the alternatives are *x* and *y*, then an answer to the question "Is it *x*?" tells you unambiguously which it was. If the answer is "No," then you know it is *y*. In a display consisting of two possible alternatives, only one unit or "bit" of information is needed. For four alternatives the minimum number of questions that would have to be asked is two. You would first ask a question that eliminates half the alternatives. For example, you ask, "Is it *x* or *y*?" If the answer is "No," then it must be *z* or *w*, in which case a single additional question tells you which it is. If there are four alternatives, this technique of first dividing the four into two and then dividing the remaining two into one gives you a guaranteed method for determining which it is in exactly two questions. The information measure of four alternatives is two. If there are eight alternatives, the number of required questions is, at most, three. By first asking whether it is in the first or last four, the problem is reduced to four alternatives, and then two more questions ensure the correct answer.

The number of bits of information in sets of discrete stimuli of the kind we have been talking about is equal to the number of questions needed to locate one element exactly. This number is called the logarithm to the base 2 of the number of stimuli. A logarithm is just a number. It is a number found by operating on other numbers, just as a sum is a number found by operating on other numbers. To find a sum you operate on a pair of numbers by adding them together. To find a logarithm, the operation is slightly trickier but no more subtle. The logarithm of a number, *x*, to the base 2, is merely the power to which the number 2 has to be raised in order to equal *x*. Thus, the logarithm to the base 2 of the number 8 is the number equal to the power to which 2 has to be raised in order to equal 8. Because $2^3 = 8$, 3 is the logarithm to the base 2 of 8. To check yourself, determine the logarithm to the base 2 of 16 and the logarithm to the base 2 of 64. You should get 4 and 6 as answers.

Logarithms for numbers that are other than integral powers of 2, that is, numbers whose powers of 2 are not whole numbers, can be found by using a table of logarithms.

Now, things become rather more complicated. In the sets of stimuli that we have been talking about, we have been tacitly assuming that each one can occur with equal likelihood. Suppose, however, that the chances are overwhelmingly in favor of one rather than the other of two alternatives. In that case, the guess that it is the more probable of the two is not as surprising as it would be if the two alternatives were equally probable. So it is necessary to introduce a correction on the measure of the amount of information in a set of alternatives. This correction takes into account the likelihood or probability that each of the possible alternatives will be selected. The formula for calculating the information measure for sets of stimuli with unequal presentation probabilities can be found in several of the selected readings.

But back from this short excursion into information theory to our immediate problem. The reason that information theory has been studied by people interested in recognition is that it measures the a priori difficulty of recognition. If a person is able to recognize correctly whichever of eight different stimuli have been presented to him, given that the stimuli are shown equally often, then we can say that with respect to this particular aggregate of stimuli his recognition capacity is three bits of information. How many bits of information can a person process with perfect recognition?

If stimuli are taken from one-dimensional physical continua such as sound intensity, or the brightness of light, or the pitches of various tones, and so on, then it turns out that the limits of the absolute recognition of these stimuli range between one and a half and four bits—that is, between about three and sixteen equally likely alternatives. This is a surprisingly small number. On the average, the number of equally likely alternatives that can be perfectly recognized is in the neighborhood of seven. This is a rather universal result when we consider only homogeneous stimuli that differ in one "dimension." If we add a second dimension to the stimuli, for example, making the sounds that we use vary in both loudness and pitch, then we can improve the recognition from about two bits to about three and a half. The added information obtained by increasing the number of dimensions is less than the sum of the information in each of the dimensions taken independently. As we add more dimensions, we continue to increase the number of different events that can be recognized, but the increase is at a decreasing rate. The absolute upper bound for stimuli of any complexity, that is for stimuli of any number of independent dimensions, is probably not greater than ten or eleven bits, i.e., one to two thousand stimuli. This number, of course, refers to equiprobable stimuli. The multitude of English words that can be recognized depends on the strong constraints in word probabilities imposed by the rules of grammar and statistical usage.

The information contained in the stimulus array can be thought of as being transmitted to the subject when he is able to recognize which of the stimuli has been shown. As we have said, the amount of transmitted information is rather small, and one wonders what could be done to increase it. We might try to spread out the differences between the stimuli. That is, instead of using tones that differ in loudness by very little, we might spread the tones out so that they differ in loudness by large amounts. It has been shown that independently of the spread between the various stimulus elements, the amount of information transmitted still reaches a maximum of three bits. Thus, there are only a few different things that can be perfectly recognized when the stimulus display is homogeneous and varies along a single uniform dimension.

This last point suggests that if one is interested in maximizing the transmitted information, the set of stimuli should consist of complex stimuli. This, however, is often not possible, because the nature of the display is constrained by the machinery that is used to generate it or by the inherent nature of the object we are trying to recognize. The physician listening for a heart murmur cannot increase the complexity of the signal. He must recognize or not as a function of what the signal happens to be. The consequences of these limitations on recognition are that people often group things so that many different stimuli are recognized as being the same. That is, people categorize things, and when they recognize, they recognize a category rather than a particular stimulus.

This phenomenon of categorization suggests that if the number of alternative response categories is fewer than the number of stimuli, category recognition for a large set of stimuli may be feasible. This is in fact the case.

It has been shown that the amount of information transmitted from a particular stimulus display is primarily determined by the number of response categories used by the observer rather than by the number of stimuli. Thus, twenty stimuli can be sorted into five categories without error, although twenty stimuli cannot be sorted into twenty categories without error.

In conjunction with the fact that the amount of transmitted information does not depend on the spread between the stimuli, this new result suggests that by recognizing in steps one may achieve better accuracy than by direct recognition. That is to say, if without difficulty we sort twenty stimuli into five categories, and then re-identify the stimuli when each category is re-presented, we may be able to achieve better recognition than if we tried to identify directly among the twenty stimuli. This stepwise or hierarchical recognition technique improves recognition by dividing the task into a sequence. The consequence is that time is traded for accuracy because the stimuli in the selected category must be presented again. The question is whether the repeated presentation of the original twenty stimuli as many times as needed would yield the same result as the piecewise method. Experiments of this kind have not been done. It remains to be seen whether the time taken to recognize is independent of the method through which recognition is achieved.

Up to now we have been talking about recognition experiments where the observer presumably knows the elements of the set of possible stimuli. We turn to the case where the observer does not have any information about the set of possible stimuli. In this experiment, recognition is much harder. This is related to the fact that more information must be transmitted as the size of the set of stimulus alternatives increases and, therefore, the a priori likelihood of correct recognition is smaller. If we tell a person that he is to recognize which of the twenty-six letters of the alphabet is flashed on a screen, he has a certain degree of difficulty. If, however, we tell him to recognize which of the first five letters is to be flashed on a screen, his recognition accuracy per letter increases. This result suggests that the person figuratively tunes himself to the set of possible stimuli that may be projected and thus recognizes as a consequence of this anticipation. But we can do the experiment another way. We first apparently flash one of the twenty-six letters on the screen, although we really flash only one of the first five. We then ask the subject which of the first five it was. Now, he could not have anticipated. And yet the result is that his accuracy is better than it would be if we had not told him that the presented letter was among the first five. This is a surprising result. It is as though he has stored the information from among the twenty-six alternatives but cannot recover it unless he is told the nature of the possible alternatives. It does not appear to be very critical whether the set of potential alternatives is indicated before or after the stimulus is presented. (This is not quite true in so far as presentation in advance gives a slight edge to recognition.)

Let us now consider the ability of the subject to recognize when the stimuli are just barely detectable. In this case, there are at least two experiments that we can do. On the one hand, we can present one or another or neither of a set of possible stimuli and ask him on every trial to recognize which it was. This means that on those trials when no stimulus was presented he is still required to make an identification. On the other hand, we can allow him to recognize which of the stimuli was presented or, if he believes that none was presented at all, to say that none was presented. The second experiment is capable of giving us more information than the first. Specifically, we can investigate what would have been said on those trials on which the observer reports inability to detect a stimulus. We can amplify the second form of the experiment by requiring detection and recognition. That is to say, we provide the subject with a set of four possible responses rather than the obvious three. The four responses are:

    i.   I detect it and it is x.
    ii.   I detect it and it is y.
    iii.   I did not detect it but I think it is x.
    iv.   I did not detect it but I think it is y.

The question of interest is whether, on the trials when a stimulus was presented and the subject reported that he did not detect it, he was more accurate in his recognition than he would be by chance alone. We presume that on the trials during which detection did not occur, he was still able to absorb some information from the stimulus display, as evidenced by the fact that his recognition responses were better than we would expect by chance alone. The fact of the matter is that this result probably does not occur. In a recent experiment an analysis was made of those recognition responses in which the subject reported that he did not detect a stimulus. These recognition responses consequent to his failure of detection were no better than chance alone would lead us to expect. Whenever the subject reported that he was unable to detect, even though a stimulus was present, he was in fact also unable to recognize. This suggests a certain priority for detection in our perceptual behavior. It also suggests that recognition experiments in which no reports of detection are allowed are not very sensible, because on those trials where the subject is unable to detect, he must distribute his recognition responses in unanalyzable ways. We get information from the subject by demanding that he give us the additional detection response. The consequence of this is the discovery that recognition is contingent upon prior detection. This is not a very startling result, except in conjunction with the fact that we previously discarded the notion of a threshold. This priority of detection, however, suggests that there is some sort of threshold, and below it no information is communicated about the stimulus.

Our initial study of detection suggested that a person continuously absorbs information about the presence or absence of a stimulus. These recognition experiments imply that this picture of what happens may not be accurate. When the subject reports that he has not detected a stimulus, that report may accurately portray his internal state insofar as he is unable to provide any other information about the stimulus when he is asked for particulars. So we see that recognition appears to depend very strongly upon detection. But this apparent priority of detection may in fact be illusory. For it turns out that detection itself is dependent upon the amount of information that the subject must process. That is, detection depends upon the subject's ability to recognize stimuli.

If detection were truly prior to recognition we would expect that a person would be able to detect a signal independently of whether or not he knew what the signal was going to be. Suppose now that we do a simple yes-no detection experiment, but tell the subject nothing about the form of the signal. We could present to him any of a variety of different pitches of a tone, or any of a variety of different colors of a light. We do not ask him to recognize which it is, but simply to detect whether or not something is present. If detection is really the most fundamental of the processes we are speaking of, there would seem to be no reason why the subject could not detect the signal regardless of the change in the signal's form. It turns out, however, that if the form of the signal is unkown to the subject, the probability of detection deteriorates. It is harder to detect an unknown signal than it is to detect a signal that is known.

Why should this be so? Some theorists have suggested that the person must first "tune" himself to the possible signals that are to be detected before he is able to detect it. It is as if the subject's anticipation of the signal is a critical variable in detection. And this is indeed the case. Thus, we see that through a study of recognition, another important factor about the detection process has come to light. Not only is the subject's expectation of the presence of a signal critical, but also his anticipation of the kind of signal to be shown affects his ability to detect it. In a sense, it is almost as simple as saying that you cannot find a lost object if you look in the wrong place. This suggests that in the detection of a signal, the person is looking somewhere for the signal, even though there is no real locus in any spatial sense.

An alternative to this theory is one that the subject, in an experiment in which the signal is not known exactly, makes a covert recognition response as well as an overt detection response. This means that the level of detection in this kind of an experiment is limited to the lower limits of the recognition response. If we first determine the recognition probability for a set of stimuli and then measure the detection threshold for the same stimuli, we expect that the same probabilities of detection occur as we observe for the recognition itself. Experiments to test this out have shown that this kind of theory can at least roughly be supported.

The consequence of these results is that when the signal is not known exactly, the subject's detection is determined importantly by recognition. Although we had already suggested the priority of detection, this generalization holds true only for signals that are known exactly. When the signals are unknown to the subject, then the recognition phenomenon may very well be the fundamental and crucial one that determines whether or not detection will occur.

In part of our discussion of recognition we have been talking about stimuli that differ among themselves to a degree sufficient for the subject normally not to confuse them. The stimuli with which we work have the property of being highly discriminable. This, of course, is not always the way nature packages its signals. Very often we may not be called upon to identify signals, but we may be required to say that one is different from another in some important respect. Thus, for example, the sonar operator aboard a submarine may be required to report that the second of two successive signals is louder than the first. The identification of the signals as representing an enemy or a friendly ship may not be relevant. The change in loudness between the signals may indicate the important fact that a target is moving closer, even though the identification of the target remains in question. When we are called upon to discriminate two signals from each other, it is much like the extension of a simple detection experiment. We can conceive of the simple detection experiment as being the discrimination between a signal and no signal. The discrimination experiment simply extends this concept to include the detection of differences between pairs (or more) of signals. In its general form we say that we are able to discriminate x from y if on some proportion of the trials better than chance we report that x is different from y. In most discrimination experiments the response of "same" or "different" is further refined to indicate the sense of the difference. That is, the subject is asked not only to tell whether x is the same or different from y, but whether x is louder or softer than y, or bluer or greener, and so on. We turn now to this collateral part of the perceptual problem, the discrimination problem.

THE DISCRIMINATION PROBLEM

At first glance, the study of discrimination seems a childishly simple pastime. After all, if two things are different, they can be discriminated. If they are the same, they cannot be. This rather naive solution remains satisfactory only until we ask how different things have to be in order to be discriminated. This is the direction of inquiry to which the experimental psychophysicist has directed his attention. The work started early in the nineteenth century with the German physiologist E. H. Weber, who became interested in how far apart two points on the skin have to be before they are detected as two rather than one. In principle, if we wanted to see whether two things could be discriminated we could present an example of the pair and ask a person to decide whether they were the same or different. The reaction of the subject to this question is one of confusion. He is not sure exactly what it means. Certainly, two things are different insofar as they are two things; they are the same insofar as they share some common attribute. Some kind of criterion seems to be needed. The unambiguous answer to the question of whether two things are the same or not is not at all straightforward and most observers object to having to make a decision of this kind. Their usual objection takes the form of asking, "What attributes of sameness or difference do you want me to tell you about?" For example, two stimuli can be the same in area and different in shape, the same in color and different in brightness, the same in loudness and different in pitch. Sameness and difference is a hard judgment to make. For this reason, Weber and his followers took a different line of attack. They asked their subjects the question: "With respect to these two different stimuli, which of them is *x*?" where *x* can stand for "louder," "bluer," "warmer," and so on. These judgments, which we shall call *comparative unidimensional judgments*, constitute the basic form of the question about discrimination.

The experimental technique commonly used in conjunction with comparative unidimensional judgments is the so-called *method of constant stimuli.* In this method, one particular stimulus, called the *standard,* is presented to the observer in conjunction with one of a number of alternative stimuli called the *comparison stimuli.* Thus, on each trial, the observer is shown a display consisting of the standard stimulus followed by a comparison stimulus and is asked to make a comparative unidimensional judgment with respect to the pair. For example, the standard stimulus can be a tone of a certain intensity and the comparison stimuli can be other tones, all of the same pitch but varying in their intensity, above and below the standard. The subject is then called upon to answer the question, "Is the second tone louder or softer than the first?"

Each comparison tone is presented with the standard tone on a large number of trials. The judgments of the subject for each pair, then, give us an estimate of the probability that for that

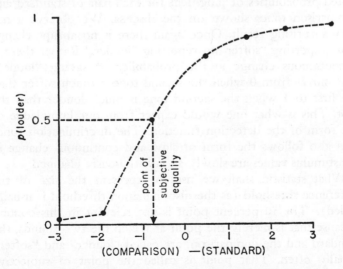

Fig. 7. Data from an experiment using the method of constant stimuli

pair the subject will say that the second or comparison tone is louder (softer) than the standard. Observe that if for any single pair one hundred judgments were obtained and on seventy-five of these trials the subject said that the second was louder than the first, then the estimated probability of "louder" equals 0.75. By the nature of the experimental design, twenty-five of the trials must have been called softer, and therefore the estimated probability of reporting that the second was softer than the first must be 0.25. It is always the case that if only two judgments are called for, then the probability of the second judgment equals 1 minus the probability of the first. The sum of the two probabilities must always be equal to 1. Even though we ask the subject to judge in two categories, we need only consider the probability of one or the other. We shall use judgments of "louder" to construct our graphs of discriminative behavior.

In Figure 7 we have plotted points that represent the estimated probabilities of judgment for each pair of standard and comparison tones shown on the abscissa. We observe a not very surprising result. Once again there is no abrupt change from reporting "softer" to reporting "louder." Rather there is a continuous change in the probability of saying "louder" that moves from 0 when the second tone is much softer than the first to 1 when the second tone is much louder than the first. This is what one would expect from our knowledge of the form of the detection function. The discrimination function also follows the form of slow and continuous change as the stimulus values are slowly and continuously changed.

What statistic shall we use to represent the size of the difference threshold (as the discrimination threshold is usually called)? The 50 percent point is not relevant in this context because that is merely the point at which the two sounds, the standard and the comparison, are called "louder" and "softer" equally often. That point is called the point of subjective equality, and is shown by the dotted line from the 50 percent point through the curve to the stimulus pair at which it occurs.

Notice that the point of subjective equality does not necessarily fall at the point at which the two stimuli, the standard and the comparison, are *objectively* equal in their intensity. It usually falls, as we have shown in Figure 7, at the point where the comparison stimulus is slightly softer than the standard stimulus. The second of two tones usually sounds a bit louder than it "really" is, and therefore the subject selects as equal to the standard, one that is slightly softer. The illusion that the second tone sounds slightly louder is called the "time error" or "time order error." It was thought to depend upon the fact that there was a time interval between the presentation of the standard and the comparison tone. Experiments have been performed to show that as the time between the tones is varied, the error changes. However, these results are difficult to repeat, and the question of the source of the illusion is still in doubt. At the moment, it is best to consider the "time error"

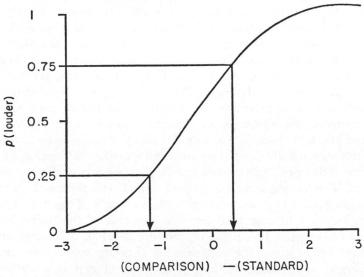

Fig. 8. A "psychometric" function obtained by the use of the method of constant stimuli

as a phenomenon for which we can provide no ready explanation.

If the 50 percent point cannot be considered a relevant statistic for the difference threshold, what can? Clearly, the difference threshold must be a relation between two points on our graph. By analogy to the absolute threshold the difference threshold is usually considered to be half the distance between the comparison stimulus at which the probability of saying "louder" is 0.25 and the comparison stimulus at which the value of saying "louder" is 0.75. If we first fair a line through the obtained points, on the assumption that the variability of the points is attributable to small errors, and therefore that the underlying behavior follows the faired line, then we have Figure 8. On this figure we have drawn a line from the 0.25 judgment and from the 0.75 judgment until they intersect the idealization of our data. From these two points we drop perpendiculars to the stimulus axis. As in Figure 7, 0 represents the standard stimulus paired with itself, 1 represents the presentation at which the standard stimulus and the first louder comparison stimulus was given, and –1 represents the point at which the standard stimulus and the first softer comparison stimulus was given, and so on. Thus, on this axis, we have plotted stimulus differences, that is, (comparison − standard), and, preserving their sign, listed them along the abscissa. Observe that the difference in stimulus values between the 0.25 and the 0.75 point is 1.8 stimulus units. By convention, this number is usually divided by two, and is called the "just noticeable difference" (abbreviated jnd). For these data the jnd = 0.9. This means that if a pair of stimuli are separated by a value equal to 0.9 stimulus units, then about half the time the subject will be able to detect the direction of the difference between them. This measure, the jnd, depends, of course, on how flat or steep the experimental data are when they are plotted in this fashion. In Figure 9 are shown two curves resulting from two different determinations of the jnd. The dotted curve, the flatter one, reveals clearly a larger difference

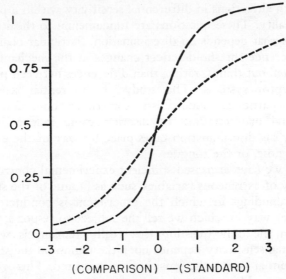

Fig. 9. Two jnd functions showing unequal jnd's

threshold than the dashed curve. In point of fact, the difference threshold of the dashed curve is 0.5 while that for the dotted curve is 1.5. Can you see the calculations that would be necessary in order to determine these values?

The existence of non-zero jnd's means that there are limits to our capacity for distinguishing between things. Of immediate concern are the variables that control this differential sensitivity. In the first place, of course, the particular stimuli, whether they be lights or sounds or shocks or odors, have a great deal to do with how sensitive we are. We are much more sensitive to slight differences in sounds than to slight differences in electric shocks. Each sense department has its own differential sensitivity, and it is of technical value to know the various limits that each sense modality exhibits. However, within a particular sense, such as hearing, it is also the case that differential sensitivity is not always the same.

The more exotic questions of discrimination are those that

deal with alterations in differential sensitivity within a particular modality. These questions are fundamental to the study of behavior that depends on discrimination. Particular changes in the difference threshold reflect changes in the mechanisms of decision about things, rather than differences between particular receptor systems. The study of differential sensitivity within a particular mode tells us something about underlying behavioral manifestations of discrimination, independent of whether the discrimination takes place by way of the eye, the ear, the nose, or the tongue.

Once we have exercised sufficient experimental control over a variety of extraneous variables, such as fatigue of the subject, the surroundings in which the experiment is conducted, the particular way in which we tell the subject to respond, and so on, then the only question that really remains is whether differential sensitivity depends upon the region on the stimulus continuum at which the sensitivity is measured. This is not to say that variables such as fatigue or what the subject had for dinner will not affect his differential sensitivity. They will. But these effects are so complex that their study constitutes a separate domain in psychology. What we have left if we keep all of these variables constant is the question of whether, for example, the differential sensitivity of loudness depends upon how loud the standard tone is. If, then, we do an experiment in which we measure the differential sensitivity at various points along the stimulus continuum, we obtain a result that looks something like Figure 10. As the intensity of the standard stimulus increases, the size of the difference threshold—that is, the amount of energy necessary to detect the difference—increases also. This is rather odd. One might have thought that the energy necessary to detect a difference would remain constant regardless of where the difference threshold is measured. However, we see in Figure 10 that the difference threshold appears to grow larger; that is, the differential sensitivity decreases as the magnitude of the standard increases. This means that it takes a larger intensity change to produce a difference

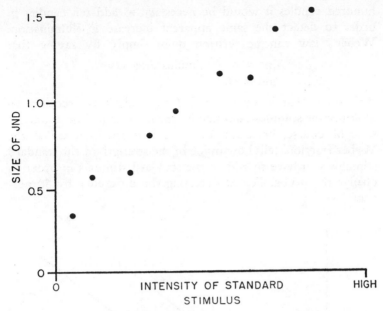

Fig. 10. Data showing the size of the jnd as intensity of standard is increased

in effect at high intensities than it does at low intensities. You can see the intuitive force of this observation if you consider that with a single candle burning in a room the addition of one more candle makes a profound difference in the apparent amount of light, whereas if one hundred candles are burning the addition of one more candle has very little effect. It may even go undetected. Weber conjectured a law, which has been given his name, about how the size of the difference threshold depended on the point at which it was measured. Weber's law states that the size of the difference threshold is a constant proportion of the intensity level at which the difference threshold is determined. That is to say, that if in a room with ten candles you had to add one more in order to detect an increase in illumination, then if the room contained one hundred candles it would be necessary to add ten candles in order to detect the same apparent increase in illumination. Weber's law can be written quite simply by saying that

$$jnd = c \times stimulus\ intensity$$
$$jnd = cI.$$

This states that in order to find the jnd, it is necessary to multiply the stimulus intensity by the number c. The number c will, of course, be a fraction, and that fraction, called the Weber fraction, tells how much of the strength of the standard stimulus you have to add to the standard stimulus in order to change the probability of detecting the difference by 50 percent.

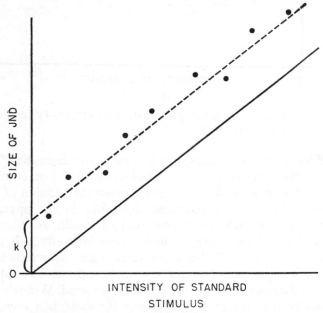

Fig. 11.   Solid line: the graph of Weber's law, jnd $= cI$. The points are the data shown in Figure 10. The dashed line is the graph of the generalized Weber law, jnd $= cI + k$

In Figure 11 we have drawn the line that Weber's law predicts. The data depart from the theoretical prediction described by Weber's law. It is easy to see why this must happen. After all, if the intensity of the standard stimulus moves toward zero, then some small percentage of the standard stimulus will move even closer to zero, and therefore, when the intensity of the standard stimulus is just at zero, no increase will be necessary in order to produce a difference in behavior. This of course cannot be the case because of the existence of the detection threshold. Thus it is obvious that Weber's law will not describe behavior if we do not take into account the fact that people have limits below which they cannot detect a stimulus, let alone tell the difference between two. We can improve the fit of Weber's law by changing it slightly to include a constant that depends upon the detection threshold. That is, we always add a little bit to the difference threshold equal to the stimulus intensity of the detection threshold. At low levels the proportion of the standard stimulus that is being added in order to produce the difference threshold is small, but the added quantity that depends upon the detection threshold is relatively large, while at high intensity levels this added quantity is relatively small. This new form of Weber's law can be stated as

$$\text{jnd} = c \times \text{standard intensity} + k$$
$$\text{jnd} = cl + k.$$

The number k represents the amount that has to be added to the weakest stimulus that can be detected in order for a difference to be perceived. It is the size of the first step away from the detection threshold. The theoretical line for this generalized Weber's law is shown in Figure 11 as a dotted line, and, as we see, the empirical results bear out this form of Weber's law.

It seems to be the case that Weber's law, or one similar to it, also holds for the point of subjective equality, that is, for the time error. The size of the time error appears to increase proportionally as the standard stimulus is increased in strength. This result suggests that the relation between the time error and the difference threshold is stronger than it might have appeared.

So far we have been talking as though we could perform the difference threshold experiment by simply asking the subject to say when tones sounded louder or softer. Obviously the same arguments that apply against this technique in the study of detection also apply in the study of discrimination. Here again, it is necessary to introduce an explicit outcome structure with its payoff function so that the motives of the subject can be brought under some degree of experimental control. When this is done, and the payoff structure is concordant with the demands of the discrimination task in the sense that positive rewards are given when the subject is correct and negative rewards when he is incorrect, the size of the difference threshold changes. This is especially true with naive, unpracticed observers. For people who have never had the difference threshold measured, the size of their Weber fraction for sounds is approximately 0.10. When appropriate payoff schedules that reward them for correct judgments and punish them for incorrect judgments are used, the fraction decreases by a factor of two.

Has their sensitivity increased? In some sense, it would be inappropriate to say that. Rather, we assume that because of the payoff function, the subject has learned what to look for in making these discriminations. Because of the information in the payoff, he is able to concentrate on those features of the stimulus display that are relevant to the experimenter. He is better able to tell the experimenter when a difference occurs of the kind that the experimenter is interested in, rather than the kind the subject may have thought the experimenter was interested in. The increased discriminative capacity shown by subjects who receive payoffs are paralleled by a shift in the location of the point of subjective equality. The difference between the point of subjective equality and the point of objective equality becomes smaller as discrimination improves. Thus, we see again that there appears to be some relation between these apparently unconnected facts, that is, between the apparent increase in the loudness of the sound tone and the sensitivity that the subject exhibits in discriminating between pairs of tones.

In almost every experiment that has been performed on the measurement of the difference threshold, the relative frequency of presentation of the standard-comparison pairs has been equal for all pairs. That is, the subject's expectations that the different pairs will occur equally often has never been disconfirmed. It is obvious, however, that by varying the relative frequency of the different pairs, we could introduce biases into the subject's behavior just as we did when we altered the relative frequency of presentations in a detection experiment. It is strange but true that no extensive experimentation has ever dealt with the question of the effects of these expectation biases on the difference threshold, but one would expect that they would behave in a way analogous to changes in the payoff structure of a detection experiment. Unhappily for the state of the science, the study of a variety of payoff structures in the difference threshold experiments has also never been accomplished. Although the discrimination experiment is one of the oldest in psychology, it has not been studied as extensively as one might think. There are many reasons for this, but a main one is a result of the work of Gustave Theodor Fechner.

Fechner, a German physicist-philosopher, became interested in these problems in the middle of the nineteenth century, and from 1850 until 1860 he conducted a series of experiments that he reported in detail in a monograph called *Elemente der Psychophysik*. In this book he concerned himself with a classic philosophical problem and proposed to show that the work that Weber had done and his own results provided a solution to his problem. The problem was the relation of the mind and the body. Fechner was concerned with how physical stimuli affected the "experience" of them. He argued that he was able to show how to measure sensations, to show the relation between the sensations as he measured them and the physical stimuli that produced them, and to show that there was a lawful relation between the physical world and the mental. This lawful relation between stimuli and sensations has since come to be called Fechner's law. Because it is a pivotal point in the study of psychophysics, we will now turn our attention to the nature of this law and the problem that Fechner hoped to solve.

We are all aware that as the physical intensity of, say, light increases, the sensation of brightness increases; that as the physical energy of a sound increases, the sensation of loudness increases, and so on. Fechner was hoping to find a way to relate the magnitude of the stimulus energy to the appearance of the stimulus in the subject's mind. To do this it was necessary to find a measure of these "appearances." Fechner was looking for what we have come to call *scales of sensation.* How do you measure the impressions that a person has? It is not an easy problem, but Fechner thought he had found the solution. He approached the problem of measuring the degree of sensation by making two important assumptions. The first of these is that Weber's law is true. This is an experimental fact, and as far as it went Weber's law appeared to hold over quite a wide range of stimulation. Even in its simplest form, Weber's law is a good approximation to changes in differential sensitivity as a function of intensity. Thus, Fechner's first assumption, the truth of Weber's law, seems reasonable.

The next assumption is more difficult to justify. Fechner assumed that the subjective impression of the difference between two stimuli separated by exactly one jnd was the same regardless of the values of the two stimuli. That is to say, if you take two stimuli at the low end of the intensity scale and they are separated by one jnd, then the impression of the magnitude of the sensation difference between them is the same as it is for two stimuli from the upper end of the intensity scale that are also separated by one jnd. Fechner went on to generalize this by saying that two stimuli separated by an equal number of jnds were equally different from any other two stimuli separated by the same number of jnd's. His assumption has often been summarized by the phrase that "equally often noticed differences are equal unless they are always or never noticed." This assumption allowed Fechner to take the jnd as the unit of subjective measurement. What he said is that each jnd is subjectively equal to every other jnd. This means that at the low end of the intensity scale where the jnd's are small, two stimuli will be separated by one sensation unit when they are physically quite close together, while at the upper end of the intensity scale, where the jnd's are physically large, two stimuli that are separated by one subjective unit will be quite widely separated physically. If we accept the truth of Weber's law, and if we accept that each jnd is equal to every other jnd in sensation, then Fechner's result is that the scale that steps off equal units of sensation will be related to the physical scale

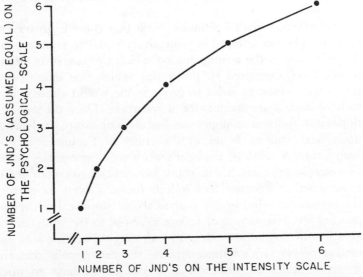

Fig. 12. The psychophysical relation proposed by Fechner

when the physical scale steps off ever larger units of physical energy. We plot this in Figure 12, where we see that as we move along the physical energy scale in equal jnd steps, the size of the jnds gets larger. But, because Fechner assumed that each jnd was *subjectively* equal, the intersection of each of these physical jnd's with an equal sensation unit gives rise to a relation between sensation and the physical stimuli that is of the form shown by the curve. Observe that the sensation increases more slowly as the physical energy increases. The curve is concave downward. In point of fact, the curve is of such a form that the sensation scale equals the logarithm of the stimulus scale. The equation for the line is

sensation scale value $= k \times$ logarithm (stimulus intensity)
$$s = k \log I.$$

This relation follows mathematically if you accept Fechner's assumptions. The subjective impressions of stimuli grow as the logarithm (to the base 10) of the stimuli. This, then, is Fechner's law.

The difficulty with Fechner's law is that there is no way to find out whether one jnd is subjectively equal to another, and this of course is the assumption on which the law rests. Many people have attempted to prove this assumption empirically, but as we can see, in order to prove it one would already have to have some scale or measure of sensation. Thus, the assumption stands more as an unproved postulate or axiom. It depends upon our intuitive belief in the truth of Fechner's second assumption. A result of Fechner's work was immediately to set into operation researches in many laboratories to try to determine whether Fechner had indeed found a way to capture the immaterial mind in the analytical and empirical science of psychology. His success or failure gave rise to the study of the question of sensation scales, and although Fechner was the motive power behind these studies, the new results that the study of scales of sensation have yielded promise to open wider vistas than Fechner had supposed.

As we said early in this chapter, one of the common forms of human behavior is the judgment of the magnitude of things. The basis of much action depends on these judgments. Insofar as people are able to do this with accuracy and expediency, something like a measure or scale of sensation seems a reasonable idea. The profound problem is how to trap this scale in our scientific nets. To see the course of this enterprise, we now turn to the study of the scaling problem.

✛ THE SCALING PROBLEM

Fechner claimed to have measured sensation; if one sensation was produced by a stimulus 25 jnd's above the detection threshold and another by a stimulus 50 jnd's above threshold, the second stimulus should appear twice as intense as the first in terms of Fechner's scale. As we have pointed out, however, without an independent scale of sensation, there appears to be no way to decide whether Fechner is right or wrong.

Many people worked to resolve the issues raised by Fechner's logarithmic scale of sensation. The line of attack many took was to find some way to measure the appearances of things directly without resorting to the indirect methods of the summated jnd. The first experimental technique for scaling sensation magnitudes directly was devised toward the end of the nineteenth century. It is called the category scaling method. With this method the subject is told that he is to judge the relative magnitudes of a variety of things (stimuli) that will be presented to him. In order to make his judgment he is given a set of categories, for example, the first seven integers. He is told that he is to place the weakest of the stimuli into category 1 and the strongest into category 7, and he may even be shown examples of these stimuli so that he knows which the weakest and the strongest are. He is then told—and this is the most important part of the instruction—that he is to distribute the other stimuli among the categories in such a way that the intervals between categories are subjectively equal. That is, the sensation level difference between categories 2 and 3 should be the same as the sensation interval between categories 5 and 6. Fifteen or twenty different stimuli that range along a physical dimension are then presented to the subject one at a time, and he assigns one of the category names to each of them. The subject is asked to do this a number of times, and then the average of the category values that were assigned to each stimulus is taken as the category scale value of the stimulus.

This experimental method appears to be exactly the same as the technique used in a recognition experiment, except that there are fewer categories than stimuli (cf. p. 120). However, we should note that in the recognition experiment the experimenter is able to decide whether the subject has rightly or wrongly assigned the stimuli to the appropriate recognition category. In the category scaling experiment the intrinsic nature of the question we try to answer implies that the experimenter cannot know in advance what the appropriate category assignments are. The subject is presumed to reveal something about his apprehension of the stimuli rather than to comply with a set of arbitrary instructions about what to name the stimuli. The failure of the subject to recognize the repeated presentations of the stimuli is not relevant in this category scaling experiment; rather it is his judgments about the relative magnitudes of the stimuli that are sought. The experimenter can never decide whether the subject is right or wrong in a scaling experiment; there is therefore no natural way to introduce an outcome structure into this kind of experiment. In scaling experiments we are forced to assume the uncontrolled ability of the subject accurately to report his sensations. As we shall see, the reproducibility of the data upon repetition of this experiment lends some support to this assumption.

If we believe that the subject has spaced the categories equally in terms of their sensation differences, then we can justifiably mark off equal intervals along a line and assign the category names to the intervals on the line. In Figure 13 the

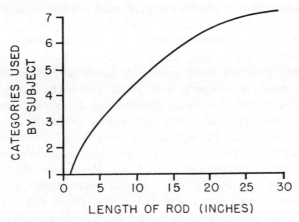

Fig. 13. A category scale for length of rods

ordinate of the graph is marked off into seven categories, each separated by an equal interval. This imposed equality of physical distance between the category labels is dependent upon our belief that the subject was doing what we said he should do. Along the abscissa of the figure are shown the intensity measurements of the stimuli in physical units. In this particular experiment the stimuli are lengths of rods shown to the subject, which vary from one to thirty inches. The smooth curve drawn on the figure indicates the relation between the length of the rod in inches and the category that the subject used to describe the rod. The curve is concave downward and follows roughly the logarithmic form that Fechner asserted was the scale of sensation.

This is resounding support for the sensation scale derived by Fechner from discrimination experiments. His result projects with amazing accuracy into the form of behavior generated by this new method of category scaling. To have predicted the form of the category scale from the results of simple discrimination data is certainly an impressive feat. The implication, of course, is that the mental mechanisms by which discrimination threshholds are generated are the same as those that give rise to the category scale. Both are presumed to represent the appearances of stimuli to the observer.

But these results, supporting as they do Fechner's conjecture, still generate some suspicion. Look at Figure 13. The length rated as category 4 is about ten inches; the length rated as category 2 is about three inches. Does this mean that a person believes that a ten inch rod is twice the length of a three inch rod? Perhaps so, but our initial intuitions suggest that this is not the way things really look. We can perform another experiment to find out. Re-present the rods to the subject and ask him to estimate their length in inches. This experiment, when repeated a few times and averaged, gives us the data plotted as Figure 14. The magnitudes of the judged lengths are plotted on the ordinate and the physical

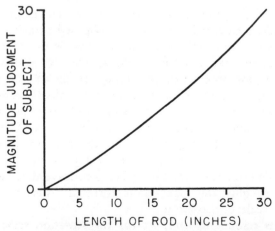

Fig. 14. A magnitude estimation scale for length of rods

lengths on the abscissa. These *magnitude estimations* no longer display the logarithmic form predicted by Fechner, but rather conform to our intuitions that subjects see lengths about as we would expect. If anything, there is a slight tendency to underestimate the lengths of the rods.

Here is a dilemma. We have two ways to get people to tell us how things look. Each has an apparent "face" validity, and each can be shown to yield highly reliable results, in the sense that repeated experiments give approximately the same data. But the two ways do not yield the same answer. Which of them is "right"? Which provides us with some understanding of the judgmental processes of the person? How can we hope to arrive at a resolution of this conflict? What constitutes the justification of one rather than another of these scales?

The aim of much scientific endeavor is to find a general understanding of a variety of observed events. A scientist does not devote himself to phenomena that are idiosyncratic. A person does not live long enough to consider in detail things that happen only once in the universe, unless they are of such overreaching importance that they cannot be ignored. Therefore one of the first things we must decide is whether this incompatibility of results of the two scaling methods is perhaps an isolated phenomenon that occurs only when these length judgments are made. Experiments have been performed in which subjects are required to make category judgments and magnitude estimations of the brightness of lights, the intensity of sounds, the impressions of hefted weights, the numerousness of dots, the durations of time intervals, the magnitudes of electric shock, the subjective amplitudes of vibration, and on and on.

If the magnitude estimation method and the category scaling method gave equivalent results in all of these experiments, then we would be justified in construing length as an anomalous stimulus and discarding the apparent problem that the experiment raised. But, if, when we plot the category judgments of these stimuli against the magnitude estimations, we do not observe straight lines relating them, then the nonlinear relation between category judgments and magnitude judgments is sufficiently pervasive to demand our scientific attention. The graphs in Figure 15 show the relation between the

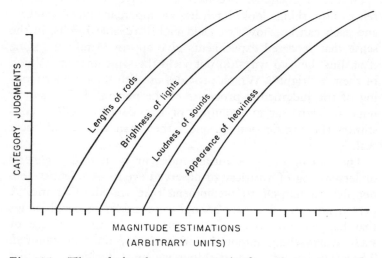

Fig. 15. The relation between magnitude and category judgments

magnitude judgments and the category judgments for a number of different perceptual continua. The magnitude judgments are plotted on the abscissa, successive perceptual continua being displaced to the right in order to spread out the curves. The category judgments are plotted on the ordinate. First of all, the curves are parallel, which indicates that regardless of the sensory continuum we are examining, the relation between magnitude judgments and category judgments is much the same. Second, the lines that describe the relation are not straight lines, hence the two modes of judgment do not give equivalent results. Rather, the lines are curved in exactly the same way that length judgments are. Thus, we see that the result observed in the judgments of the lengths of rods is not unique; rather it is true for a variety of perceptual continua. Specifically, all perceptual continua that involve intensity or quantity—in other words, that involve judgments of whether more of the same thing has been presented, whether that thing is sound or light or shock—have this characteristic property. When these so-called *prothetic* sensory continua are judged by category methods and by magnitude estimation methods, the results always reveal a nonlinear relation between the two forms of judgment.

We have established that the two forms of judgment do not give rise to the same subjective scale. We have further shown that this lack of equivalence between two methods of scaling is a common phenomenon which exists for a variety of sensory continua. We are forced, therefore, to the position of defending one or the other or both as representing the nature of the appearance of things. We turn now to the question of what constitutes the criteria upon which the acceptance of one rather than another of these sensory scales is appropriate. Four kinds of criteria are commonly used to justify the validity of a result. They are:

1. The consistent repeatability of the result.
2. The explanation of the result in terms of some more basic theory.
3. The prediction of new findings based upon the result.
4. The invariance of the result in the face of manipulation of ostensibly nonessential characteristics of the experiment.

The first of these criteria is met by both of the methods, insofar as we are able to repeat the experiments under a variety of conditions.

The second criterion, the dependence of the result upon some more primitive or basic theory, would appear to give the category scale the edge. Fechner's law states that the form of the sensation scale should be the logarithm of the stimulus intensity. That is, the intervals between the successive jnd's are presumed equal and therefore, if the categories contain an equal number of jnd's, Fechner's result should follow. Thus, the category scale can be thought of as depending upon the underlying Fechnerian theory and, in a sense, as being supported by the existence of such an underlying theory. However, the assumption that equal differences in jnd's give rise to equal sensation differences is just that: an assumption. If Fechner had made a slightly different assumption, namely, that equal ratios of jnd's give rise to equal sensation ratios, then instead of a logarithmic relation between the subjective impressions of things and the intensities of things, we would predict that there would be a power relation between subjective impression and stimulus intensity. A power relation is of the form

$$\text{sensation scale} = k \times (\text{stimulus intensity})^n$$
$$S = kI^n.$$

Now it just so happens that all the magnitude estimation scales when plotted against the stimulus intensity are, in fact, power functions. Thus, by simply changing one of Fechner's assumptions, but still preserving Fechner's theory, we can explain the magnitude estimation scale as well as the category scale. It is merely an historical accident that one of these assumptions rather than the other was used in the original formulation. But the theory itself, when coupled with one or the other assumption, can justify either of the obtained results. So we see that the second criterion for making a decision between the two kinds of subjective scales does not quite provide the kind of leverage we need.

The third criterion asks us to be able to predict other results from the values of the two scales that we find. Can this be done for either of them? The category scale, depending as it does upon judgments of differences between stimuli, suggests an experiment that, if the category scale is true, should lead to a predictable result. In this experiment we ask a subject to equate the differences between two pairs of stimuli. If we arrange, for example, four lights, as shown in Figure 16, and make the intensity of lights A and B different from

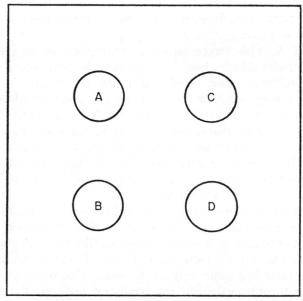

Fig. 16. The light panel for judgments of differences of ratios

each other by some fixed amount, and then light up C at an intensity still different from either A or B, we can ask the subject to adjust light D until the difference between C and D is equal to the difference between A and B. If we then know the category scale values of lights A, B, and C, we should be able to predict—because we also know the predicted category scale value of light D—what the stimulus intensity of light D should be. When this experiment is performed, the results confirm the category scale in the sense that we can predict the physical intensity at which light D will be adjusted in order that the perceived difference between C and D should equal that between A and B.

An analogous experiment can be performed based upon the ideas that underly the magnitude estimation scale. In this case, we present light A at a fixed intensity and have the subject adjust light B until it is some brightness equal to, say, half the brightness of light A or perhaps twice the brightness of light A. This fractionation or multiplication experiment yields results which should be predictable from the magnitude estimation scale. And when the experiment is conducted, it turns out that the fractionations and multiplications that the subject makes are approximately as predicted from the magnitude estimation scale for these particular continua. So again both scales lead to new experiments and enable us to predict with some precision what the outcomes of these new experiments will be. Again we are at an impasse in making a decision between them.

The fourth criterion for deciding between two conflicting results is somewhat less obvious in its implementation than the other three. This principle proposes that the scales which we obtain by various experimental methods should be related in their form and value only to the object that is being scaled and not to other extrinsic and irrelevant features of the experiment. In the case of sensory scales, we would expect the scale values to be related to the stimulus intensities only and not to other aspects of the experiment. But the experimental design seems to contain nothing other than the stimulus intensities themselves and the instructions. The instructions, obviously, are intimately connected to the scale that we obtain, because they instruct the subject about how he is to make his judgment. However, there is one part of the experiment that is under our control and that should not lead to changes in the scale if the scale is truly dependent upon the values of the stimuli and independent of other aspects of the experiment. This particular variable, or feature, is the composition of the ensemble of stimuli that we choose to present. If we present a large number of very weak stimuli and one or two very strong ones, we should find essentially the same scale values as when we present a large number of very strong stimuli and a few weak ones. If the appearance of the stimulus depends only upon the stimulus that is presented, and not upon the rest of the stimuli that are going to be or have been presented, then the scale values should remain fixed regardless of the particular collection of stimuli that we use in the experiment.

We can easily vary the spacing of, say, sounds that we present to the subject and have him give us category values for each of two variations. We can then repeat the experiment with the same two groups of stimuli and obtain magnitude estimates from the subject. The results are shown in Figures 17 and 18. In Figure 17, the filled circles are the obtained

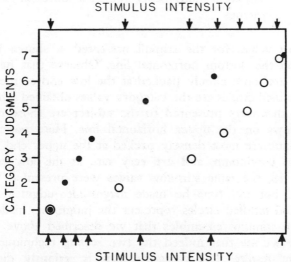

Fig. 17. Category judgments for two different stimulus spacings

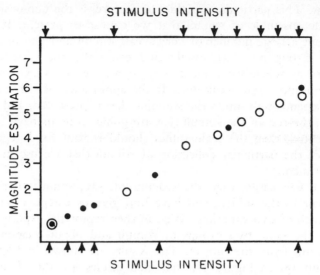

Fig. 18. Magnitude judgments for two different stimulus spacings

category values for the stimuli presented as shown by arrows on the bottom horizontal line. Observe that here the stimuli are more closely packed at the low end of the scale. The unfilled circles are the category values obtained when the stimuli that were presented to the subject are those marked by arrows on the upper horizontal line. Here notice that the stimuli are most densely packed at the upper end of the stimulus continuum, and are very rare at the low end. In Figure 18, the same stimulus values were presented to the subject, but this time he made magnitude judgments. The filled and unfilled circles represent the judgments made with the two stimulus ensembles that we described above.

Now we see that indeed the two scaling techniques give different results. The category scale is seriously distorted when the particular stimuli that are used for constructing the scale are changed. The magnitude scale, on the other hand, is invariant with changes in the stimulus ensemble. This result suggests that the magnitude scale values of stimuli are "attached" to the stimuli by the subject, whereas the category scale values of the stimuli are "attached" not to the stimuli themselves, but rather to the stimulus-within-the-context of the display in which it appears.

The category scale value for a particular stimulus is not as intimately associated with the stimulus as is the magnitude value. In consequence, many psychophysicists have come to believe that the magnitude scale reveals more about the sensory effects of stimuli, and therefore more about the bases of the judgmental process of people when they are called upon to act with respect to the magnitudes of stimuli in their environment.

Unlike many other branches of psychology (although by no means all others), laboratory studies in psychophysics make use of highly reproduceable stimulating conditions and give rise to repeatable data that can be easily transformed into numerical values. As a consequence of this "quantitative" feature of psychophysics, much theoretical work that depends upon the use of very sophisticated mathematical techniques has been done. In fact, the primary motivation for the conduct of many psychophysical experiments now is to test various mathematical formulations about the nature of human judgment and decision making in these relatively "pure" contexts. Mathematical theories in psychophysics are being coupled with other theories from its sister field of learning and one forms the impression that a coalition of activity in these two theoretical areas will be forthcoming very shortly. As a consequence, we can expect to see highly developed theoretical work providing us with a deeper understanding of the nature of human behavior in these restricted situations. The basic faith of the scientists working in these fields is that an understanding of behavior within this restricted context will provide a base for generalization to the more elaborate

forms of behavior we find in common experience. But whether
or not we will ever understand the complex actions of the
person in his natural habitat, we are sure to gain new insight
into the bases of behavior on which the complexities of human nature may ultimately depend.

⊕ SELECTED READINGS

DETECTION

Green, D. M. Psychoacoustics and detection theory. *J. acoust. Soc. Amer.*, 1960, *32*, 1189-1203.

Licklider, J. C. R. Three auditory theories. In Koch, S. (Ed.). *Psychology: A study of a science*, New York: McGraw-Hill, 1959, 41-144.

Luce, R. D. Detection and recognition. In Bush, R. R., E. Galanter, and R. D. Luce (Eds.) *Handbook of mathematical psychology*, New York: Wiley (in prep.).

Miller, G. A. Sensitivity to changes in the intensity of white noise and its relation to masking and loudness. *J. acoust. Soc. Amer.*, 1947, *19*, 609-619.

Shipley, E. F. A model for detection and recognition with signal uncertainty. *Psychometrika*, 1960, *25*, 273-289.

Shipley, E. F. Detection and recognition with uncertainty. Unpublished doctoral dissertation. University of Pennsylvania, 1961.

Stevens, S. S., C. T. Morgan and J. Volkmann. Theory of the neural quantum in the discrimination of loudness and pitch. *Amer. J. Psychol.*, 1941, *54*, 315-335.

Swets, J. A. Is there a sensory threshold? *Science*, 1961, *134*, 168-177.

RECOGNITION

Attneave, F. *Applications of information theory to psychology*. New York: Holt, 1959.

Luce, R. D. Detection and recognition. In Bush, R. R., E. Galanter, and R. D. Luce (Eds.) *Handbook of mathematical psychology*, New York: Wiley (in prep.).

Miller, G. A. What is information measurement? *Amer. Psychol.*, 1953, *8*, 3-11.

Miller, G. A. The magical number seven, plus or minus two: some limits on our capacity for processing information. *Psychol. Rev.*, 1956, *63*, 81-97.

Pollack, I. The information of elementary auditory displays. *J. acoust. Soc. Amer.*, 1952, *24*, 745-750.

Pollack, I. The information of elementary auditory displays: II. *J. acoust. Soc. Amer.*, 1953, *25*, 765-769.

DISCRIMINATION

Boring, E. G. *A history of experimental psychology*. New York: Appleton-Century-Crofts, 1950 (ed. 2).

Luce, R. D. *Individual choice behavior*. New York: Wiley, 1959.

Luce, R. D., and E. Galanter. Discrimination. In Bush, R. R., E. Galanter, and R. D. Luce (Eds.) *Handbook of mathematical psychology*, New York: Wiley (in prep.).

Thurstone, L. L. *The measurement of values*. Chicago: University of Chicago Press, 1959.

Torgerson, W. S. *Theory and method of scaling*. New York: Wiley, 1958.

SCALING

Galanter, E., and R. D. Luce. Psychophysical scaling. In Bush, R. R., E. Galanter, and R. D. Luce. *Handbook of mathematical psychology*, New York: Wiley (in prep.).

Stevens, S. S. Mathematics, measurement, and psychophysics. In Stevens, S. S. (Ed.). *Handbook of experimental psychology*. New York: Wiley, 1951, 1-49.

Stevens, S. S. On the psychophysical law. *Psychol. Rev.*, 1957, *64*, 153-181.

Stevens, S. S., and E. Galanter. Ratio scales and category scales
for a dozen perceptual continua. *J. exp. Psychol.*, 1957, *54*,
377-411.

Torgerson, W. S. *Theory and method of scaling.* New York:
Wiley, 1958.

3 ✦ ETHOLOGY

An Approach toward the
Complete Analysis of Behavior

ECKHARD H. HESS
THE UNIVERSITY OF CHICAGO

THE WORK ON IMPRINTING HEREIN DESCRIBED WAS SUPPORTED IN PART BY GRANT M-776 OF THE NATIONAL INSTITUTES OF HEALTH, PUBLIC HEALTH SERVICE, DEPARTMENT OF HEALTH, EDUCATION, AND WELFARE, BETHESDA, MARYLAND; BY THE WALLACE C. AND CLARA A. ABBOTT MEMORIAL FUND OF THE UNIVERSITY OF CHICAGO, CHICAGO, ILLINOIS; AND BY THE WALLACE LABORATORIES, NEW BRUNSWICK, NEW JERSEY. IN SOME INSTANCES OUR ONLY SOURCE OF INFORMATION WAS THE WRITINGS OF KONRAD LORENZ AND IRENÄUS EIBL-EIBESFELDT; THE AUTHOR IS INDEBTED TO THEM FOR THE MATERIAL WHICH HE HAS PARAPHRASED.

✦ INTRODUCTION

In the first book ever written on ethology, Niko Tinbergen used the following definition: "Ethology is the objective study of behavior" (1951).

From the public relations standpoint, particularly for the American psychologist who has long been proud of the objectivity of his own behavior research, this definition could scarcely be more unfortunate. Coupled with this implication that ethology is the only objective behavior research method, there was an added annoyance: ethology was intrepidly resuscitating the almost dead idea of genetic transmission of behavior characteristics, distinguishing species and breeds within species. All in all, these two factors were a powerful combination deterring the easy acceptance—or even the perusal—of the ethologists' program and research findings.

In order to contribute to a more sympathetic appraisal, we shall attempt to give a general view of what ethology is, what it attempts to do, and what it has accomplished.

Up to the present time, ethology has been developed mainly by zoologists who also had a keen interest in the problems of animal behavior. The fact that most of these researchers and theorists have not published their findings in the English language is another factor responsible for the relative lack of general knowledge on ethology in the United States. Ethology has, however, grown so rapidly during the last decade that it has now come to the attention of psychologists in this country.

The major premise of ethology is that the study of animal behavior must begin by obtaining as complete a knowledge as possible of the behavior of the species in question during the entire life cycle. A collection of such observations on one species is called an ethogram. It simply describes what an animal does, not why it does it. This goes beyond the usual naturalistic approach, since the various behaviors are then classified and compared with those of many other species, particularly related ones. The ethologists consider it very important that the animals be observed in surroundings that closely approach their natural habitats. It is preferable, if possible, to study them in the wild rather than in captivity, because in captivity it is more difficult to keep the animals in a state of optimum health and, when they are not in a state of optimum health, some aspects of behavior may not be manifested. In addition, captive animals often engage in abnormal stereotyped behavior. The best alternative is to rear animals to be both tame and unconfined, so that they have no fear of man and thus can be easily observed.

After the different behaviors have been classified and compared, the next step is their analysis in the light of the factors entering into or influencing these behaviors. A study is made of the probable evolution, ontogenetic development, survival value or function, and the physiological bases of these behaviors.

All these steps are followed because ethologists believe that all facts on behavior must be acquired before any hypotheses are formulated. They have come to this conclusion because behavior is so multiform that a wealth of evidence can always be compiled in support of any theory, no matter how capriciously constructed.

The ethologists' first concern has been to concentrate on behaviors that are normally performed by animals rather than on learning processes, because it is their philosophy that the basic material already present in an animal must be perfectly known before changes in this substratum as a result of learning can be studied. Some psychologists, viewing the ethologists' emphasis on innate behaviors, have mistakenly assumed that they do not feel learning to be very important. This is not at all the case; indeed, they consider learning to be of highest importance; it is one of the many mechanisms that produce behavior in an animal. They do not subscribe to the viewpoint that a given behavior is either wholly learned or innate; only the basic components or units are one or the other. This will be considered in more detail at the close of our discussion.

The early pioneers of ethology—C. O. Whitman, O. Heinroth, W. Craig, and K. Z. Lorenz—began the discipline as a purely phylogenetic and comparative investigation of behavior. Since its beginnings it has proceeded from observation and description to causal analysis, and is now becoming more and more physiological in approach, since ethologists fully recognize that physiological processes underlie the behavior of an organism. In fact, ethology is sometimes called *behavioral physiology*. And research into the genetic basis of inborn motor patterns is developing as an extremely important area of ethology.

As a result, ethology's early, simplified concepts have become more complex and sophisticated as more and more facts have been brought into light by careful investigation, thus placing the earlier concepts in the category of special cases. Indeed, ethology has grown so rapidly that it would be impossible to give a complete exposition of it in this review.

It is this mushrooming growth of ethology that now makes an understanding of it especially important to psychologists in their search for systems of behavior that correspond to empirical facts and have a coherent, consistent, theoretical meaning. To be sure, psychologists and ethologists have used very different—and at the same time, equally objective—approaches to the problems of behavior, but it is this very fact that results in each being able to profit by the findings of the other discipline. Indeed, ethological methods have penetrated a few areas of psychological research, and ethologists have evolved their discipline to the point where they feel able to begin making some judgments about the function of learning processes. The idea of imprinting, which originated from ethologists, has received a great deal of attention in this country and will accordingly be discussed in detail during our examination of ethology.

Two other examples of the inroads ethology is beginning to make into psychology will be given. First, behavior geneticists are now emphasizing a fact long known to ethologists: experimental results must either be restricted to the animals from which they were obtained, or else tested on many species before they are used to provide the basis for generalization. Even breed or strain differences play an important role in behavior manifested by animals in an experimental situation. And, as a second example of growing awareness of the subject, the 1962 edition of *Annual Review of Psychology* contains, for the first time in the series, a chapter on ethology.

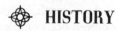 **HISTORY**

EARLY FORERUNNERS OF ETHOLOGY

In 1702 and again in 1716 Baron Ferdinand Adam von Pernau, a German zoologist, described the behavior of several species of birds, members of which he had kept tame or partly tame, just as did Whitman, Craig, Heinroth, and Lorenz more than two centuries later. He described feeding habits, migration, nesting, social behavior, territoriality, voice, bathing, and feeding of young. For example, he pointed out that some species he observed had to learn their species-specific song, but other species sang in the species-specific way without having had the chance to hear the song from another species member. Long before Mendel's work more than a century later, von Pernau investigated the transmission of characters from parents to offspring.

Then in 1740 Hermann Samuel Reimarus, a professor in Hamburg, discovered the maturation of instincts that had nothing to do with learning. In his 1762 book, *Allgemeine Betrachtungen über die Triebe der Thiere*, he pointed out that the distinction between innate and acquired skills must be made in animals as well as in man. These innate skills he called instincts or drives. Some of these instincts, he points out, are present from birth.

In one of a number of examples he gave as proof of this proposition, he quoted the French scientist R. A. F. Réaumur's observations (1734-1742) on bees and wasps; they are capable of quite complicated behavior patterns, like collecting food, immediately after hatching from the pupa. Furthermore, young of species that are able to locomote immediately after being born and that have been separated from their mothers or species members right after birth will perform certain actions without having been shown how to do them. Reimarus pointed out that in many instances behavior patterns adapted for the use of certain organs are performed before these organs are developed. For example, young male goats will try to push each other with their heads before they have grown horns, and young boars try to slash each other with sideways blows of their heads long before their tusks have grown. This he took to be proof that the use of these organs was not learned by trial and error.

Charles Darwin must certainly be given credit as an early forerunner of ethology. His 1872 book, *The Expression of Emotion in Man and Animals*, lists many complex behavior patterns, characteristic of a species, that do not need to be learned, as shown by their performance immediately after birth or hatching. Darwin reported many observations and made interpretations on the behavior of different animals that were later to be emphasized by the ethologists of this century, an example being his emphasis on the physiological bases of behavior.

In line with his theory of evolution, Darwin studied innate

behaviors from a phylogenetic point of view, treating them like morphological characters; he noted that many basic actions, such as hair raising, which is observed in man, dogs, cats, monkeys, peccaries, elk, birds, horses, and cattle, are common to wide classes of animals. "It seems hardly credible that the coordinated erection of the dermal appendages, by which the animal is made to appear larger and more terrible to its enemies or rivals, should be altogether an incidental and purposeless result of the disturbance of the sensorium" (Darwin, p. 102).

Darwin stated that there is, furthermore, selection for these instinctive behaviors, since these actions are susceptible to slight variation within a species, just as bodily structures are, and any variations which were beneficial and important enough would tend to be preserved and transmitted to succeeding generations. He also mentioned behavorial rudiments—once useful actions—still performed by a species. For example, dogs will be seen to scratch out nonexistent earth or grass before lying down to sleep on a hard floor; they will similarly attempt to bury their excrement in a hard floor, even though there is nothing to cover it with. Following the same approach, he believed that emotional behavior in man was based on the inheritance of characteristics that were useful to animals but are no longer so to man. Thus it is seen that Darwin took care to inquire into the historical causes and functions of behavior in order to understand it.

In 1873, D. M. Spalding, an English naturalist, wrote his article, "Instinct, with original observations on young animals," and stated emphatically that there are species-specific behavior patterns that are as genetically fixed as morphological characteristics. An example of his research was his keeping of nestling swallows in narrow cages so that they were unable to flap their wings in order to practice flying movements. When these birds were released at an age when swallows normally fly, they were able to fly quite well.

In 1894 the English naturalist, Lloyd Morgan, made public his famous canon that in no case can a behavior in higher animals be attributed to higher psychical functions if it can be demonstrated to be the result of a lower function. His naturalistic observations (1891, 1894, 1896) on the behavior of animals formed the basis for his law, and it had the very important effect of placing animal behavior and human behavior in proper perspective.

Before the turn of the century Jacques Loeb, a German zoologist and physiologist, proposed his theory of tropism (1886, 1888a,b, 1889, 1918). He was thoroughly mechanistic in his viewpoint, and his theory of tropism advanced the proposition that all behavior was explicable on the basis of local physicochemical reactions toward or away from stimuli impinging on the animal, just as had been demonstrated in plants. The theory of tropisms as a general explanation for behavior systems, however, was severely criticized by another mechanist, the American zoologist H. S. Jennings. In his 1906 book, *Behavior of The Lower Organisms*, as well as in an earlier 1904 publication, Jennings took exception to the theory of tropism because, according to his observations on the behavior of a number of lower organisms such as amoeba, paramecium, hydra, and infusoria, it explains only parts of behavior. "The organism responds as a whole, by a reaction involving all parts of the body" (p. 270), Jennings declared. He went on to say (p. 274) that:

'The tropism as applied to animal behavior in the sense we have considered is not an elementary factor; it is only a more or less artificial construction, made by combining certain elements of behavior and omitting others that are of most essential significance. It makes use of certain simple phenomena that actually exist, but elevates these into a general explanation of directed behavior, for which they are utterly inadequate. The prevalence of this local action theory of tropisms as a general explanation of behavior in lower organisms is based only on an incomplete knowledge and an insufficient analysis of the facts of behavior.'

In this statement one can see the core of the ethologists' criticisms of atomistic theories of behavior that attempt to resynthesize all behavior from a few elements that actually do exist but can lead to false conclusions because other elements of behavior are ignored.

Jennings insisted that behavior depended on and was determined by physiological conditions as well as stimulation as such. Behavior can be *spontaneous;* it is not always a reaction to a change in environment. Thus internal physiological processes as well as external stimulating events were factors influencing behavorial acts. It was his view that behavior is regulatory, varied, and becomes preserved through repetition.

Jennings also set up as a fundamental principle for the study of behavior the gathering of an animal's *action system.* "In studying the behavior of any organism the most important step is therefore to work out its action system—the characteristic set of movements by which its behavior under all sorts of conditions is brought about" (1906, p. 107). The action system, furthermore, consisted of "habits" combined into a *connected* or coordinated system. Thus, in his work on the behavior of lower organisms, he described and took inventory of their movement patterns and integrated them with the whole organism in relation to its environment. In discussing the topic of the development of behavior, he pointed out that just as an individual organism selects the adaptive response out of the many and diverse possible reactions, natural selection picks out the adaptive reacting individuals among the diversely acting individuals.

Like Darwin, Jennings pointed out the continuity of behavior in lower and higher organisms, since all essential features of behavior in higher animals could be traced back to lower organisms, just as with physiological processes.

Jakob von Uexküll (1909), whose independently achieved methods and results were in remarkable agreement with those of Jennings even though their philosophical views were quite divergent, also held that the observation of all there is to be observed in the behavior of a species must go *before* the quest for explanation of single items of behavior. Von Uexküll's major contribution was the discovery that, out of the many environmental data, each animal grasps only a few as perceptual signs; these signs have a releasing effect upon certain of his behaviors. According to von Uexküll, these signs alone represent the things that constitute an animal's world—the *Umwelt*[1]; they stimulate the animal's sensory receptors and at the same time offer points of attack for the animal to react upon with his effectors or motor apparatus. The meanings of these perceptual signs may be learned or innate. Von Uexküll's *Funktionkreis* or "functional circle" was the symbolic representation of the cycle in which an animal perceives these perceptual signs and reacts to them, this reaction in turn altering the sensory qualities of these signs, upon which the animal again reacts (see Fig. 1). Thus the *Funktionkreis* consists of a

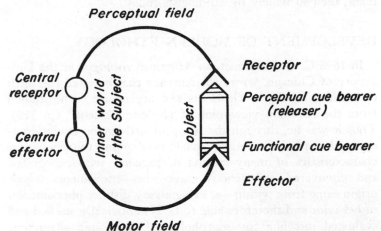

Fig. 1. Diagram of von Uexküll's *Funktionkreis*, showing how, according to von Uexküll's conception, the animal and it sensory world are interrelated so as to constitute a systematic whole. (From von Uexküll, J., *Streifzüge durch die Umwelten von Tieren und Menschen*, Berlin: Springer, 1934.)

[1] In other words, the *Umwelt* is the totality of the external stimuli to which an animal reacts behaviorally.

circular chain of causes and effects running through the organism and its environment. Von Uexküll pointed out that only certain cues initiate certain behaviors in an animal. For example, a moth courts the odor on a paper on which a female had been standing, not the odorless female standing nearby under a glass bell (Fabré, 1879-1910).

Although von Uexküll thought that behavior was preformed or based on a pre-established plan, thus rejecting the Darwinian idea of evolution, this philosophical bias never interfered with his objective causal analysis of behavior, which made no inferences regarding the subjective state of the animal. He was thus responsible, together with Jennings, for setting up the method of the analysis of the whole organism and its environment, used so widely by ethologists today.

DEVELOPMENT OF MODERN ETHOLOGY

In 1898 C. O. Whitman, an American zoologist at the University of Chicago, wrote the sentence that initiated the birth of modern ethology: "Instincts and organs are to be studied from the common viewpoint of phyletic descent" (p. 328). Thus it was he, through the study of orthogenic evolution as opposed to random mutation while cataloguing morphological characteristics of many species of pigeons, who recognized and discovered endogenous movements—movements whose origin came from within—as being a very distinct phenomenon of behavior and therefore able to be systematically studied and evaluated just like any morphological taxonomic characters. It was his contention that "as the genesis of organs takes its departure from the elementary structure of protoplasm, so does the genesis of instinct proceed from the fundamental properties of protoplasm. Primordial organs and instincts are alike few in number and generally persistent" (p. 329). He also criticized the notion that instinctive actions have clocklike regularity and inflexibility, calling it greatly exaggerated; actually, he contended, instinctive movements have only a low degree of variability under normal conditions, the most machinelike instincts always revealing some degree of adaptability to new conditions; thus he echoed Darwin's views.

At very nearly the same time, 1910, Oskar Heinroth, a German zoologist studying ducks and geese, independently came to very similar conclusions. While Whitman's observations on the taxonomic value of innate behavior had been more or less incidental, Heinroth was the first to demonstrate with empirical evidence that the concept of homology applied just as much to movement patterns as to morphological characters, so that these could be used to reconstruct phylogenetic relationships (see page 200).

Heinroth did not set up any hypotheses about the newly discovered homologies of movement patterns. He described them, studied them, and pointed out the similarities and dissimilarities between various species, genera, and families.

Wallace Craig (1918), Whitman's student, took the first step from the purely descriptive to the analytic stage when he formulated a certain lawfulness in these behavior patterns. He observed that an animal does not only react to a stimulus, but searches, by appetitive behavior, for a certain stimulus situation which allows a consummatory act to run off. Craig defined appetitive behavior as follows: "appetite (or appetence) is a state of agitation which continues as long as a certain stimulus which may be called the appeted stimulus is absent" (p. 91). Craig went on to explain that when a consummatory reaction is released "the appetitive behavior ceases and is succeeded by a state of relative rest" (p. 91). Aversive behavior was similarly defined, but the period of rest comes when the aversive stimulus has been removed.

These consummatory acts were the same as the stereotyped species-specific movement coordinations described by Whitman and Heinroth. In most cases this consummatory act is at the end of a long chain of behavior patterns involved in the appetitive behavior. In some cases, however, the consummatory act occurs so quickly that the appetitive stage is not apparent,

but by withholding from the animal the opportunity to perform the consummatory act, appetitive behavior is clearly
seen. The fixity of these consummatory acts was shown by
the fact that sometimes a species-specific consummatory act
that is of selective value in nature is made by the animal in an
inappropriate situation, as pointed out by Darwin in the case
of dogs trying to cover their excrement in a bare concrete
floor. Thus the confusion between desired ends (goals) and
the species-preserving function of behavior was eliminated
through this analysis, since Craig's standpoint was that the discharge of the consummatory act, not survival value, is the goal
of appetitive behavior.

Craig pointed out that the appetitive and aversive factors
in instinctive behaviors showed that mere chain reflexes were
not the only constituents of such instinctive behaviors. An
appetite, furthermore, is accompanied by a certain *readiness
to act*, and many of the behavior patterns performed during
the appetitive behavior are not innate or completely innate,
but must be learned by trial. Thus a cat out looking for food
may go to a certain place because he once caught a mouse
there, or he may find that he must surmount some unexpected
obstacles. But the end action—the consummatory act—of the
series of behaviors in the appetitive chain is always innate, as
shown by the occurrence of incipient consummatory acts
during the appetitive behavior, when the adequate stimulus for
the consummatory action has not yet been received.

Craig's scheme was only a beginning that Konrad Lorenz,
Heinroth's student, took up and further developed, thus ini-
tiating the present period of ethology as a science. In 1935 he
described the behavior of birds, drawing from his observations
on tame or partly tame birds and paying special attention to
the formation of social relationships. In 1937 and 1950 Lorenz
elaborated on Craig's behavior analysis by proposing his
scheme of *action-specific energy*. He found that the ease with
which a given stimulus elicits or releases the corresponding

behavior through the innate releasing mechanism (I.R.M.) is dependent on how long it has been since the animal has last given that response. Thus action-specific energy, that is, energy for a particular action, is being produced continuously in an animal's central nervous system, but is held in check by some inhibitory mechanism until the appropriate stimulus releases this energy to certain muscular systems and the reaction takes place. The longer the animal has gone without performing the action in question, the more easily this behavior can be triggered off or released. In fact, in the case of a very prolonged absence of relevant stimulation, this behavior can go off without there being any observable stimulus present. This special case he called the *Leerlaufreaktion* or *vacuum activity*. Similarly, if the relevant stimulation is repeatedly given, the animal's response can decrease to the point where he gives none at all. Lorenz's conceptualization of the way in which a readiness to react is built up and then dissipated through reaction was an extension of Craig's scheme of appetitive behavior seeking the discharge of the consummatory act. One and the same physiological event are probably responsible for the occurrence of appetitive behavior as well as for the raising and lowering of the threshold for response to the stimuli.

Lorenz was careful to point out that this action-specific energy concept did not have anything to do with the exhaustion of or recuperation of muscular systems.

Niko Tinbergen, through his studies on the releasers for innate behavior patterns, further enlarged on the Craig-Lorenz scheme of behavior. Like Lorenz, he postulated (1950) the removal of a central inhibition when an innate behavior pattern is released. He demonstrated, furthermore, that behavior patterns in themselves can function as releasers, as Lorenz had suggested (1935), this finding being based on his studies on the behavior of the three-spined stickleback (1942). Tinbergen (1950) proposed that there was a hierarchical order of appetitive behaviors and consummatory acts. Both Tinbergen and

G. P. Baerends (1956) have demonstrated that the lawfulness of behavior in intact higher organisms and the neurophysiological events in lower organisms are parallel.

Thus inspired by the work of Lorenz and Tinbergen, ethology began to expand into the neurophysiological bases of behavior. That these neurophysiological bases existed in fact and had a clear correlation with behavorial events was shown by the work of Erich von Holst (1933 *et seq.*), P. Weiss (1941a, b) W. R. Hess (1927, 1949, 1954, 1956), and K. D. Roeder (1955). Von Holst and Hess demonstrated the existence of neurological organization underlying various behavior patterns by stimulating a particular brain region of birds and cats with electrodes. The elicited patterns of behavior in response to electrical brain stimulation were the species-specific behavior patterns which ethologists had already observed in these particular species. Hess's elicitation of integrated threat, fighting, sleeping, and eating behaviors upon electrical stimulation of the cat's brain are examples of the behaviors observed. The *integration* of these behaviors was a particularly important finding; for example, cats not only went to sleep but also searched about for a place to sleep. Other areas of neurophysiological research have included von Holst's studies on the relationship between the rhythms of nervous impulses and of muscular movements, Weiss's proof of central nervous determination of primitive movement coordinations, and Roeder's demonstration that behavior is created spontaneously within the central nervous system. Recently, von Holst and von St. Paul have published a monumental paper on the interaction of different behavior patterns through the method of simultaneous electrical stimulation of adult chicken brains (1960). Their findings represent a landmark in ethological theory and evidence, and will accordingly be discussed in detail later.

There are many other modern ethologists who have made significant contributions to the growth of their discipline. Indeed, it would be a staggering task to attempt to treat all of them adequately.

ETHOLOGICAL CONCEPTS

FIXED ACTION PATTERNS

The fixed action pattern, or more simply, fixed pattern, is one of the most fundamental concepts of modern ethology. In fact, ethology was founded on the discovery of this phenomenon by Heinroth and Whitman, who were the first ones to describe it.

The fixed action pattern is defined as a sequence of coordinated motor actions that appears without the animal having to learn it by the usual learning processes. The animal can perform it without previous exercise and without having seen another species member do it. The fixed action pattern is *constant in form*, which means that the sequence of motor elements never varies.

These patterns are not equivalent to the well-known reflexes, nor are they chain reflexes; this statement will be discussed in connection with neurophysiological evidence for ethological tenets. There are many differences between the fixed action patterns and reflexes; however, an adequate discussion of these differences is beyond the scope of this paper. It may be mentioned, nevertheless, that the frequency with which the fixed action pattern is performed depends in part on how long it is since it was last performed; this is in accordance with Lorenz's postulation of specific action potential. This is not the case with reflexes. The animal engages in appetitive behavior that ends in the performance of the fixed action pattern, or consummatory act. No such appetitive behavior ending in the discharge of a reflex has been found. What is more, as we shall see later on, rhythmic movements such as those of locomotion are not necessarily equivalent to chain reflexes.

The appearance of such fixed action patterns in animals isolated from their own species is clear evidence of their genetic fixedness. Even though experimentally isolated animals may never have had any experience with the particular objects or situations involved, they will still perform the fixed pattern when the appropriate situation arises, as demonstrated by squirrels that were reared in isolation and were never given any objects to handle. Nevertheless, the squirrels attempted to bury nuts or nut-like objects in a bare floor upon their first encounter with them, making scratching movements as if to dig out earth, tamping the object in the floor with the nose, and, finally, making complete covering movements in the air (Eibl-Eibesfeldt, 1956a).

The fixed action pattern, appearing as it does in animals that have been isolated from their own species and deprived of experience relevant to this behavior, is therefore a constant characteristic of the species in question, being based, presumably, on specific central nervous system mechanisms that are inherited, just as are other morphological and physiological characters. In line with this, they are, furthermore, characteristics of genera and orders right up to the highest taxonomic categories. The fact that they are always to be found in more than one species proves their taxonomic value. They can be used, in fact, to differentiate between very closely related species.

The fixed action patterns are quite resistant to phylogenetic change through evolution, more so than morphological characters. For example, a morphological structure (such as a colored skin patch or an enlarged feather) connected with a fixed action pattern may often appear after the fixed action pattern has come into existence in the species, or the fixed action pattern may remain but the morphological structure may disappear. The first case is illustrated by the mandarin duck's pointing to an enlarged and colored wing feather during courtship. This pointing has derived, through the process of ritualization, from wing-preening, which presumably occurred before the wing feathers had become enlarged and specially colored. The last case is illustrated by the behavioral rudiments that have been observed in animals.

Krumbiegel (1940) compared the behavior of long-tailed and short-tailed monkeys and found that when a long-tailed monkey runs along a branch, its tail moves from the right to the left and back again, thus achieving balance. These same compensatory movements are to be observed in the short stumps of the short-tailed monkeys, even though there is obviously no value at all in these movements for balancing. Similarly, hornless domestic cattle and goats attempt to fight with their heads in the same way as their horned relatives.

Finally, mutant drosophila flies with no wings still perform the wing-preening movements typical of the species (Heinz, 1949).

Not only may the fixed pattern persist even though the relevant morphological structures have disappeared, but it also may persist even though the biologically appropriate situation no longer exists in the normal environment of the species. The injury-feigning ruse of a number of birds when their nest containing young is approached by an intruder or a predator is well known. On the Galapagos Islands, there are no mammalian predators, and most of the birds no longer show this distraction behavior when their nest is approached by man. However, the Galapagos dove still does this, running and fluttering from the nest as if it had a broken wing, in order to distract the attention of the intruder from the nest (Eibl-Eibesfeldt, personal communication).

In the same fashion, a kind of ontogenetic development, similar to Haeckel's well-known "phylogenetic recapitulation" of organs, has been observed in some cases where a primitive behavior pattern precedes the more recent one during ontogeny of the individual. There are some species of birds (the lark, the raven, and the starling) belonging to the *Passeres* whose original form of ground locomotion was hopping, but that now live on the ground and run. It is most interesting to find that the juveniles of these species hop in biped fashion before they run (Lorenz, 1937).

It is therefore clear that the fixed action patterns are extremely conservative in the evolution of a species. In only one case has rapid phylogenetic change in fixed action patterns been observed. This happens in the sexual behavior of closely related species that live in the same territory. In such cases the courtship behavior of these two species must of necessity become differentiated from each other if crossbreeding is not to occur. Thus changes take place in the motor patterns and vocalizations by means of which the sexual partner of the same species is selected during courtship. For example, closely related songbirds inhabiting the same ecological niche, as P. Marler (1957) has shown, have very different songs and courtship movements, whereas other fixed patterns that do not play a role in the ethological barrier between the species have remained the same.

Evolutionary changes that occur in fixed action patterns are similar to those that occur in morphological or physiological characteristics. Thus selection pressure may favor the development of a clear-cut execution of a fixed pattern that has much survival value, or cause it to disappear when it has no survival value. In some cases, of course, behavioral rudiments or vestigial behavior may remain even though there is little survival value.

A phylogenetic change during evolution is the altering of the function of a fixed action pattern in a species that has changed its manner of living. This was demonstrated by one of Tinbergen's group at Oxford, Esther Cullen (1957), who analyzed the behavior of a gull species, the Kittiwake, which now lives on cliffs rather than at the shore. Many fixed patterns changed their function completely, but were still the same in form, so that their homologies with the patterns of the gull group to which this particular species belonged were quite apparent. For example, the young, unlike those of other gulls, cannot run away from strange adults, and consequently have developed an attack-inhibiting appeasement gesture. In related gulls this gesture appears only in sexually mature animals during mating.

Ethologists have postulated that there are two stages in the evolution of motor patterns. In the first, there is a quantitative increase or decrease of motor elements—perhaps actual disappearance in some cases—and in the second, there is a coordinative coupling and disengagement of almost unalterable basic motor units. These basic motor units were shown by Lorenz's film analyses of courtship in ducks. This coupling of previously independent motor elements into a fixed sequence is part of the phylogenetic process that J. S. Huxley, an English naturalist, called ritualization in 1914.

Another phylogenetic process in ritualization is one in which a recently formed fixed pattern may become motivationally autonomous of the situation that originally aroused it, or dependent on another motivation. An example of this process is to be seen in the different forms of the female's "inciting" movement during courtship in different species of swimming ducks (Anatinae). In the original form of this behavior, the female attempts to separate the male from the group by inciting fights between her partner and other males. To do this she runs toward the strange male, but at a certain point fear overtakes her, and she runs back toward her mate. When she is close enough to him, however, aggressiveness again takes hold of her, and she stops and turns toward the strange male. This results in her standing at the point of equilibrium, near her mate, but stretching her neck toward the other male, making inciting movements. Here the angle between her body and her stretched-out neck is a function of her position and those of the two males. This behavior constitutes the unritualized form of incitement. Now, in some other species, the behavior has become so fixed that the female simply stands near her mate and moves her head back over the shoulder, regardless of where the strange male is. This shows that the movement is now performed solely as a courtship movement by the female. The interpretation that this behavior constitutes ritualized incitement is supported by the fact that still other species perform actions which are intermediate between these two extremes when in a similar situation (Lorenz, 1941).

Still another phylogenetic process in the ritualization of behavior is one in which the fixed pattern is no longer performed in different degrees of intensity, but in one intensity only. Thus the degree of motivation is not expressed in the intensity of the behavior, but in how often the behavior is repeated, much as the urgency of a telephone call may be recognized by the frequency of ringing rather than in loudness. All fixed patterns with a single or typical intensity function as means of communication between species members; selection pressure would in these cases operate to enforce a quite simple and unmistakable form of the movement (Morris, 1957).

Another very interesting evolutionary process in the development of fixed patterns is to be found in fighting behavior between members of the same species. Here actions that injure the opponent have been removed to the end of the sequence of fighting behavior by raising the threshold for its release to a very high level. This results in the development of ceremonial "tournaments" with a very small likelihood of actual bodily harm, a development that has clear survival value to the species, since fighting behavior will maintain its function of spacing out members of a species without causing injury to species members.

The result of ritualization, in summary, is that actions come to be performed in a mimetically exaggerated way in special situations. The same species may be observed to perform both forms of the fixed action pattern, ritualized and unritualized. As different and related species perform ritualized and unritualized forms of these movement patterns, as well as forms intermediate to these extremes, the homologies between these forms can be used to reconstruct phylogenetic relationships.

During the past few years ethologists have expanded from the phylogenesis of these fixed action patterns to their physiological bases. At the present time very little is known regarding their neuroanatomical bases, but it seems probable that they share a common physiological base, and the investigations so far conducted strongly indicate that they are based on inherited and structured neurophysiological mechanisms. For the time being, nevertheless, the fixed action pattern is defined in purely functional terms.

RELEASERS AND THE INNATE RELEASING MECHANISM

An animal, like man, does not give a particular response to *all* of the stimuli it perceives; most of them are only *potential* stimuli, to some of which it may learn to respond. Instinctive behavior, in particular, is evoked in response to only a few of the stimuli in an animal's environment; these stimuli are called *sign stimuli*, or *releasers* of the behaviors which they elicit.

An example of these facts is to be found in the behavior of the common tick, which was described in detail by von Uexküll (1909). The tick does not respond to the sight of a host, but when an odor of butyric acid from a mammal strikes the tick's sensory receptors, the tick drops from the twig to the host, finds a spot on the skin which is about 37° centigrade, and begins to drink blood. Only a few stimuli elicit the tick's behavior, this behavior being without doubt innate.

But the simplicity of releasers can sometimes lead animals into grave situations. For instance, a patient tick climbs up a slippery twig to waylay its prey, a nice, juicy mammal. When it has reached the end of the twig, it is above a rock on which a fat, perspiring man has been sitting. The rock therefore emanates the typical odor of butyric acid, and is just the right temperature. So the tick jumps, and lands on the rock— whereupon, in trying to suck from the rock, it breaks its proboscis.

This description shows clearly that only a few stimuli elicit the tick's behavior, this behavior being without doubt innate.

Another example is the carnivorous water beetle *Dytiscus marginalis*. It does not react to the sight of prey—even though it has perfectly well developed compound eyes, as is easily demonstrated when a tadpole in a glass tube is presented to it —but to the chemical stimuli emanating from the prey through the water. If a meat extract solution is put into the water, the beetle engages in frantic searching behavior, clasping inanimate objects (Tinbergen, 1951). These two examples of the few stimuli that release innate behavior patterns make it easy to understand why a male robin will attack a bundle of red feathers but not a dummy of a male, perfect in all respects except that it lacks the characteristic red breast (Lack, 1939).

Animals react automatically to sign stimuli, with little insight; the behavior is just run off. The lack of insight is well demonstrated by the hen's failure to rescue a chick that it can see struggling under a glass bell, but that it cannot hear. It will come to its rescue immediately, however, if it does not see him but can hear his distress cries (Brückner, 1933).

Sign stimuli, or releasers, furthermore, almost always release only *one* reaction, an example being the fact that the smell of butyric acid can release only jumping in a tick. This property differentiates sign stimuli from an acquired picture, where the response seems to depend on a configurational stimulus or Gestalt complex, which may be so altered by small changes or additions so that the original is not recognized. A tame bird, for example, may become quite frightened when it sees its keeper wear glasses or a hat for the first time. In addition, the response given to an acquired stimulus may be changed; a dog may learn to avoid a particular place instead of approaching it.

Sign stimuli also differ from *Gestalten* in that when several of them (usually attached to the same object) that produce the same response are present, they do not interact in determining the animal's response; instead, their effects are completely additive. This is in contrast to the Gestalt psychologists' view that an object is *more* than the sum of its component parts. The additiveness of releaser stimuli was demonstrated by Seitz (1940) when he studied the fighting response of the male cichlid fish *Astatotilapia Strigigena* (Pfeffer). He found that the following stimuli released fighting behavior: (1) silvery blueness, (2) dark margin, (3) highness and broadness by means of fin erection, (4) parallel orientation to the opponent, and (5) tail beating. All of these are characteristics normal to an intruding and attacking male. Seitz found that each of these, presented singly, would elicit the fighting response about equally. This remarkable finding provides a fundamental distinction between releasers and acquired *Gestalten*, since only the whole is responded to in a *Gestalt*. Furthermore, if two of these stimuli were presented simultaneously, the elicited fighting response was twice as great. The intensity of a reaction, therefore, can depend not only on what sign stimuli are present, but how many are present. Seitz called this phenomenon the "law of heterogenous summation" (*Reizsummen regel*).

Weidmann and Weidmann (1958) recently tested the law of heterogenous summation quantitatively and found it to hold, in most cases, in a strict arithmetical sense. They counted the number of pecks made by black-headed gull chicks, while they were begging, at cardboard models. If they presented a round and a rectangular model to the chick, one would receive more pecks than the other. But if they made both models red, each received the same increase in the total number of pecks.

Although sign stimuli often consist of a quality such as butyric acid for the tick, or red feathers for the male robin, and differ from *Gestalten* in many ways, most releasers, like *Gestalten*, consist of relational characteristics between stimuli. Indeed, the registration of relationships between stimuli is a fundamental attribute of perception, since the strength or distinctiveness of a perception is to a large part dependent on the contrast or relationship between, or distinctiveness of, stimuli.

For example, a male stickleback reacts with fighting behavior to the red on a rival male. But this red must be on the rival's belly, for if the red is on the back, the stickleback will not attack (Tinbergen, 1951).

Similarly, Tinbergen and Kuenen (1939) showed that the young thrush's gaping response was to a particular stimulus relationship. They constructed a round cardboard model with two different-sized heads attached to it. Tinbergen and Kuenen found that the thrushes directed their gaping toward the larger of the two heads. They then took off the two heads and placed them on a smaller round cardboard. The young thrushes now directed their gaping toward the smaller head, thus showing that it was the relationship between the sizes of the head and body that elicited gaping.

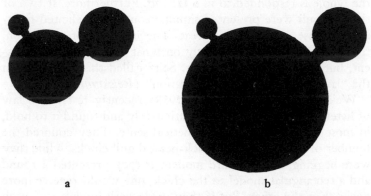

a   b

Fig. 2. The two double-headed models used by Tinbergen and Kuenen in their study of the stimuli eliciting the gaping response in young thrushes. The body of model *a* is 4 cm.; the body of model *b* is 8 cm. The small heads are 1 cm.; the large heads are 3 cm. When model *a* is presented, the small head is found to elicit gaping, but when model *b* is presented, the large head now elicits gaping. This shows that the ratio between the size of the head and of the body is the stimulus quality releasing gaping in young thrushes. (From Tinbergen, N., and D. J. Kuenen, *Zeitschrift für Tierpsychologie*, 1939, *3*, Verlag Paul Parey, Berlin.)

Since releasers can consist of relational qualities, these relations can be made even stronger in some cases through transposition or exaggeration. For instance, Koehler and Zagarus (1937) studied egg recognition in the ringed plover. If a normal egg having dark brown spots on a light brown background was presented together with another egg having black spots on a white background, the birds preferred the black and white eggs, because the spots contrasted more strongly with the background. More remarkable was their preference for abnormally large eggs, even ones they could not sit on. A herring gull behaves similarly (Baerends, 1957, 1959, and Kruijt, 1958). Such stimuli that release a response stronger than that released by the natural stimulus are *superoptimal*, or supernormal.

Magnus (1958) also convincingly demonstrated superoptimality of releasers, this time in the silver-washed fritillary butterfly, *Argynnis paphia* L. Magnus first found that the color yellow-orange, the same as in the female's wings, released courtship responses in the male. The female also flutters its wings, and the resulting alternation between color and dark releases the male's courtship behavior, as Magnus showed by placing yellow-orange and dark strips on a revolving cylinder. Surprisingly, Magnus further found that increasing the speed of the rotating cylinder so that the color and dark alternation was more rapid than the rate used by the female resulted in greater effectiveness in eliciting courtship. The greater the speed of rotation of the cylinder, the greater the courtship responses, right up to the physiologically demonstrated flicker fusion frequency for the species when the color and dark alternation was so rapid that it could not be seen. This was indeed a very dramatic demonstration of supernormal releasers.

The susceptibility of animals to superoptimal releasers provides us with an insight as to the reason for the development of bizarre morphological structures in some animals such as the peacock. These strange structures are used in courtship of the female. It is clear, also, that parasitic birds capitalize on this phenomenon, since the young parasite is usually larger and more babyish than are the host's own young, so that it is actually preferred, with resultant neglect of the host's own young (Cott, 1940). Heinroth described the situation accurately when he called the young cuckoo a "vice" of its foster parents (1938).

When the different stimuli that act as releasers are examined, it is apparent that they are all very clear and simple in character—the color red on the belly or breast, a head-body size ratio, an odor, a movement, and so on. At the same time, they are unmistakable distinguishing characteristics of the appropriate biological situation—characteristics that are highly improbable in any other biological situation. This fact, when coupled with the selection pressures that must operate so as to bring about the ability to recognize without fail certain biological situations essential for the survival of the individual and of the species, accounts for their reliability in eliciting the required and adaptive response in natural conditions.

Their great simplicity, in fact, means that they can be imitated for certain purposes. The fisherman utilizes a releaser when he places a silvery lure into the water in order to attract and catch a pike (Baerends, 1950). There are some flowers which give off a putrid odor that attracts flies, and fertilization of these flowers is thus carried out by the flies. Still other flowers look like a female bumblebee's body and are fertilized in the male bumblebee's attempt to copulate with it.

Releasers, or sign stimuli, are also used for interspecies communication. An example of this is to be found in the fish symbioses studied by Eibl-Eibesfeldt (1955b). There are certain large species of fish in the Carribean, the groupers (*Epinephelus striatus*), that allow their teeth and gills to be cleaned of particles and ectoparasites by the neon goby, *Elacatinus oceanops*. The fish wishing to be cleaned makes a movement inviting the cleaner fish to enter its mouth and pick its teeth, and makes another movement signaling it to come out from the mouth. The principle of imitation is also to be found in this case (Eibl-Eibesfeldt, 1959). These fish do not normally allow any other fish to come near it, and in the Indopacific oceanic regions they permit only fish looking and behaving like cleaners of that area, the *Labroides dimidiatus*, to approach it. However, there is another species, *Aspidontus taeniatus*, which has taken advantage of this by having a certain coloration and by imitating the movements of the cleaner fish. When they come close to the large fish, they fall on it, biting out chunks of flesh, and the fish must flee. However, these parasites do occasionally pick ectoparasites from larger fish.

Now that we have considered the nature of the releaser, or sign stimulus, let us complete the picture by taking a look at the *innate releasing mechanism*, known for short as the I.R.M. As has been earlier mentioned, an inhibitory block has been postulated by Lorenz (1937) and Tinbergen (1950) to prevent the continuous discharge of internally produced energy. The I.R.M. functions to remove this inhibition when it receives sensory impulses arising from a releaser stimulus. This brings us to an important rule in evaluating the relative effectiveness of a given stimulus as a releaser for a fixed action pattern, in the light of the fading of reactivity due to repeated stimulation, and reaction recovery during a period in which no performance of the reaction takes place (see pages 170-171). If the animal is under low motivation, a strong releaser is required in order to elicit a reaction; whereas if the animal is highly motivated, a weak stimulus is sufficient to elicit a response of the same strength. Therefore, it is necessary to test the potential effectiveness of different releasers in relation to each other. This can be done by making certain that the animal is under the same motivation when exposed to each of them, or by exposing the animal to a standard stimulus just prior to the presentation of the stimulus in question. Thus the difference in responsiveness between the different stimuli and the antecedent standard stimulus is the basis for evaluation. Only in these ways can it be determined whether a stimulus is a normal, subnormal, or supernormal releaser.

The I.R.M. operates as a receptor of key stimuli and must be adapted to the world as it exists; this is necessary to make sure it will respond only to stimuli that unfailingly characterize a particular biological situation, and no other. If a particular response is elicited by several sign stimuli belonging to a certain biological situation, then the presence of most of them in that situation guarantees the elicitation of the response in question. A pike cannot attach any releaser or sign stimuli to the fish on which it preys in order to differentiate it from a fisherman's lure; therefore the species must adapt the I.R.M. accordingly. However, within a species or where interspecies communication takes place, natural selection can quickly result in the evolution of special sign stimuli or releasers that will be understood easily by the reacting animal.

Not only morphological structures but also behavioral patterns performed by another animal may function as releasers, as Tinbergen has shown in his study of the courtship behavior of the three-spined stickleback (1942). In such cases there is a reaction chain, each animal's action serving as a releaser for the other animal's subsequent response. Thus, the appearance of the female initiates the male's zigzag dance toward the nest, which in turn releases a following response in the female. The male, in response to her having followed him, shows her the nest entrance, and she reacts by swimming into it. On seeing her in the nest, the male touches her tail with a quivering motion, with the result that she lays the eggs and then swims out. The male then swims into the nest and fertilizes the eggs. Reaction chains, where they exist, enable the male to select a female of the same species. As Baerends (1950) points out, they also serve to select fully mature and healthy females, since any others would fail to respond correctly after the first couple of links in the chain.

Another feature of the I.R.M. is that in some cases its selectivity for sign stimuli may increase during the life of the individual. Such a process occurs in all members of the species, not in just one individual.

The increased selectivity may be of either of two types:

1. *Narrowing of the range of stimuli evoking a particular response through the dropping out of individual stimuli.* This occurs by means of habituation or one-trial negative conditioning. For example, a bird becomes habituated to the motion of leaves, other members of its species, etc., with the result that

it no longer responds with fright to them. Its fright behavior in the face of predators, however, is absolutely unaffected. Similarly, a toad will at first snap at all small objects, but after a single unhappy experience will avoid bees and wasps.

2. *Selection and strengthening of one releaser out of a large range of potential releasers, with the result that only this releaser is responded to and not any of the others.* This occurs in the socialization process of many animals, and this instance is known as *imprinting*. Soon after hatching, for example, a gosling has the disposition to follow almost any moving object and to behave as if that object were its mother. After this experience only this object, and no other, is treated as if it were the mother. Thus a gosling imprinted to a green box will not have anything to do with its real mother, but will stay close to the green box. This shows, of course, that the socialization process in the natural situation occurs in the same fashion. The subject of imprinting and its difference from ordinary types of association learning will be discussed in a later section.

In both cases of the increased selectivity of the I.R.M. during the life of the individual, it is clear that it results in behavior which has greater survival value.

SIMULTANEOUS AROUSAL OF DIFFERENT DRIVES

Most often people think of behavior as being influenced by one drive at a time. Actually, however, behavior can most frequently be seen to be influenced by or be a result of more than one activated drive, thus making the analysis of behavior quite complex. There are several types of such behaviors: successive ambivalent behavior, simultaneous ambivalent behavior, redirected behavior, and displacement behavior.

In the case of successive ambivalent behavior, it is seen that the animal alternates between incompletely performed movements belonging to the conflicting drives. When two males of a territory-owning species (such as the stickleback or herring gull) meet each other at the common boundary of their two territories, each is influenced by the other in two ways. First, because the other is so near the territory, the owner is roused to attack. But the stranger also causes hesitance and avoidance, for it is not in the owner's territory, but just outside it, and furthermore in its own territory. Each male is therefore in the same conflict, one which usually finds expression in an ambivalent reaction: attack and retreat in quick and repeated alternation.

Simultaneous ambivalent behavior, however, is also to be found. In such a case both tendencies are simultaneously, rather than alternately, aroused. An example of this is the threat posture of the cat, which, according to Leyhausen (1956), results from the animal retreating more rapidly with the front paws than with the rear ones, or advancing with the rear paws while retreating with the front ones. Lorenz (1953) has shown that fear and aggression occur simultaneously in the dog, with at least nine different expressions possible as a result of mixing three different degrees—high, medium, and low—of either drive.

Redirected behavior is another type in which two conflicting behaviors manifest themselves. This occurs when one behavior is inhibited or suppressed by another motivation. For example, an animal feeling aggressive towards a member of its own species (its mate, for instance) may at the same time be inhibited in its attack. Hence, the aggression may be redirected, and the animal will attack another animal or even an object if no third animal is available. Thus, prairie falcons defending their nest from a human intruder may swoop down toward him, but at the last moment fear overtakes the falcon: it makes a sudden swerve to the side and flies to attack by-passing birds.

Since cases in which behavior is determined by only one drive are relatively rare, the different behaviors of animals result from independently varying sets of motivations. In accordance with this knowledge, Oehlert (1958) demonstrated the existence of a mechanism of sex recognition that is widely distributed throughout the animal kingdom. In *Cichlasoma biocellatum* and *Geophagus brasiliensis*, two species of cichlids studied by Oehlert, and perhaps in many other species in which the sexes do not have a distinctive sexual dimorphism, the only sexual difference in behavior consists of the fact that three drives—sex, aggression, and fear—which are always activated simultaneously when two strange fish meet, can be mixed in different ways in males and females. In the males just about every possible mixture and superposition of sexual and aggressive behavior elements can be made, but the flight drive, even when minimal, will immediately inhibit the sexual drive. In the female, however, flight behavior can mix very easily with sexual behavior, whereas aggressiveness immediately suppresses sexuality. This difference between males and females is enough to guarantee the formation of male-female pairs. In the same way, fear suppresses male sex behavior and aggression inhibits female sex behavior in grouse and crows (A. A. Allen, 1954, and Lorenz, 1931).

Still another type of behavior may occur when two motivations are in conflict with each other. This is the *displacement activity* discovered independently in 1940 by both Tinbergen and Kortlandt. Very often in conflict situations the animal may show behavior patterns that do not belong to either of the two conflicting drives, but that are completely different. At first such "irrelevant" behavior is surprising, but after further study it is found that a particular irrelevant act is often typical of a particular set of conditions. Since the intensity of the displacement act is correlated with strength of the conflicting motivations, Tinbergen proposed that the irrelevant or displacement act is activated by the energy from the conflicting drives. Thus such displacement acts were *allochthonous*, as distinct from the case in which they are motivated by their own drive, when they are *autochthonous*.

For example, fighting domestic cocks may suddenly peck at the ground as if they were feeding (Lorenz, 1935, Tinbergen, 1939). In this case the irrelevant feeding results from a conflict between aggresiveness and fear. Quite often such pecking on the ground has been observed in other birds. The prairie horned lark does this during territorial fights (Pickwell, 1931), and so does the lapwing between attacks of an intruder disturbing it at its nest. Male snow buntings will peck at the ground during boundary disputes (Howard, 1929).

Many other types of displacement activities have been observed. The three-spined stickleback makes nest-building movements (displacement sand digging) during boundary fights with another male (Tinbergen and van Iersel, 1947), and herring gulls pick up nesting material during boundary disputes. Sexual movements such as wing-flapping and gurgling, which normally occur in courtship behavior, are shown by cormorants when fighting, and sky larks burst into violent song just after having escaped from a predator (Tinbergen, 1952). Cormorants also perform sessions of "false brooding" during nest fights (Kortlandt, 1940a), and the avocet may suddenly sit down during exciting hostile encounters (Makkink, 1936). Even sleep may occur as a displacement activity; this was first discovered by Makkink (1936) in the avocet and has been observed since then in various other waterbirds such as the oyster catcher, turnstone, and common sandpiper, and in male snow buntings, always in an aggressive situation.

It is apparent even from this short review of displacement activities that they often occur when the fighting and escape drives are simultaneously aroused. They are also very common in sexual situations. They can, of course, be aroused by combinations of other drives.

From what has been found concerning displacement activities, it is clear that such activities are usually dependent, at least in part, on internal impulses. The so-called innate "comfort movements" such as preening, shaking the feathers, wiping the bill, bathing, and so forth, most often depend on internal impulses and also appear as displacement activities in both hostile and sexual situations. Displacement preening is quite common during courtship, and displacement bathing has been observed regularly in the sheld duck when copulation was interrupted for some reason (Makkink, 1931). Scratching of the fur is a very common displacement activity in mammals up to the primates (Portielje, 1939, and Tinbergen, 1940). Another fact in considering the nature of displacement activities is that they are more likely to occur when conflicting drives are relatively intense. For example, in the boundary clash between males of territory-owning species, ambivalent behavior consisting of attack and retreat in alternation occurs as long as the conflicting drives of aggressiveness and fear are not too strong. But when these drives are very intense, displacement activities appear. Tinbergen (1952) therefore hypothesized that displacement activities were outlets through which strong but thwarted drives could express themselves in motion.

In sexual situations, displacement activities may occur as a result of sudden cessation of external stimulation emanating from the partner, or from conflict. Also, it has been suggested (Verwey, 1930, Kortlandt, 1940b) that copulation in birds brings about a situation which they normally avoid, that is, bodily contact with another individual. Therefore, the precoition situation may evoke in each individual a tendency to keep away from or to attack the partner as well as the expected one of approach.

However, no experimental evidence has been found that supports Tinbergen's hypothesis. Recently, Andrew (1956), Sevenster (1958) and van Iersel and Bol (1958), by studying grooming in birds, displacement fanning in the three-spined stickleback, and displacement preening in terns, respectively, suggested that inhibitions exerted by one or both of the conflicting systems on an activity are temporarily removed as a result of the conflict between these drives. These authors hypothesize that if the two conflicting motivations are balanced, then not only their own motoric manifestations, but also the inhibiting effect on the third motor pattern is removed.

This new conceptualization agrees with a number of well-known facts regarding displacement activities. For example, displacement activities occur particularly when specific motivations that strongly inhibit other motivations and dominate the entire organism, such as flight, escape, and copulation, come into conflict. Furthermore, the fixed patterns that occur as displacement activities are almost always those that are repeated many times daily and that do not usually require a high motivation level. Also, the form of the displacement movement has often been observed to be correlated with the body position into which an animal is forced by his primary conflict: a movement for which this body position is the basis is made in a large number of cases. This last is a point made by Tinbergen (1952) in connection with his theory.

Sevenster (1958) supported his hypothesis by the finding that the presence of adequate external stimuli can facilitate the appearance of certain types of displacement activities. For example, if food is thrown to fighting cocks, then displacement feeding increases. Sevenster could increase the fanning of the nest by the stickleback as a displacement activity by bringing about the appropriate conflict situation and at the same time maintaining a high CO_2 concentration in the water. Van Iersel and Bol (1958) also found that displacement bill-shaking, which occurs in sandwich terns when in conflict between escape and incubation drives, was increased in rainy weather. These phenomena would be hard to explain if displacement were based only on irradiation of energy, channeled strictly in a certain direction by the structure of the central nervous system.

On the other hand, there are several facts that could be better explained by the earlier hypothesis than by the new theory. The new theory, for example, fails to explain why in the majority of cases where there is a particular conflict, only a particular displacement activity is performed. This is an important point, because in closely related species the same small motor patterns are performed, but in the same conflict situation different specific displacement activities occur. Furthermore, according to the inhibition theory, the *balance* between the two conflicting motivations is responsible for the occurrence of displacement activity, whereas it has been shown that the intensity of the displacement act is proportional to the absolute drive level of the conflicting motivations. Lastly, if the inhibition hypothesis were correct, then displacement activity would have to be performed with the same *irregularity* as its autochthonous forms, as, for instance, in the case of a bird; it does not preen itself ceaselessly when the preening drive is not under inhibition by other drives.

Finally, these different types of mixed-drive behavior—successive and simultaneous ambivalence, redirection and displacement activities—are not mutually exclusive and may often be found to exist in the same behavior sequence. For example, as Baerends (1958) has shown, the courtship of the male cichlid fish, *Cichlasoma meeki*, has successive ambivalence in the zigzag dance (the *zigs* being incipient attacks and the *zags* being incipient leading-to-the-nest), redirection in its incipient attacks toward plants, and displacement activity in a peculiar quivering movement interpreted as displacement digging.

HIERARCHICAL ORGANIZATION OF BEHAVIOR

Lorenz and Craig distinguished between two types of behavior: the appetitive and aversive behaviors, and the consummatory act. Appetitive behavior consists of initially variable searching behavior that becomes more and more specific until the simpler and more stereotyped consummatory act, in response to a releasing stimulus situation, is performed. Aversive behavior has some similarity with appetitive behavior, but consists of behavior that continues until a disturbing situation is removed, and the animal reaches a state of equilibrium. Here the goal is not the discharge of specific behavior patterns, but the cutting off of appetitive behavior that in this case is undirected locomotion.

The distinction between appetitive behavior and the consummatory act is not an absolute one; there are many forms intermediate to them. But these concepts serve to mark the extremes, since appetitive behavior is variable and plastic, whereas the consummatory act is relatively fixed and stereotyped.

Appetitive behavior is characterized in three ways. The first is by its motor pattern, usually one of locomotion. The others are its orientation component and the stimuli to which the animal is particularly responsive. Since the first and second components may remain the same while the third changes, as seen when a hungry squirrel (1) climbs (2) up trees (3) looking for cones; and when a squirrel motivated to build nests (1) climbs (2) up trees (3) looking for twigs and bark, 'appetitive behavior is usually classified according to the third component. Therefore, in the first case, the squirrel is showing appetitive behavior for food, while in the second case it is showing appetitive behavior for nesting material.

The consummatory act itself is made in response to one or more releasers and is composed of an orientation component, the *taxis*, and a motor component, the *fixed action pattern*. These two aspects of the consummatory act were pointed out by Lorenz and Tinbergen (1938) during a study of the egg-rolling response of the greylag goose. But before we discuss this, let us briefly examine the nature of the taxes, since the fixed action pattern has already been discussed in detail.

Taxes are oriented locomotory reactions of motile organisms. When exposed to a source of stimulation, the body as a whole, or a particular part, is oriented in line with the source of stimulation. Movement toward the source is said to be positive, while movement away from the source is negative. There are many types of taxes recognized by ethologists, and some of the most important are klinotaxis, tropotaxis, telotaxis, and transverse orientation (Fraenkel and Gunn, 1940).

Klinotaxis consists of the animal traversing a short distance, stopping, making a turning movement from one side to the other, and then finally moving toward one side according to whether it is nearer or farther away from the source of stimulation. The animal then travels a short distance further, and then repeats the whole procedure. In this way an animal gradually gets nearer or farther away from the source of stimulation. Tropotaxis is like klinotaxis except that there are no trial movements, but a gradual turning toward or away from the stimulation. Telotaxis, however, is direct locomotion toward the source of stimulation, without trial movements, and looks as if it were goal-directed. Transverse orientation may or may not involve locomotion, and is illustrated by the light compass reaction shown by bees navigating toward or away from the hive, and by the dorsal light reaction of fishes swimming always belly down, that is, belly away from the light.

Instinctive behavior is complex, being composed of several elements: reflexes, taxes, and fixed action patterns or instinctive movements. In the egg-rolling reaction of the greylag goose we find two separate components in this behavior. If an incubating goose is presented with an egg outside of her nest, she will reach out with her neck toward it and roll it back into her nest with her bill, balancing it in its course with little sideways movements. If, after it has begun this action, the egg is taken away, the goose will continue to perform the action to the very end. However, the bill is moved directly, without the balancing movements, toward the nest. Hence the movement of the bill toward the nest is a pure fixed action pattern, being released but not guided, while the balancing movements are guided by continuous external stimulation from the egg. Tinbergen (1951) has compared the taxic component and the fixed action pattern with the steering and propulsory mechanisms of a ship, respectively.

Another example of the simultaneous presence of fixed action patterns and of taxic movements is to be found in the wing-cleaning behavior of the common fly. The fly moves its legs over and under the wings, making little scrubbing movements. If, however, the wings are removed, the fly still moves its legs around in the region where the wings had been, but will not make the tiny scrubbing movements. This shows that the action of passing the legs over and under the wings is a fixed action pattern, while the little scrubbing movements were guided by the stimulation offered by contact with the wings (Heinz, 1949).

Often the same stimuli both steer and release the reaction, and in some cases the taxic steering component is absent in certain consummatory acts such as swallowing or blinking. Although the distinction between the fixed action pattern and the taxis is not absolute, the isolation of the fixed action pattern has contributed a great deal to the analysis of behavior.

However useful the distinction between appetitive behavior and the consummatory act, the Lorenz-Craig scheme of appetitive behavior leading to the consummatory act has been found to be a rather simplified case. Normally, particular appetitive behavior does not usually end in a consummatory act, but, rather, leads to a stimulus situation that initiates another and more specific appetitive behavior (Baerends, 1941 and 1956, and Tinbergen, 1950). A chain of appetitive behaviors gives rise to a temporal sequence of "moods" or readinesses to act, anchored in the central nervous system. We shall illustrate this by considering the reproductive behavior of the male stickleback.

In spring the gradual increase in length of day is responsible for bringing the fish into a reproductive motivation. It does ot immediately acquire a red belly, but first begins migrating nto shallow fresh water. The rise in water temperature, as it goes further inland, together with the visual stimulation arising from suitable territory consisting of heavily vegetated sites, then releases the entire reproductive behavior. Only then, after it has established its territory, does the male stickleback acquire its characteristic red belly. At this point it begins to react to particular stimuli that previously had no effect on it. If males caught during migration are put together in a bathtub, they all will remain in a school except one who establishes a territory by the drain plug chain. This chain is the only structured element in the bathtub; it is for this reason that a territory is established there. Furthermore, it provides enough territory for only one male. This male will then fight at the appearance of a stranger, begin to build a nest with suitable material, and court passing females. Since the male's behavior depends principally on the stimulus situation, this makes difficult the prediction as to precisely what it will do. Fighting, for example, is released by the stimulus *red belly* on a male intruding into its territory, but it cannot be predicted which of the five known fighting movements will occur, each being, again, dependent on still further and highly specific stimuli. If the stranger bites, the territory owner will bite in turn, or if the stranger beats with its tail, the owner makes the same response. Fleeing will elicit chasing, and threatening will elicit threatening in turn. In summary, the stimuli emanating from a suitable territory will activate the fighting, building, and mating drives. The more specific stimulus, *red-bellied male*, activates only a general readiness to fight; the specific movements made are dependent on even more specific stimuli.

Thus one can organize different levels of integrations into a hierarchical system. In this way it is clear that there are chains of behavior tendencies that are connected in higher and lower levels of integration. The adaptive advantages of the mood hierarchy rather than a stereotyped series of single fixed action patterns lie in its adaptability to several situations. For example, a hunting peregrine falcon initially seeks prey of any kind, this behavior being of a rather general appetitive type. If it sees a group of prey birds, it dives down toward them and isolates a single bird from the swarm. If it has met with success, it performs the very specific behavior patterns of killing the prey, pulling out its feathers, and eating it (Tinbergen, 1950). The adaptability of the mood hierarchy lies in the fact that if a falcon should happen to meet a single bird by accident, the previous part of the chain will drop out, and it immediately proceeds to kill, pluck, and eat it.

It seems evident that a structural organization within the central nervous system must exist which parallels the lawfulness of behavior, particularly the mood hierarchy. Tinbergen (1950) has illustrated this in the diagram shown in Figure 3,

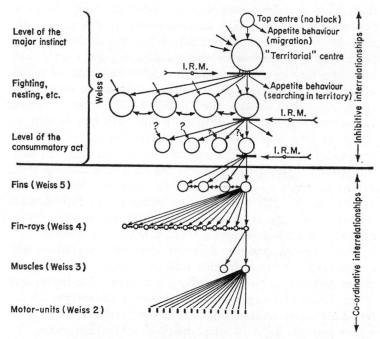

Fig. 3.   Tinbergen's diagram of the hierarchical organization of instincts, superimposed on Weiss's diagram of the hierarchical organization of central nervous mechanisms, Weiss's highest level incorporating the same phenomena as those placed in Tinbergen's hierarchy. (From Tinbergen, N., 1950.)

which, of course, represents only functional units and does not attempt to represent anatomy or localization of functions. The number and kind of appetitive links, as well as the innate releasing mechanisms (I.R.M.) that respond to certain stimulus situations and the chain of built-in fixed patterns that are also their final goals or consummatory acts, are rigorously derived from empirical observations of behavior.

Close relationships exist between Tinbergen's results and those of P. Weiss (1941b), who showed a similar hierarchical organization of the central nervous system mechanism in motor processes that are almost exclusively below the level of integration of the goal-forming fixed patterns. Since Weiss had specified that the highest level of his hierarchy was the behavior of the animal as a whole, Tinbergen assumed that the two hierarchies were physiologically similar, and therefore he added Weiss's diagram below a horizontal line under his own hierarchical organization, making Weiss's uppermost level equivalent to his own system.

In this scheme Tinbergen ignored a complication that he recognized: some of the same behavior patterns at the lowest level, for instance those of locomotion, can be among the final effecting links in several hierarchical organizations of a higher order as a common final pathway, so that under certain circumstances the chains diverge and then converge again. Tinbergen's results and hypothesis are highly valuable because they provide a link to a real physiology of the central nervous system. Further evidence regarding this will be discussed later when we turn to neurophysiological evidence for ethological concepts.

⊕ ETHOLOGICAL METHODS AND AREAS OF RESEARCH

We have already described the basic starting point of the ethological approach, the *ethogram*, in the introduction. We shall now consider the various methods, all subsequent to the cataloguing of the behavior of a species. The phylogenetic relationships between the behaviors of different species, the probable evolution of these behaviors, and their genetic and neurophysiological bases can be determined only after an exhaustive inventory has been made of the fixed action patterns, etc., of the species involved.

PHYLOGENESIS

It is very clear from our previous discussion that there are fixed action patterns which do not need to be learned but which are part of a species, just as are its bodily structures and physiological mechanisms. These fixed action patterns are, furthermore, based on these structures and mechanisms, the central nervous system being particularly important in determining their form.

Just as it is realized, when the similarities and dissimilarities of higher and lower forms of recent animals are compared, that all animals inhabiting this planet are derived from common sources, it can be shown that their behavior is similarly derived. Thus behavior characteristics can be said to be homologous, and these homologies are recognized by the same procedures as those used by comparative morphologists. The principal criteria by which homology of behavior is judged by ethologists are as follows (Remane, 1956):

(1) *Similarity in structure*, that is, similarity in the spatiotemporal pattern of muscular contractions or movements. The more fixed action patterns correspond with each other in their special characteristics—such as internal causal factors and releasing situations—as well as in the coordinations themselves, and the more complex these characters are, the more likely they are to be homologies. Sometimes, however, similar structures, bodily or behavioral, can evolve independently of phylogenetic relationship in different groups of animals as a result of adaptation to the same environmental conditions; in such cases they would be *analogies*. For example, food hiding in very different species might at first look homologous, but the

similarity would actually be due to function and not to common history, as there are only a few ways in which food can be stored. Such analogy of behavior is more likely, furthermore, when similar behavior patterns are to be found in different species whose mode of living is the same (tree-nesting, seed-eating) or that live in the same biotope (wood, earth, silt) but which have relatives in other biotopes and with a different manner of living, and therefore lacking these particular behavior patterns. Homology, rather than analogy, however, is more likely in expressive movements which serve as signals understood only by members of the same or very closely related species.

(2) *Similarity in order of occurrence of movements*, or topography. Certain activities can often be found to follow each other with regularity. If, for example, two species have the same sequence of movements, as a, b, c, d, e, f, g, but one species makes its movement e somewhat different from that for the other species, the correspondence in the temporal occurrence in the sequence indicates homology. For example, two species of fish, *Tilapia mossambica* and *T. nilotica*, perform comparable but different tail-wagging movements. These movements, however, occur at precisely the same places in the male's courtship of the female (Baerends, 1958).

(3) *Linkage by intermediate stages*. Hence even different fixed patterns in different species consisting of different movements or different orders of movements can be homologized as long as they are connected to each other by intermediate stages shown by other related species of the same taxonomic group. If enough intermediate stages between disparate forms are compared, this will prevent the mistaken homologizing of these similar-appearing activities in the two related species.

When structures or movement patterns, even of a simple type, are quite universal in their distribution in a group of related species but are not present in unrelated species, they are very probably homologies.

Just as organs in one and the same animal can be compared,

behaviors in one and the same animal can also be compared. For example, morphologists conclude that a crustacean's feeding legs are actually modified walking legs, because there are a series of organs representing intermediate stages between them. These serial homologies are called *homonomies*, and can also be found in behavior, since behavior patterns, in adapting to different functions, often have been variously modified, with the different forms used by the same animal. This is the case with many ritualized movements and the original movement from which they are derived, as we have earlier mentioned. For example, drinking in its ritualized and unritualized form can be observed in the same animal.

Let us give some examples of homologous behavior. A widespread behavior, one that has existed for a long time, is scratching, found in most four-limbed animals. A lizard scratches itself by bringing one hind leg laterally over the front leg of the same side to the head, which is slightly bent towards the scratching leg. Many other reptiles, mammals, and even birds scratch themselves in a similar fashion, dogs and cats being common everyday examples (Heinroth, 1930). Many birds can be seen to lower their wings in a most peculiar way and reach forward in front of the shoulder with the leg. It would seem that it would be less clumsy for the bird to move its claw directly to its head without moving its wing, which is normally folded on its back and out of the way. Apparently, then, the bird reconstructs the spatial relationship of its four-legged ancestor and still behaves as if it had an obstructing front leg. A few species, such as storks, herons, and pigeons, have developed the habit of scratching the other way around, but most species stick to the original over-the-shoulder technique. Large parrots which feed with their claws use the more direct method, but parakeets scratch over the shoulder, and do not pick up food in their claws. There are some exceptions; for example, the Australian broad-tailed parakeet has learned to eat with its claws, and brings them directly to the head. But when scratching, it still brings its claw over its lowered wing, and cannot be trained to do otherwise (Lorenz, 1958b).

A very clear demonstration of homologous behavior patterns is in the courtship behaviors of ducks, as studied by Heinroth (1910) and Lorenz (1941). By comparing many species, Lorenz traced in detail the evolution of some of the highly peculiar courtship postures of ducks. For example, males of many species perform an up-down movement with the head and bill while courting the female. Some species, however, do not perform this action, but in its place in the sequence of movements they make a drinking response. This drinking behavior has the same appeasement effect on the female as does the up-down movement. The similarity of these two actions and their identical place in the sequence of movements indicates that they are homologies. In fact, this also shows that the up-down movement actually is a ritualized form of the original drinking movement. What is more, this conclusion is confirmed by the fact that there are other species which show intermediate forms of these two behaviors.

Schenckel (1956 and 1958) recently analyzed the courtship display of different species of pheasants and related fowl, and demonstrated that the frontal display of the true pheasant, peacock pheasant, Indian pheasant (monal), and peafowl during courtship has derived from a ceremonial feeding of the female by the male. We will give a few details to show how he arrived at this conclusion.

The behavior pattern in its original and relatively unritualized form can be seen in the domestic cock. The cock will often scratch the ground, utter a high, short cluck, bend its head and nod while its beak is pointing to some food particle, and at times lift the food. This behavior results in attracting the attention of the females; the females come and begin to peck at the ground in front of the cock even if there is really no food there. In this way the cock and hen establish an intimate relationship analogous to a parent-child relationship; this interpretation is confirmed by the infantile posture the female assumes in order to subordinate herself to the male.

Similar behavior can be observed in the common pheasant, *Phasianus colchicus*.

The Impeyan pheasant *Lophophorous impeyanus* bows in front of the female, spreading his tail feathers and pecking energetically on the ground. When the hen comes in response to this, the male raises and spreads its tail and wings while bending its head low, and the female then begins to search for food in front of him. The male peacock pheasant *Polyplectron bicalcaratum* assumes a similar posture. After scratching the ground as does the domestic cock, but before presenting food to the female, it bends down, spreading its tail and wings. When the female is close by it moves its head rapidly back and forth towards her. If food is presented to the male at this time, it will take it and present it to the female, thus showing that its behavior is symbolized feeding.

In the peacock the behavior is so ritualized that, without having studied the behavior of related species, it would be rather difficult to explain its origin. The courting peacock presents its back to the female, spreads its tail feathers with shaking movements, and makes a few steps backwards. Then it bends the spread tail forward, while its neck is raised and its beak is pointing to the ground, and makes fanning movements with its tail. The female then runs in front of the male and pecks on the ground. He may prolong the courtship by again turning his back to her so that she has to run around him. The result of the ritualization is that few of the original feeding ceremony elements can be recognized. In this case the original elements are the pointing of the beak, the backward stepping, and the reaction of the female. The spreading of the wings and tail, which are also observed in pheasants that still perform demonstration feeding, has, in this instance, become even more ritualized and goes beyond the demonstration function. Young peacocks, however, often spread their tails while scratching the ground and pecking, thus confirming Schenckel's view.

Thus by comparing different species the evolution of certain behavior patterns may be traced. During the course of ritualization the original behavior patterns are transformed so as to become a mimic exaggeration in the amplitude and frequency of the movement, just as they are transformed by the evolution of additional structures. For instance, the ceremonial feeding of *Gallica* birds and pheasants has been transformed and accentuated by additional shaking movements, feather spreading, swelling of exposed vascularized skin structures, and sounds.

It is also clear that the original meaning or function of a behavior pattern may change during the course of evolution: it may become motivationally autonomous or dependent on another motivation, as earlier mentioned. An example is that of grooming, which is used in social interaction as an expression of friendliness and peaceful intentions. Thus, a friendly dog greets by licking and nibbling. Movements exactly like those used in grooming may also be used in other animals as a greeting ceremony to a member of its own species before any physical contact has been made, and they are homonomous with the original grooming behavior.

In general, any kind of behavior that indicates a certain mood of an animal can be ritualized into an expressive movement. For example, preparations for attack such as mouthopening, standing up, and so forth, have changed into symbolic threat movements toward another species member or a predator. Such incipient movements that indicate what an animal is about to do have been called *intention movements*. Sometimes simultaneously occurring and conflicting intention movements of attack and flight are apparent in expression movements, as we have found to be the case when behavior is determined by different drives that have been aroused simultaneously.

There are, in many cases, striking similarities between highly ritualized movements that can with certainty be traced to homology. However, some movements that are similar in entirely unrelated species, such as the rattling of the rattlesnake and the porcupine, certainly were acquired independently, and are analogous. Expressive movements such as these are conventional signals in a given species; therefore, different meanings may be attached to similar movements by different species—for example, tail-wagging in the dog and cat—depending on the motivational situation from which they have derived. Ethologists consider what a movement signals to be a phylogenetically evolved convention, comparable to the words in man's languages.

GENETICS

Investigations of the genetic basis of inborn behavior patterns began only in recent times. S. von Hörmann-Heck (1955 and 1957) crossed two species of crickets, *Gryllus campestris* L. and *G. bimaculatus* de Geer, in order to study the inheritance of, and the effects of crossing on, four behavioral characters. She obtained fertile hybrids and was able to show that in three of these characters the inheritance was based on monofactorial transmission; in addition, interesting combinations of characters was found.

W. von de Wall, at the Max-Planck-Institute in Seewiesen, has been carrying on careful study of the transmission of courtship behavior patterns in crossbred progeny of different species of ducks (W. von de Wall, in preparation). His studies have proven the ethological postulation, originally based on comparative studies of these ducks, that certain complete series of fixed action patterns were primary, or original, in a group of species, but that the absence of some of these fixed patterns in any species is a more recent phenomenon. Hybrids, obtained by crossbreeding different species, performed motor elements that, even if those were not present in either of the parent species, are distributed in the species group to which they belong. Some hybrids perform integrations and coordinations that, again, are not present in any of the parent species, but are present in certain other members of their species group. Of the few second generation (to be referred to as F₂) hybrids obtained up to now, such as *Anas* (Dafila) *spinicauda* × *Anas*

(Poecilonetta) *bahamensis,* each showed several interesting integrations of motor patterns. One individual, however, showed a complete sequence of coordinations that is not found in any of the parent species nor in any other of the swimming ducks (Anatinae), this sequence presumably being one that has disappeared in the entire species group.

Two males of the F_2 generation of such a cross have been observed over an extensive period of time. The morphological characteristics of these drakes are not at all different; however, they show some behavioral differences from each other when they court females. For example, Drake A sometimes will begin the up-down movement with a forward bending of the head and a specific sideway shaking of the bill that throws up a stream of water; these two movements initiate the grunt-whistle in *spinicauda* and many other *Anas* species. Neither in the F_2 Drake B, nor in the F_1 generation of these hybrids, nor in any other ducks species, has this motor sequence ever been seen. But, most remarkably, this motor sequence occurs in almost identical form in an F_1 drake resulting from a cross between *Anas flavirostre* × *A. bahamensis.* Again, this sequence is one that must have originally been performed by ducks but has disappeared in all present-day species. Drake B regularly shows the so-called bridling movement in courtship, whereas Drake A never performs it. In *spinicauda* this movement occurs only in copulatory afterplay, while in *bahamensis* it occurs in a rudimentary form in pre-courtship behavior. Drake B also performs a combination of motor sequences that is unique to it: this is the bridling and tail-up that, in other duck species, is the element of the head-up tail-up sequence. In addition, Drake B has a genuine head-up tail-up sequence that A has never been observed to perform.

Von de Wall's observations have been supplemented by those of Ramsay, of McDonogh School, Maryland, who began his research in 1956 and has just published a brief paper on this subject (1961). He crossed a male black duck and a female mallard. The courtship displays of the two parent species are essentially identical, but the F1 generation hybrid performed several sequences that were characteristic of neither parent species. In one case there was an elimination of a movement after a particular one: it never gave the nod-swimming following the head-up tail-up display. In the mallard this display is omitted only 7 percent of the time and in the Black Duck 20 percent of the time in the typical sequence. These percentages are based on approximately seventy-five recorded observations for each animal. In this hybrid the movement sequence of bill-shaking, grunt-whistle is reversed. Sometimes in the parent species this sequence is tail-shaking, bill-shaking, grunt-whistle. In the hybrid this is reversed to grunt-whistle, tail-shaking, bill-shaking. This hybrid also showed other occasional deviations from pattern such as head-up-tail-up, down-up.

These investigations make it quite clear that whereas the basic components, or fixed action patterns, do not change in character as a result of crossing, it is possible to rearrange these components. This in itself is almost certainly proof of the correctness of the ethologists' hypotheses.

Courtship behavior is not the only type of behavior with which ethological genetic studies have concerned themselves: Dilger (1962) of Cornell University, has investigated nest material carrying in F1 hybrids of a male *Agapornis roseicollis* parrot and a female *A. personata fischeri*. Both of these species cut strips of paper or leaves and take them to the nest to be used for building. *Fischeri* carries the strips to its nest in its bill. *Roseicollis*, however, tucks the strips under the lower back and rump feathers, with their plumage erected while the material is being tucked, and then flies off to the nest. The remarkable thing about this difference in behavior between these two closely related species is that both have body feathers modified with tiny hooks whose main function is to bind the feathers more closely to the body, but *roseicollis* also uses them for holding strips of material under the feathers.

The sequence of the *roseicollis* female's behavior is composed of the following elements: the cutting of the strip, grasping of the strip, bringing the head back over the shoulder, erecting the lower back and rump feathers, tucking the strips between these feathers, bringing the head into the normal position, and lowering the back and rump feathers. This sequence is an innate pattern, the only changes due to experience being the subsequent standardization of the size and shape of the strips. Strips that are accidentally dropped are not picked up, but new ones are cut to take their place. *Fischeri*, which carries the cut strips in its bill, however, will pick up strips which lie on the ground.

The nest-building behavior of the F_1 hybrids resulting from a cross between these species was most interesting. They cut the leaves and tried to tuck them under their feathers, but their attempts never succeeded, for a variety of reasons. Sometimes the birds would tuck the strip under the feathers but be unable to let go of it. In such cases, after repeated attempts had been made, the strip would be abandoned and a new one cut. In some other cases the hybrid might be able to let go of the strip, but the feathers would fail to hold the material, probably from not being pressed against it. Sometimes the hybrids would try to put the strips in inappropriate locations such as the breast, belly, flanks, or wings. Quite commonly, the tucking behavior would change into preening behavior. It was very clear that the hybrids were displaying a conflict between the tendency to carry material in the feathers and the tendency to carry material in the bill. They were successful in getting material to their nests only when they carried it in the bill. But even when they carried the strip in the bill, which happened very rarely during their first attempts at nest building, they engaged in tucking movements.

After two months of experience the hybrids made fewer tucking attempts before carrying leaf strips in the bill to the nest. Nevertheless two years passed before their behavior became more efficient and more like their *fischeri* parent's. Even so, they continued to perform tucking movements. These movements themselves were better performed, but never were successful as a means of carrying leaf strips to the nest.

In all these cases where the inheritance of behavior patterns

is studied through the crossbreeding of different species that
have different or similar behavior characteristics, it is obvious
that it is necessary to study carefully the characteristics of the
parent strains in order to assess correctly what similarities persist and what changes take place. Picking at random another
example of the crossbreeding of parents with widely divergent
behavior characteristics, there is McClearn's study (1959) of
the effects of crossing two highly inbred mouse strains that
were quite different from each other with respect to exploratory tendency, as measured by various tests. The F_1 generation
proved to be intermediate to the parental strains in three measures of exploratory tendency. One of these, the number of
crossings into a square in the middle of an open field, is illustrated in Figure 4.

Herter and Sgonina (1938) found that differences in temperature preferences of inbred strains of mice were explainable

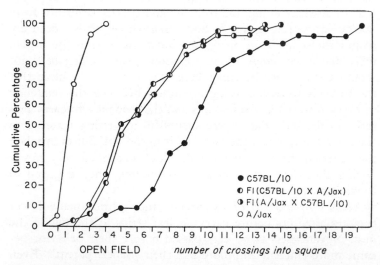

Fig. 4.   Cumulative distributions for parental strains and reciprocal F_1s for number of crossings into square in
Open Field test. (From McClearn, 1959.)

by the different skin structures in these strains. However, other genetic differences, such as those described for the two species of parrot, appear ascribable to differences in the central nervous system itself. Behavior traits often prove to be controlled by several genes, as experiments with *Ephestia* insects have shown. Normally, this species digs tunnels within the food mass. When they are about to pupate, they crawl up to the surface of the food mass and spin a cocoon. However, one strain was observed to leave the food at an earlier time, crawl around on the cover of the dish, spinning continuously, and thus producing a mat of silk. Backcrosses between hybrids of mat-spinning and normal strains and backcrosses between F_1 and F_2 generations have been studied with respect to the behaviors shown, and the conclusion is that the trait is determined by several genes (Caspari, 1948, and Cotter, 1951).

Ethological research on the genetics of behavior is still in its infancy and promises to become increasingly important. Many implications concerning the mode of genetic transmission and the origin of behavior have already been made. Genetic behavioral research has also attracted a number of excellent researchers in the United States, for example, at the Roscoe B. Jackson Memorial Laboratory in Maine, where temperament studies are being conducted. We can fully expect genetic problems of behavior to be a fruitful area of research in which many pioneering contributions will be made.

NEUROPHYSIOLOGY

Some people, critical of the ethological viewpoint, thought that there were serious neurophysiological difficulties in viewing instinctive drives as having their origin within the central nervous system, and as being independent of stimulation from peripheral sense organs.

When Lorenz observed that behavior was spontaneous, he was led to assume that central nervous excitation was constantly being produced within the animal. He also postulated that this constant energy production does not lead to incessant activity of the animal, because special blocks inhibit the expression of this energy into action. These blocks are removed by another mechanism—the I.R.M.—that selectively reacts to specific stimuli only. Now a whole body of neurophysiological evidence has accumulated to support Lorenz's scheme.

The neurophysiological work of ethologists has done much to change earlier neurophysiological ideas. Classical physiologists were of the opinion that the task of the central nervous system was to transform an incoming stimulus into motor impulses; therefore, all movements of an organism were reflexes or chain reflexes. In other words, all the central nervous system did was to change sensory impulses into appropriate motor actions. But von Holst's work has shown this conception to be rather inadequate.

Von Holst isolated a nerve cord of the earth worm (1932, 1933) and found that there were salvos of rhythmical impulses corresponding exactly to the contraction of the segments in the normal creeping movements of this animal. To test the classical chain reflex theory, he completely cut off the sensory nerves running to the brain of an eel, thus making a spinal animal (von Holst, 1937b). According to the chain reflex theory, the contraction of one segment during the sinuous swimming movement should change the tension of the succeeding segment, and by means of proprioceptors, or sense organs that transmit information about muscular movements, induce the contraction of the next segment. Therefore, an eel deprived of such information from the proprioceptors should not be able to swim. But instead, after the trauma of the operation had passed, the eel began to swim. If von Holst restrained the middle part of the eel so that this segment could not move, the undulating movement that started from the front end appeared in the right phase and time in the rear end, thus excluding the role of mechanical transference. Therefore, central factors, that is, mechanisms within the brain itself, coordinate the sinuous movement without the aid of sensory receptors, and no chain reflexes are involved. There were many others of von Holst's observations that tended to disprove the classical chain reflex theory.

In his search for the co-ordinating factors involved in muscular movements, von Holst studied the locomotory activity of fishes that do not travel by sinuous movement of the whole body, but by rhythmical movements of fins (1936a, b, 1937b). Von Holst recorded the fin movements of spinal fish whose sensory nerves had been cut along the pathway to the brain, and found that the rhythms of different fins influenced each other by means of a central or brain mechanism. There were two kinds of fin movements, dominant and dependent. The dominant movements tended to influence the dependent ones in varying degrees, resulting in either absolute or relative co-ordination of the fins. Such influences were clearly due to a central factor, not to peripheral sense organs, for the passive movement of a quiet fin did not influence the rhythm of any other fins (von Holst, 1935).

Furthermore, von Holst found muscle rays—that is, single nerve fibers transmitting motor impulses to one muscle—to interact in a similar way, except that the "magnetic effect" of a dominant over a dependent rhythm was much stronger than that found for fins, thus resulting in a much greater absolute coordination. As a result of these investigations, it was concluded that central nervous automatisms, rather than peripheral stimulation—that is, sensory information—determine locomotor rhythms.

Von Holst also studied a phenomenon that was discovered by Sherrington in 1892 and known as *spinal contrast* (1937a). The sea horse is a relatively sedentary fish. Most of the day it stands with its back fin completely folded; but when the sea horse begins to swim, this fin is erected and undulated. If the medulla is cut, thus making a spinal fish, uninhibited locomotion will not be observed (as when other fish have their medullas cut), but instead the back fin rests in a half-erected position. If this fish is pressed in the region of the gills, the fin becomes completely folded, and if after a while the fin is removed from this restraint, the fin erects itself more than before for a short while. Depending on how long the fin was restrained, some actual swimming may occur briefly. This is the basis of the spinal contrast.

The explanation for this strange phenomenon is that the central nervous energy production for swimming is very weak and must be stored up for a while in order for locomotion to occur. It is not yet known what the physiological mechanisms are, or what sort of energy is involved. The important facet of von Holst's results is that they constitute potent support for Lorenz's hypotheses on constant central nervous energy production.

The neurophysiology of other fixed action patterns has become an expanding and important area of ethological research. Von Holst (1957) and W. R. Hess (1956) found that they were able to elicit well-coordinated, complete movement sequences identical with those of normal behavior, von Holst stimulating electrically certain portions of chicken brains, and Hess doing the same with the cat. Hess's elicitation of rage and integrated sleep activity is well known.

Recently, von Holst and von St. Paul (1960, 1962) proved the existence of a hierarchical organization of the mechanisms underlying behavior while studying the functional structure of behavior by means of wireless brain stimulation of free-moving chickens (Jechorek and von Holst, 1956). Their work gave strong support to the long-held opinion of ethologists that there must be a structural organization within the central nervous system which parallels the lawfulness of behavior observed by the ethologists, and particularly the hierarchical organization of behavior as shown by Tinbergen.

Von Holst and von St. Paul elicited a great number of different behavior patterns in their chickens. Complex behavior patterns were distinguished by four characteristics:

1. The sequence in which the different behavior acts belonging to the activated complex pattern were performed was always the same. Continuous electrical stimulation or increasing

the strength of the electrical stimulation caused these part acts always to occur in the same order.

2. This sequence is usually obtained by means of constant moderate stimulation voltage.

3. Observers of animal behavior will find such a sequence of movements to be a natural one.

4. These sequences are functional patterns of biological importance for the survival of the individual or of the species. They are the same as the fixed action patterns.

In these cases it appears that von Holst and von St. Paul stimulated an "instinct," the different acts appearing according to their individual thresholds, in an orderly sequence.

Von Holst and von St. Paul gave many examples of the coordinated sequences they observed. For instance, they could release the whole sequence of the "disgust" reaction; this consists of tongue movements while the neck is stretched out and the head is bent downward. Saliva is secreted as if to wash out an unpalatable object, then shaking of the head and scratching occurs. If the electrical stimulus is turned off, the chicken wipes its beak on the ground as a final cleaning movement. In such cases von Holst and von St. Paul probably have stimulated the physiological correlate of a sensation or "hallucination," that is, a central nervous pathway arising from the cheek or mouth.

Among other reactions elicited were flight from a ground predator or from a bird of prey, each very different from the other. In one case, the animal would first fixate a spot on the ground, give a warning call, start to walk, make aiming movements with the head as if fixating a branch to land on, and, finally, fly up, as if a ground predator were approaching. In other cases, the chicken finally hides in a bush, as if a bird of prey were in view.

A great wealth of such complex adaptive behavior patterns has been released. Sleeping, seeking food and eating, seeking water and drinking, flight behavior, aggressive behavior against a rival or predator, and many others could be activated. Some of them go off *in vacuo;* others need to be released by the

presence of a specific stimulus, in which case it might appear
to the naive observer to be just motoric restlessness. But in most
cases it can be easily demonstrated that the chicken is actually
looking for some specific object, by offering food, which he
may ignore, or a hen, which he again ignores, and so on, until
water is offered and the animal begins to drink.

Another outstanding finding was that all these sequences of
behavior are composed of single acts that can be obtained in
isolation by stimulation of certain brain areas. Cackling is a
part of the flight reaction, but pure cackling can be elicited.
If cackling is part of the flight reaction, then when electrical
stimulation is continued or increased, the chicken will start to
walk around and then finally take off. In the case of pure cackling, however, continuing or increasing stimulation will result
only in more cackling. The chicken then behaves like a "cackling machine", and stimulation is in the motor pathways.

Since many of these part acts appear as parts of instinctive
behavior patterns, von Holst and von St. Paul attempt to find
what sequence of innate behavior pattern they belong to, just
as in the case of "motoric restlessness." When they succeed in
finding this, then it may be said that they are activating a whole
instinct in its hierarchical organization, and that the point of
stimulation is very close to sensory pathways, with the animal
acting as a whole. This proof of the hierarchical organization
of behavior as advanced by Tinbergen has greatly complicated
conceptions about the structure of animal actions. In view of
this, it is quite remarkable that the earlier concepts on which
Craig's and Lorenz's much too simple action schemas were
based have maintained their full applicability, even if further
analysis is required.

Another extremely important area of von Holst and von St.
Paul's investigation (1958, 1960, 1962) was the interaction of
different behavior patterns elicited simultaneously. The simplest
form of interaction was that of *superposition*. Both activities
remain independent of each other, as is the case with pecking

and turning of the head. In the case of *overlapping*, on the other hand, both activities superpose, but, at the same time, change in their intensity. "Alerting" with stretched neck, and looking around while making wide head movements, if stimulated simultaneously, results in alerting with a neck less stretched out than usual and shorter head jerks. If there is an equilibrium between the two tendencies, then *oscillation* may be observed, as when "alertness" and feeding are both activated, and movements belonging to each are alternated.

The simultaneous electrical stimulation of complementary behavior patterns, such as turning to the right and turning to the left, can result in each other's *cancellation*. This is different from the case of the *transformation* that occurs when agression and flight are stimulated at the same time. Such a process results in a completely new behavior pattern consisting of rapid running around with fluffed feathers and calling. This is very much like the behavior of a hen whose nest is being approached by a dangerous intruder. But one must be careful in applying categories schematically to the behaviors observed. As von Holst points out, what might be classified on the basis of observation as transformation could be the outcome of different physiological mechanisms. If, for example, the fleeing tendency is evoked in a hungry chicken, and also a sleeping stimulus which conflicts with fleeing, then it will be found that the animal may feed briefly before sleeping. In this case, fleeing has suppressed feeding, but fleeing in itself is suppressed by the sleeping stimulus; hence, feeding behavior is actually liberated.

This brings us to another type in their schema, *suppression*. Von Holst and von St. Paul use this expression only when one behavior pattern is not apparent but when, at the same time, it can be demonstrated that it has not been nullified. For example, sitting down while in the brooding mood can suppress the cackling mood. But when the electrical sitting and cackling stimuli end at exactly the same time, a short cackling is observed. Thus, the suppressed activity becomes apparent as an afterdischarge. Hence, the activated drive existed in a latent form but was blocked at some point on the motor pathways. But when such afterdischarge is not observed, the more neutral term *prevention* is used to label this phenomenon. This is the case when "scolding" is interrupted by sitting down. Von Holst and von St. Paul found that there are some dominant activities that suppress others even at low intensity. This is particularly the case with different flight reactions, notably "freezing." The quantitative effect of the different behavior patterns upon each other has been measured. In one case the reaction was disgust, which expresses itself by a certain posture, and the other reactions were pecking on the ground and turning of the head. If the electrical stimulus for the disgust reaction is kept constant and the thresholds for the other reactions are measured for each different constant value of the disgust stimulation, then it will be seen that the disgust reaction raises the threshold for the turning of the head only slightly, while the pecking drive, being related to the feeding drive, seems to be more contrary to the disgust reaction, and its threshold is sharply raised. On the other hand, the neutral turning of the head mixes more easily with the disgust posture.

In summary, it is quite clear that the ethologists' neurophysiological research differs a great deal from the usual reflexology. The emphasis on the causal bases of behavior integration is quite evident in the demonstration that the coordination of many movement patterns, particularly those of locomotion, arises from impulses generated by the central nervous system. There are two ways in which this has been demonstrated: by the removal of impulses from peripheral sense organs and by direct stimulation of points in the brain, both of which result in the appearance of these coordinations. The far-reaching implications of these neurophysiological findings have indeed opened a vast area of research, as well as having confirmed the ethological propositions on the nature of appetitive behavior and fixed action patterns, particularly the hierarchical organization of behavior.

THE DEPRIVATION EXPERIMENT

The deprivation experiment, or Kaspar Hauser experiment, is a particularly good method for separating the learned and innate elements of behavior. In such an experiment, animals are separated from members of their own species, and are deprived of certain experiences, so that no information regarding the situation to which the behavior pattern in question is adapted is obtained.

The deprivation experiment is designed to answer the following questions: (1) Are there any motor patterns and taxic components that develop in the individual without learning taking place? (2) Is there experimental verification for the ethological assumption that motor patterns which can be shown to be homologous (on the basis of the phylogenetic comparison of species) must therefore be independent of learning? (3) What is the role of individual learning in changing or developing the behavior pattern, and in integrating innate elements, if any, with learned ones into a functional whole?

A deprivation experiment does not always give a yes-or-no answer as to whether a given behavior pattern is learned. The only positive conclusions that can be drawn from the results of a deprivation experiment is that certain behavior elements are *not* learned, since if an animal is deprived of information regarding the situation to which a behavior pattern is adapted and yet the behavior pattern is executed on the very first exposure to the appropriate situation, then this behavior pattern must be innate. In such a case we can assert with confidence that the behavior pattern is not learned.

But if the opposite result is obtained, namely, that the behavior pattern in question is not executed, this does not necessarily mean that it must be learned by the animal. In many cases it can never be confidently concluded that a given behavior pattern is learned, for the following reasons.

In the first place, conditions of captivity and deprivation may not be maximally conducive to a state of optimal health in the animal. Impairment of health, even though such a defect is not apparent to the eye, can prevent normal behavior from appearing. As has been earlier mentioned in the case of reaction chains, unhealthy females cannot respond correctly to more than the first couple of links in the chain. The fixed action patterns can suffer a loss of intensity and the thresholds for them can be raised; the I.R.M.'s can lose much of their normal selectivity; and social inhibitions can diminish or disappear. These facts have long been known to zoo-keepers. For example, even if captive animals can be induced to breed, rearing of the young often fails because the parents eat or kill their young. Lorenz (1958a) once tried to raise some red-backed shrikes, which are well known for their impaling of prey on a thorn. Lorenz noticed that the fledglings performed wiping movements along the perches and bars of their cage. Since he suspected that this behavior was the beginning of the impaling action, he offered them artificial thorns. At first, the birds paid no attention to them, but when one happened to hit a nail in a wiping movement and had its prey catching on it, it would suddenly go into a frenzy of activity and impale the prey. Thereafter, it directed the wiping movements to the nail. This would appear to be a clear case of learning to impale prey on thorns. Later on Kramer repeated the same experiment, and at first found the same thing Lorenz had. But when he improved the birds' diet, it turned out that these birds did not need any trial-and-error conditioning to the thorn, but when offered one, used it immediately. When presented with a rubber dummy of the same shape, they persisted in directing their impaling movements toward the unsuitable object, and lack of success was completely unable to bring about negative conditioning (G. Kramer and U. von St. Paul, unpublished).

Hence, whenever some incompleteness is observed in the behavior patterns of an experimental animal raised in a deprivation experiment, pathological deficiencies of these types must be taken into consideration. They are indeed very likely when the measures taken in order to exclude possible experience are of a kind that seriously interfere with the animal's well-being. Rearing animals under abnormal conditions such as those of restraint or certain diets may constitute such grave interferences with their bodily health that severe disturbances in unlearned behavior are absolutely predictable. To ascribe them solely to the elimination of individual experience, Lorenz maintains, is biologically naive.

To this end, the experimenter must be completely conversant with the inventory of motor patterns, or ethogram, that the species he is studying performs, and also with the symptomatology of the pathological disturbances likely to occur in the deprivation experiment.

In the second place, even though a deprived animal's health is optimal, he still may not perform the behavior pattern in question simply because it has not been exercised, and as a result some atrophy, similar to that in muscles when they are not used, may have taken place. If a lock is not used for a long time, its key may not be able to open it. This does not mean that the lock needs to "learn" to turn, but simply that it must be put into the necessary physical condition in order to turn when the key is inserted into it. Since the I.R.M. has been called a "lock" that a special "key"—the releaser—opens, this analogy is particularly apt in making this point clear.

Thirdly, the stimulus situation in which the animal is tested may not be optimal for releasing the behavior pattern in question. This must be checked and counterchecked by placing a normally reared animal into the experimental test situation and by placing an experimental animal into the normal environment of the species.

An illustrative experiment is offered by Eibl-Eibesfeldt's (1955a) investigation of nest-building in rats. This research had received its impetus from Riess's (1954) findings that rats reared in isolation and never given the opportunity to handle objects did not build nests when placed in a cage with paper strips, nor did they retrieve young, but scattered the paper and the young about the cage. Riess therefore concluded that the rat learns by experience in handling objects to build nests and retrieve young. Lehrman (1953) suggested that the rat might collect food and other material near its sleeping place, and observe that they served to conserve heat. Thus, it would build a nest as soon as it felt cold.

Eibl-Eibesfeldt (1955a) realized that the causes of the rats' failure to build nests could be ascribed to their exploratory behavior when placed in a new environment, and also to lack of a definite nest locality or shelter. He took ten virgin rats, experienced in nest-building, and placed them in a test situation duplicating Riess's. None of these rats built within the first hour, but spend their time exploring, and scattering the paper much as Riess's rats did. Only three of them built within five hours.

Eibl-Eibesfeldt therefore repeated Riess's experiment and went even further in insuring that no manipulatory experience occurred, by amputating the rats' tails, since he had observed that deprived rats would carry their tail to a corner and deposit it there. He tested thirty-seven virgin female rats from two to three months old for nest-building behavior in their own cages, and found that eight of them started nest-building immediately, nineteen built within five hours, and six did not build at all. These results were clearly different from Riess's, but Eibl-Eibesfeldt checked his protocols and found that all those rats that had built immediately had formed the habit of sleeping in a particular corner of the cage.

To test the possibility that the structural bareness of the test situation resulted in the failure to build nests, he took another group of forty-five deprived virgin rats and placed a little tin partition in one corner of the cage at the same time as he offered them nest-building material. Thirty-three of these rats immediately built nests, even when the tin partition was placed in a corner they did not regularly sleep in. Three more built within one hour and nine more built within five hours.

Going into further analysis, Eibl-Eibesfeldt studied various movements made in nest-building by experienced and inexperienced rats. These movements were alike in both groups. The only difference was that the experienced rats seemed to follow more of a plan or scheme than the inexperienced ones. For example, inexperienced rats might perform a motor pattern in an early stage of nest-building when these movements could not serve their functions. Hence rats do seem to learn to integrate sequences of motor patterns in order to better adapt them to their function. These behavior patterns, nevertheless, were immediately available to the animals like ready-made tools.

The fact that ethologists have emphasized that one can assert definitely only what behavior patterns are *not* learned has led some critics to counter that the ethologists' standpoint constitutes a highly protective theory. In actual practice ethologists do, in certain cases, make the conclusion that adaptiveness of behavior to a given part of the environment is due to individual learning and not to phylogenetic processes. Ethologists have found there are many cases in which the special adaptiveness of behavior cannot possibly be accounted for by phyletic adaptation, just as there are many cases in which the information underlying adaptation cannot possibly be traced back to individual learning.

One other methodological principle, fully applicable to experimentation other than deprivation research, is that consistent results can be obtained only if subjects of similar genetical constitution are used. Many of the controversies and divergent results arise from the disregard of this very important fact. There has been, for example, a discussion of Tinbergen's studies of the innate predator response of turkeys, pheasants, and greylag geese when a silhouette of a bird of prey is perceived moving slowly across the sky. Hirsch, Lindley, and Tolman (1955) found that white leghorn chickens failed to give this response, and concluded that Tinbergen's hypothesis was "found to be untenable under controlled laboratory conditions." This Lorenz (1961) argues, is just as meaningful as if Dr. Somebody had demonstrated the presence of dark pigments in the hair of wild common hamsters and if someone else were to write "the

Somebody theory that there are dark pigments in the fur of wild hamsters has been tested on white laboratory rats and found untenable under strict laboratory conditions." It is clear that no one is justified in drawing such a conclusion. This example makes clear the importance of species differences and even breed differences in the analysis of behavior, as behavior geneticists point out.

AN EXAMPLE OF ETHOLOGICALLY INFLUENCED ◈ RESEARCH IN THE UNITED STATES

Although behavioral research in the United States is largely behavioristic in orientation, directed toward analyses of ways in which behavior can be modified, there are a few researches in this country that owe their impetus to ethology. Although the example given here is unabashedly drawn from the author's own research, this is not intended to exclude other researchers, usually zoologists, who are doing commendable ethological work.

IMPRINTING

The very idea of imprinting as an early experience during which a young animal forms a strong social attachment to a mother-object has been responsible for firing the imagination of many workers who have become increasingly aware of the fact that early experiences of many kinds can have permanent effects on an animal's behavior. This, together with the many ways in which the imprinting phenomenon differs from the simple association learning processes commonly studied in the psychological laboratory, has resulted in the arousal and maintenance of a great deal of interest and research in imprinting in the North American continent.

Unfortunately, however, some of the research in the past has been robbed of potential usefulness, because the prevalence of the conceptual framework of association learning in experimental psychology caused a Procrustean effort to fit the imprinting phenomenon into the association learning framework. Although the intensive effort to find and formulate laws of learning (in hopes of accounting for the causal bases of all behaviors) did show that certain behaviors once thought to be instinctive were indeed modifiable by learning, the realization is growing that there are still certain behaviors that are so persistent in character and resistant to modification by reinforcement that they cannot be satisfactorily explained by conventional laws of learning. In such cases, and imprinting is one of them, other explanatory devices must be constructed. This does not mean that untestable hypotheses concerning the nature of imprinting must be devised, for the good work carried out by many investigators, including H. James, Peter Klopfer, Howard Moltz, and M. Schein, has demonstrated that such is not the case. Thus, the gap between ethologically oriented and behavioristically oriented researchers has recently narrowed, and common areas of agreement are being formed. Recent reviews on the topic of imprinting have been made by Hess (1959) and Moltz (1960).

Konrad Lorenz was the first to bring widespread attention to this phenomenon of imprinting, and he gave it its name (1935). In a broad sense, imprinting refers to an early experience that has a profound influence on the later adult social and sexual behavior of an animal with respect to the choice of objects for these behaviors. Although earlier workers noted this phenomenon, Lorenz was the first to point out that it appeared to occur at a critical period, early in the life of an animal. He postulated that the first object to elicit a social response on the part of a young animal later released not only that response but also related responses such as sexual behavior. Imprinting, therefore, was important in the consideration not only of animal behavior, but also of the wider problems of biological evolution and speciation. For example, Craig (1908) reported Whitman's unpublished experiments with wild pigeons, in which he found that in order to be able to cross two different pigeon species, he had first to rear the young of one species with foster parents of the other species. After such an upbringing, these animals actually preferred to mate with the other species. Such interspecies sexual fixations have been observed since then in other birds, some fishes, and two mammals—the alpaca and vicuña.

Heinroth and his wife (1924-1933) raised by hand the young of almost every species of European birds, and noted that many of the social responses of these birds were transferred to their human caretaker as a result of this experience.

Although imprinting has been studied mainly in birds, it also has been observed in other animals. Instances of imprinting have been reported in insects (Thorpe, 1944), in fish (Baerends and Baerends-van Roon, 1950), and in some mammals. These mammals in which the phenomenon has been found—alpaca and vicuña (Hodge, 1946), sheep (Grabowski, 1941, Murie, 1944), deer (Darling, 1938), zebra and buffalo (Hediger, 1938) —are all animals in which the young are mobile almost immediately after birth. Controlled experimental work with mammals, however, has just begun.

It is now thought that processes very much like imprinting exist in every social species, particularly those in which there are parent-young relationships. However, in the case of species in which there are extended periods of parental care, it is apparent that the period of primary socialization occurs over a more extended length of time than it does in, say, chickens or ducks. Dogs, for example, cannot be made into pets if they have not had contact with human beings during the period of primary socialization. Freedman, King, and Elliott (1961) have found that the age of three and a half to nine-to-thirteen weeks of age approximates a critical period in dogs for socialization to human beings, with the age of seven weeks being the most sensitive time. Similarly, if kittens are not handled during the period after the eyes are open up to the time of weaning, they always remain somewhat wild and fearful of people. Finally, it is evident (Goldfarb, 1943, Bowlby, 1951, and others) that orphaned children can grow up to be incurably unsocialized, being unable to maintain friendships or to establish permanent social relationships, and so on, if not given the opportunity to undergo normal socialization at an early age, due to lack of contact with people.

The first systematic investigations on imprinting were published in 1951. Independently, in this country and in Europe, the work of Ramsay and Fabricius (1951 a, b) gave the first indications of some of the important factors in the process. Most of Ramsay's experiments dealt with exchange of parents and young, although he also imprinted some waterfowl on such objects as a football or a green box. He noted the importance of the auditory component in the imprinting situation, the effect of changes in coloring in parental recognition as well as the recognition of the parents by the young. His findings also showed that color is an essential element in recognition, while size or form seemed to be of less importance. Fabricius carried out experiments with several species of ducklings and was able to approximate the critical age at which imprinting was most successful in several species of ducks.

After this pioneer work by Ramsay and Fabricius, no relevant papers appeared until 1953 and 1954. Ramsay and Hess (1954) published a paper on a laboratory approach to the study of imprinting. A paper by Margaret Nice in 1953 and one by Hinde, Thorpe, and Vince in 1956 include most of the pertinent materials published after Lorenz's classic statement of the problem up to 1956.

Since 1951, my associates and I have carried out a program in imprinting at McDonogh and Lake Farm Laboratories, Maryland, and at our laboratories at the University of Chicago. Many thousands of animals, including many different breeds and species, have been used. Most of them have been mallard ducklings and chickens.

Methodology. Our birds (ducks and chicks) were incubated and hatched right in our laboratory. They hatched in the dark, and each animal was placed in an individual box marked with the exact hour at which the animal hatched. The bird, in the box, was kept in a still-air incubator and kept there until it was to be imprinted. After the animal had undergone the imprinting experience, it was returned to the box and kept there until testing. Only after testing was completed was the young bird placed in daylight and given food and water.

The apparatus we used in the imprinting procedure consisted of a circular runway, about five feet in diameter, and is pictured in Figure 5. A mallard duck decoy was suspended from a rotating arm and was internally outfitted with a heating element and a loudspeaker which played an arbitrarily chosen rendition of *GOCK, gock, gock, gock.* The animal was placed, in the dark, about one foot away from the decoy, a pulley arrangement opening the bird's box. The experimenter placed himself behind a one-way screen and turned on the lights and sound. After a short interval the model began to move around for a specified amount of time, usually less than one hour. After the lights were again turned off, the animal was returned to its box until it was to be tested. No human contact was needed, since a trap door arrangement dropped the animal into its home box.

The testing procedure consisted of giving the young animal a choice between going to the male decoy to which it had been imprinted or going to a female decoy alike in shape but different in color. The male model made the *gock* call while the female model gave the call of a real mallard female calling her young. Four test conditions followed each other in immediate succession, and the choice of the animal in each condition was noted. If the duckling gave the positive response of walking to or staying with the object to which it had been imprinted—the male decoy—in all four of the tests, then imprinting was regarded as complete, or 100 percent. These tests involved choices between (1) stationary and silent male and

Fig. 5. The apparatus used by Hess in his studies on imprinting. It consists principally of a circular runway around which a decoy, suspended from a moving arm, rotates. Here a duckling is shown following the decoy. The controls of the apparatus are in the foreground. Normally a curtain or a one-way screen is placed between the apparatus and its controls so as to prevent the duckling from seeing the experimenter. (From Hess, E. H., 1959a. Reprinted from *Science* by permission.)

female models, (2) stationary and calling male and female models, (3) silent male model, calling female model, both stationary, and (4) stationary and silent male model, calling and moving female model.

Imprinting versus Learning. The most salient feature of the imprinting phenomenon is its many differences from simple association learning. There is now a wealth of experimental evidence to show that imprinting differs fundamentally from association learning in several respects, and to demonstrate the problems in dealing with behaviors that owe a great deal to genetic factors rather than exclusively to environmental ones.

For example, a principal distinguishing feature of the imprinting phenomenon is its *critical period*, which, as Lorenz postulated, means that there is a particular time in the life of the animal during which exposure to the mother-object will have the most extensive and lasting effects on that animal's social behavior. This fact is one which must be considered in distinguishing imprinting from ordinary association learning, as there is no critical period for association learning.

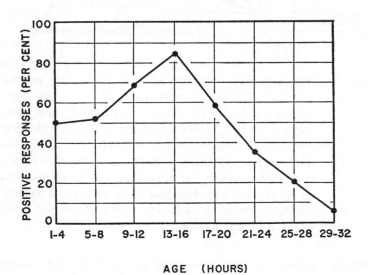

AGE (HOURS)

Fig. 6.   The critical period in which ducklings are most easily imprinted is demonstrated by this graph, which shows the mean test scores made by ducklings in each group that had been imprinted at different ages, calculated in hours from the time of hatching. (From Hess, E. H., 1959a. Reprinted from *Science* by permission.)

Our experimentation with imprinting in ducklings and chicks offers ample evidence for the existence of the critical period (Hess, 1957). To determine the age at which an imprinting experience is most effective, we imprinted our ninety-two ducklings at various ages after hatching. In this series of experiments the imprinting experience was standard: the duckling followed the model one hundred and fifty to two hundred feet around the runway during a period of ten minutes. Figure 6 shows the scores made by ducklings in the different age groups. It appears that some imprinting occurs immediately after hatching, but a maximum score is consistently made only by those ducklings in the thirteen-to-sixteen-hour-old group. This result is indicated in Figure 7, which shows the percentage of animals in each age group that made perfect imprinting scores.

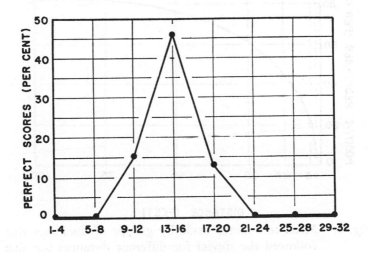

AGE (HOURS)

Fig. 7. Another way of demonstrating the critical age is by plotting the percentage of animals in each age group that made perfect test scores, or 100%. (From Hess, E. H., 1959a. Reprinted from *Science* by permission.)

There is another difference between imprinting and association learning. Learning a visual discrimination problem with food reward is quicker and more stable when practice trials are spaced than when they are massed. That such is not the case with imprinting is shown by the following experimental study we carried out.

We decided to vary independently the factors of length of exposure time and the actual distance traveled by the ducklings during the imprinting period. Since a ten-minute period had been found sufficient to produce testable results, we ran a series of animals varying the distance traveled but keeping the time constant at ten minutes. Each group of ducklings

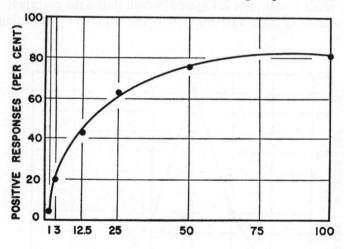

DISTANCE (FEET)

Fig. 8. Mean test scores made by groups of ducklings that followed the model for different distances but that all had the same amount of exposure time. The strength of imprinting is thus a function of the distance traveled during the imprinting experience. (From Hess, E. H., 1959a. Reprinted from *Science* by permission.)

followed the model for different distances, these distances being one foot, twelve and a half feet, twenty-five feet, fifty feet, and one hundred feet. All ducklings were imprinted between twelve and seventeen hours of age to keep constant the variable of the critical period of sensitivity. The results showed that increasing the distance over which the duckling had to follow the imprinting object increased the strength of imprinting. A leveling-off of this effect appears to occur after a distance of about fifty feet (Hess, 1957). These results are shown in Figure 8.

We also investigated the effects of the length of exposure time to the model when the distance followed was kept constant. Since the distance of twelve and a half feet could be traveled by the duck in periods of two minutes, ten minutes, and thirty minutes, we used this as a unit. Imprinting scores made by animals in each of these three groups were essentially identical. We also found that there is no significant difference between ducklings allowed to follow for a distance of one hundred feet during ten minutes and those allowed thirty minutes to cover the same distance (Hess, 1957). Both of these results are shown in Figure 9.

It is very clear, therefore, that the strength of imprinting is apparently dependent not on the duration of the imprinting period, but on the effort expended by the duckling in following the imprinting object. We did other supplementary experiments that confirmed this notion. For example, if the ducklings had to follow the model up an inclined plane, this resulted in greater imprinting than in ducklings following the same distance on level ground. We concluded that we could even write an equation for imprinting: the strength of imprinting is equal to the logarithm of the effort expended by the animal in following the imprinting object during the imprinting experience, or $I_s = \log E$.

Another example of the fact that it is the effort expended by the animal that is crucial in determining the effectiveness of the imprinting experience during the critical period in duck-

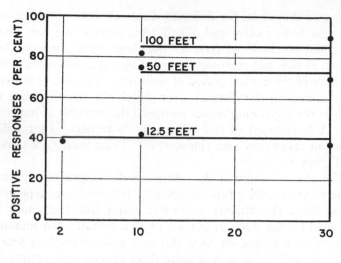

TIME (MINUTES)

Fig. 9. Mean test scores made by groups of ducklings that followed the model for different distances and different amounts of exposure time. It is apparent that the ducklings that followed the model for the same distance but during different amounts of time showed the same degree of imprinting strength; therefore, time in itself had little effect on the strength of imprinting when the distance traveled was held constant. (From Hess, E. H., 1959a. Reprinted from *Science* by permission.)

lings is offered by our attempts to produce imprinting by means of presenting auditory stimulation to mallard eggs. The sound of a female mallard calling her young was played for forty-eight hours before hatching. When tested after hatching, these young did not choose this sound any more frequently than they chose the *gock* call used in our experiments. Therefore, auditory imprinting, while the mallard is still in the egg, is considered unlikely on the basis of these results, particularly in view of the fact that it is not possible for the animals still in the eggs to exert much effort toward the source of sound (Hess, 1959a).

It is well known that in discrimination learning, recency in experience is more effective for retention of learning. In imprinting, however, primacy of experience is the maximally effective factor. This difference is demonstrated by the following experiment. Two groups of eleven ducklings each were imprinted to two different imprinting objects. Animals of Group I were first individually imprinted to a male mallard model, and then to a female model. Group II, on the other hand, was first imprinted to a female model, and subsequently to a male model. Fourteen of the twenty-two ducklings, when tested with both models present, preferred the model to which they first had been imprinted, showing primacy. Only five preferred the model to which they had been imprinted last, showing recency, and three showed no preference at all (Hess, 1959b).

The administration of punishment or painful stimulation is well known to result in avoidance of the associated stimulus in discrimination learning. But in imprinting, such aversive stimulation actually causes an enchancement of the effectiveness of the imprinting experience. For example, it has been repeatedly observed that a young mallard duckling whose toes are stepped on while he is being imprinted to a human being during his critical period does not run away with fear; on the contrary, he stays even closer to the punitive imprinting object. This naturalistic observation has been substantiated in recent unpublished experiments by J. Kovach in our laboratory. It was found that the administration of electric shock in the imprinting situation during the critical period enhances the following tendency in chicks, whereas it diminishes imprintability *after* the critical period. Thus, the use of electric shocks results in an even more sharply defined critical period for imprintability, and the notion of the critical period is thereby resubstantiated independently. Figure 10 gives a representative

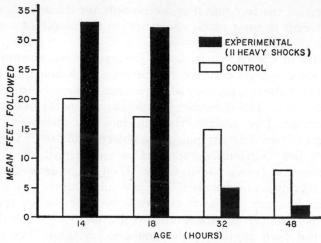

Fig. 10. Number of feet that chicks of two different major
treatment groups, one shocked and the other not
shocked, followed the imprinting object, by age at
first exposure to the imprinting situation. The
shocked chicks were given eleven heavy shocks of
3 mamp. intensity, ½ sec. duration, during the imprinting experience; the nonshocked control chicks
were given none.

set of figures from the pilot study. Each subgroup had at least
ten animals.

We have carried out experimentation with chicks in which
we found that the administration of meprobamate (Miltown)
or carisoprodol (Soma) had no effect on the ability of these
animals to learn a simple color discrimination problem with
food reward when they were under the influence of either
drug, as compared with animals that had not been given either
drug. All three groups learned equally efficiently, and furthermore, animals run the next day, after the effects of the drugs
had worn off completely, all showed the same degree of retention. However, the effects of these drugs in the case of

imprinting are very different (Hess, 1960, and Hess, Polt, and Goodwin, 1959).

We became interested, a few years ago, in the effect of tranquilizers on imprinting behavior, because we found that the end of the critical period was accompanied by the development of innate or unlearned fear responses during the imprinting situation. We thought that perhaps tranquilizers would extend the critical period by removing these animals' fear. First, we used meprobamate on ducklings, and found that it did indeed render the animals fearless when they were under its influence in the imprinting situation. But when the animals were tested, they showed no effect of the imprinting experience.

In the face of this most surprising result, we had to look for an explanation. The explanation, we decided, lay in the Law of Effort and the muscle-relaxant effects of meprobamate. So we tried another drug, carisoprodol (Soma) which is a congener, or chemical derivative, of meprobamate. It is an almost pure muscle relaxant, without the tranquilizing effects of meprobamate.

We ran three groups out of a total of forty-two mallard ducklings and eighty-nine "Vantress Broiler" chicks. One group was imprinted while under the influence of meprobamate, another while under the influence of carisoprodol, and a third group served as a control, having been given distilled water in order to equalize the effects of fluid intake and the necessary handling for administration. We found that both drugs, particularly carisoprodol, interfered with the retention of imprinting when these animals were tested after the effects of the drugs had worn off, twenty-four hours later.

That the drugs interfered with the *process* of imprinting and not with its retention was shown by another condition to which some animals in these groups were subjected: they were imprinted normally and tested under the influence of a drug. This procedure had no effect whatever on the retention of the imprinting experience: the animals behaved normally.

The hypothesis of ours that the interfering effects of these drugs lies in their muscle-relaxant effect is further supported by other investigations (Hess, 1957) in which we found that perfectly good imprinting can be obtained when the animals are under the influence of chlorpromazine.

So far, in our treatment of the topic of imprinting and its differences from association learning, we have concentrated on the reaction of following a certain model, as an indicator of the progress of imprinting during the first exposure to this object and also as an indicator of the effectiveness of this experience. However, while the animal is being imprinted, he also engages in other innate activities which can be observed and recorded. For example, the animal may emit "distress notes," or "contentment tones," remain silent, or fixate an object. This suggests that it is worthwhile to study these other behaviors in order to gain information about the imprinting process, and indeed, this is the case.

For example, "distress notes" and "contentment tones" can be used as indicators of the state of fearfulness in the animal being imprinted. It is quite easy to differentiate between these two calls in chickens, for the "distress notes" are a series of high-intensity, medium-pitch tones, of one-quarter-second duration and little pitch modulation, while "contentment tones," on the other hand, are a series of high-pitch, low-intensity notes, of one-twelfth-second duration or less, and considerable pitch modulation. The names that have been given to these calls are purely labels and their meanings should not necessarily be taken literally.

The presence or absence of fear behavior, together with other behaviors engaged in by the chick, is an important indicator of the developmental changes that would account for the limits of the critical period. Why should the critical period occur when it does, and what causes it to end?

We noted, as indicated in our studies on the effects of drugs, that the end of the critical period was accompanied by the development of innate fear responses. It is obvious that fear will prevent an animal from engaging in the kinds of social behavior that are necessary for imprinting to occur. Fabricius (1951b), in his early laboratory work on imprinting, as well as other investigators since then, observed that there is a steady increase in the amount of fear shown by a duckling during the first hours of life when he is confronted with an imprinting object.

But even if increasing fear is correlated with the end of the period of imprintability, at this point we still do not know what factors enter into the limitation of the beginning of the critical period. Why is it that newly hatched ducklings or chicks do not imprint just as well as those that have reached the age of thirteen to sixteen hours? Anyone who has observed newly hatched animals will notice at once that they do not walk as well or as fast as the older animals. Perhaps, then, we should look for an explanation of the beginning of the critical period in our Law of Effort. If a young animal is not able to follow the imprinting object, then of course it cannot expend as much effort in actual following as one that walks well. If the model is moving, the young bird will lose it. However, imprintability at the time of hatching is not zero, since the model may return to the young bird, and it can expend effort in trying to follow it.

With these two propositions in mind, we studied the development of fear responses and of locomotor ability in chicks from the time of hatching to the age of thirty-six hours (Hess and Schaefer, 1959). First we took 137 White Rock chicks and divided them into nine age groups. Each was observed individually in an imprinting experience. If an animal emitted distress notes in the presence of the model or moved away from it, it was considered to have shown fear. We then tabulated the number of animals in each age group that had shown fear while exposed to the imprinting object. We found that among the different age groups, the number of fearful animals in each group increased steadily with increasing age. During the very early hours of their lives, from the time of hatching up to about the age of thirteen to sixteen hours, these animals show little or no fear. After that time, the number of animals showing fear increases sharply, until the age of about thirty-three to thirty-six hours, when all chicks in that age group showed fear. These results are summarized in Figure 11.

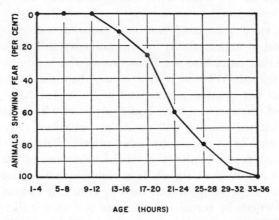

Fig. 11. Percentage of White Rock chicks in each group that showed fear responses to a potential imprinting object. (From Hess, E. H., 1959c.)

Then we took another group of sixty Vantress Broiler chicks of White Rock stock, divided them into six different age groups, and studied the development of increasing locomotor ability (Hess, 1959c). We gave each chick three trials within one hour so as to observe the effects of practice as well as of developmental stage. We found that groups consisting of chickens between the fourth and sixteenth hour after hatching showed improvement in locomotion during the three trials. However, the conditions of the experiment were such that after the sixteenth hour after hatching, a relative plateau of locomotion was reached, since there was great fluctuation between trials and a leveling of average speed. In addition, there was a clear increase in the ability to locomote with increasing age between the fourth and sixteenth hours. The results of this experiment are graphically illustrated in Figure 12.

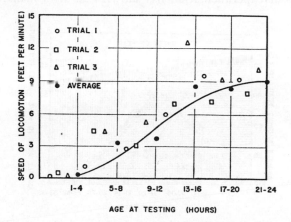

Fig. 12. Mean speed of locomotion of Vantress Broiler chicks of different ages and with different degrees of prior practice. (From Hess, E. H., 1959c.)

If we arrange our data on a graph so that the percentage of animals showing fear and the percentage of animals able to move at the rate of at least three feet per minute or more are drawn, the area under these two curves resembles the area under the curve for the critical period for the same breed, with the peaks coincident at exactly the same age period—thirteen to sixteen hours after hatching. This is shown in Figure 13.

There are probably several reasons why the empirical curve for imprintability is consistently lower than the theoretical curve for imprintability as determined by the development of fearfulness and locomotor ability. For example, the suitability of a potential imprinting object may not be the same for all species, and the imprintability of the breed is another limiting factor. Since some breeds and species have higher imprintability than others, the area under their empirical curves of imprintability would be greater than those for the other breeds, and also more closely approach the theoretical curve. For example, our experimentation has shown that wild mallards dis-

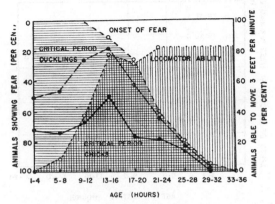

Fig. 13. The hypothetical period of imprinting sensitiveness as determined by the superposition of the fear and locomotion curves, together with actual curves of imprintability in chicks and mallard ducklings as a function of age, as shown by mean test scores. (From Hess, E. H., 1959c.)

play a much greater degree of imprintability than do any breed of chickens. The curve of imprintability for these mallards is also shown in Figure 13, and it can be seen that it agrees much more closely with the theoretical curve. However, the important aspect of our results is that on the basis of the data we obtained with our chicks, the curve of imprintability should be very much like a normal distribution curve, with a peak at a certain hour after hatching and lower points before and after that time. The curves for the critical period that have been established in our laboratories for chicks and ducklings have exactly that shape. The fact of interest to emphasize here is not the absolute identity of the points of the theoretical and empirical curves, but the resemblances between them.

The correlation between the termination of the critical period and the maturing of the fear response is an important finding. This has already been singled out by Ramsay and Hess (1954) and Hess (1957) as relevant to the imprinting process. In fact, as the stage of our present knowledge indicates, it seems likely that all animals showing the phenomenon of imprinting will have a critical period that ends with the onset of fear. Thus we can predict, in a series of animals, knowing only the time of onset of fear responsiveness, the end of imprintability for that species. Freedman, King, and Elliott (1961) have recently verified that such is the case for dogs. Even in the human being one could thus theoretically place the end of maximum imprintability at about five and a half months of age, since observers have placed the onset of fear at about that time (Bridges, 1932; Spitz and Wolf, 1946). Weidmann (1958) has recently mentioned the possibility that the onset of the fear response may limit the duration of the critical period for imprinting in ducks while Gray (1958) has proposed a similar scheme for humans.

The importance of fear in relation to the imprinting phenomenon has been documented by Moltz, Rosenblum, and Halikas (1959). They found that while the tendency of Peking ducklings to follow a mother-object closely declines with age, in accordance with the increasing independence from the protection of the mother, the arousal of anxiety would cause them to seek close proximity to the mother-object and to follow it around even when they were at an age when they normally would not do so. Furthermore, they found that ducklings in the presence of a model to which they had been imprinted were less susceptible to startles and other fear responses. This they attribute to the model's having acquired anxiety-reducing properties for the ducklings.

In summary, the notion of the critical period is a rather important one in considering the imprinting phenomenon. Not only do animals show different degrees of imprintability according to their age, in hours after hatching, but the critical period is also correlated with other behaviors in the chick, the ability to locomote, and the appearance of the innate fear response to strange objects. The idea of the critical period also has been substantiated by the fact that punishment or painful stimulation (within limits), such as electric shocks, actually will cause the young animal to imprint more intensively on the mother-object—but only if it is at the stage of maximum imprintability; otherwise, the punishment will decrease any disposition the animal might have to follow the mother-object.

The critical period concept, however, has met with resistance on the part of some researchers. The principal reason for this is that animals can often be trained to lose their fear of an alien species (or of their own species, if never before encountered) when they are past their critical period, and even to follow members of this species. This is one reason imprinting has been thought by some to be association learning of the species to which the young animal belongs. Further, the critical period can occur so early in the life of the animal that it may not be noticed by experimenters.

In addition, conflicting reports regarding the location of the critical period arise because different measures are used. To cite one instance, Jaynes (1957) stated that whereas the greatest following of a mother-object during the initial imprinting exposure occurs early in the first day of life, animals exposed to an imprinting object for the first time during the second day of life showed the strongest amount of following when tested ten days later. The use of the degree of following of a mother-object during a much later age thus led Jaynes to different conclusions regarding the location of the critical period from those Hess (1957) was led to. Hess's conclusions were arrived at on the basis of the choice, made twenty-four hours after the imprinting experience, by animals exposed to the object to which they had been imprinted as well as to another they had not seen before.

When a young animal is tamed during a period later than the critical period, this is an association learning process, and conforms to all the classical laws of association learning: it can be erased, it is stronger with increased training, and so on. The fact that animals can be tamed is the source of the occasional confusion between imprinting and association learning. However, taming can occur at almost any time during the life of an animal, whereas imprinting can occur only during a very limited period. In addition, the effects of imprinting are relatively permanent, even when it has taken place in quite a brief period of time, in contrast with the extensive training often necessary for complete taming. It appears, then, that imprinting results in a more truly social bond than taming does, inasmuch as imprinting can determine what objects constitute social or sexual partners for an animal, whereas taming does not. Finally, the social bond created by the imprinting process is extremely difficult to erase, since an animal raised by a particular species during the sensitive period usually will not dissociate himself from them even when treated cruelly. The faithful mistreated dog is an excellent example of this. The point is that the imprinting experience during the critical period establishes in the animal an image of the species to which it belongs. Thus the mistreated dog who stays close to his oppressive master does so because he is closely bound emotionally to the human species, having had close contact with human beings during his critical period of primary socialization. In fact, it would seem as if he considers himself more of a human being than a dog, as indicated by his failure to detach himself from the company of his owner.

In conclusion, the recent trend in experimental research in imprinting is an encouraging one. H. James (1959), for example, has been studying the disposition of chicks to approach a flickering light. Like the imprinting response, this disposition diminishes with increasing age at the first exposure. There is no decrement of the response, however, once it has been acquired. Also, if chicks are reared together rather than isolated, the response does not appear. Furthermore, a decoy, or a model of some kind, if presented in proximity to flickering light, will be sought out as a companion later on even if the flickering light is absent. Schein and Hale (1959) have studied the long-range effects on turkeys of rearing them in isolation from their own species and of communal rearing with their own species; they then observed what objects the turkeys chose to direct their sexual and other social behaviors in later adult life.

✥ THE ETHOLOGICAL VIEWPOINT ON LEARNING PROCESSES

Many theorists and experimentalists representing the behavioristic orientation have vehemently objected to ethological principles. Behaviorism, as is well known, was founded on the explicit rejection of the idea of innately determined behavior and on a wholehearted commitment to the belief that all behavior is acquired by the individual through learning processes. Since many behaviors that had once been thought to be innate were found to be learned, this strengthened the behaviorists' faith that when all laws of learning were found and formulated, all behavior could be accounted for.

Hence, it was inevitable that the rise of ethology during the last half century, and particularly during the past decade, when Tinbergen's (1951) and Thorpe's (1956) books were published, should present a challenge to behavioristically oriented psychologists to defend their positions.

Lehrman (1953, 1956) and Hebb (1953), as well as Beach (1954), Kennedy (1954), and Schneirla (1956) have brought forth the following criticisms of ethology:

(1) Hebb (1953) declares that the ethologists utilize a false dichotomy of learned and innate behavior. In particular, he feels, ethologists define learning and instinctive behavior in a mutually exclusive fashion, equivalent to attempting to prove the null hypothesis. In other words, *innate* is *not learned* and

learned is *not innate*. Hebb (pp. 46-47) argues that "there are not two kinds of control of behavior and that the term 'instinct' implying a mechanism or neural process independent of environmental factors, and distinct from the neural processes into which learning enters, is a completely misleading term."

(2) Even though conceding that an animal's inherited bodily structures determine potential behavior, Lehrman's (1953) position is that all actual behavior is determined by experience. Furthermore, even if an animal is born or hatched with the behavior in question, no one can exclude the possibility that there were learning processes in the egg or *in utero*.

In support of his contention, Lehrman cites Kuo's (1932a–d) observations on the development of pecking in the chick embryo. Chicks peck immediately after hatching, a behavior that we would regard as innate. But Kuo observed that at an early stage the heartbeat moves the chick's head passively. At the same time the yolk sac, moved by amniotic contractions, stimulates the head tactually; these amniotic contractions are synchronous with the heartbeat. Later, the chick reacts to external stimulation by bending its head actively, and at the same time opens and closes its beak during nodding. Much later, liquid forced into the mouth by the head and beak movements is swallowed. The movements become more and more stereotyped and the previously independent head, bill, and throat movements become linked into a functional, integrated pattern. Kuo believes that this integration is brought about by learning. He explains the first arousal of the head lunge by visual stimuli by assuming that impulses from the optical region spark over the midbrain centers, which previously had elicited this behavior in response to rhythmic tactile stimulation.

(3) Ethological concepts are merely the artificial abstraction of "aspects" or functions of behavior. Lehrman (p. 351) affirms his opinion that they do not correspond to real physiological mechanisms but are "undesirable reifications of hypothesized mechanisms."

Lorenz, a principal defender of ethological tenets, has pointed out (1960) that all these behavioristic criticisms of ethology are based on the assumption that the central nervous system has no inherited structures in it, but consists of a conglomeration of equipotential elements that can be modified without limits through learning processes; this assumption was based on the fact that earlier neurophysiological research was unable to find definite functional structures in the brain. However, he takes these criticisms as a good opportunity to clarify certain concepts.

As for the supposed dichotomy of learned and innate, no ethologist ever doubted, as some critics imply, that learning processes are of the greatest importance in the behavior of organisms. What is more, ethologists have often discussed the interlacing of innate and learned elements of behavior. For example, there have been observations on birds who make innate nest-building movements but have to learn which materials to use. Eibl-Eibesfeldt's (1956a) experiments on the prey-killing technique of the polecat give clear examples of the *intercalation* or unit by unit interweaving of learned and innate elements; for example, the killing bite, that is, the sinking of the teeth into the animal and shaking at the same time, is innate, but the animal learns, in a few trials, to direct the killing bite to the prey's neck.

Although ethologists use the terms "innate" and "learned," this does not mean that they conceive of two parallel and independent neural mechanisms determining behavior. Learning processes do constitute a natural unit, from the ethological point of view, and probably have similar physiological processes. But it is an error to think that ethologists postulate only *one* neural behavior-determining process into which learning does not enter. Rather, as we are well aware by now, they have discovered *many* physiological processes that innately determine behavior and that are as different from each other as they are from learning, for the same reason that a tooth differs from a nose or foot. Such mechanisms as the I.R.M., fixed action pattern, orientation, and optomotoric reactions not only have different origins but also are completely different from each other in their functions. Placing all of them together into a single neurophysiological group would certainly result in their being defined only by the exclusion of learning processes, and such a neurophysiological group would be just as meaningless as an anatomical group composed of knees, hands, and nose, and defined as *not-teeth*.

It is with these different physiological processes in mind that ethologists have spoken of the intercalation of learned and innate behaviors. Just as learned and innate behaviors interweave with each other, different innate behavior mechanisms intercalate with each other, as shown in the analysis of the fixed action pattern and taxic orientation components in the egg-rolling behavior of the herring gull.

The ethologists' answer (Lorenz, 1958a) to the second objection of the behaviorists—the possibility of learning in the egg or *in utero*—is that such a criticism fails to take into consideration the fact that every inborn structure of behavior—the fixed pattern, I.R.M., and so on—is highly adapted to the environmental needs of the organism. This is not deliberately to disregard the possibility of such early learning, but when immediately available complex behavior fits the environment so perfectly, there are only three ways in which it could be accounted for if phylogenetically evolved behavior patterns do not exist. One, which the behaviorists themselves would surely reject, is that the chick just happens, by pure chance, to learn the coordinations that enable it to peck food after hatching. Since every normal chick shows this behavior immediately after hatching, chance cannot be operative. Hence, such a mechanism is both impossible and improbable.

A second alternative interpretation, also incompatible with behavioristic views, is that there is a pre-established harmony between what the chick learns in the egg and how it must behave after hatching. Such an interpretation would indeed be "preformationism"—a bias that behaviorists have accused ethologists of having.

Last, there may be phylogenetically evolved teaching mechanism within the chick that causes it to learn to use its muscles in such a way as to peck. This possibility is not suggested as a *reductio ad absurdum*, but represents a real possibility, since information concerning the environment would be decoded twice, first in the development of the teaching apparatus, and second, in the trial-and-error muscular learning. Unfortunately for the behaviorists, however, the attempt to avoid the assumption of genetically fixated movements leads to the assumption of an equally genetically fixated teacher!

Certainly, whatever position is adopted—that of genetically determined movements or that of genetically determined teaching mechanisms—must also account for the fact that, as Lorenz points out, although avian species presumably all have the same ontogenetic experience in the egg, as described by Kuo, some do not peck, but gape, in order to obtain food immediately after hatching. Others, such as ducks, dabble, or shove bills into the parents' mouths, as do pigeons.

Lorenz (1961) considers, however, that the major flaw in postulating learning processes in the case of certain complex innate behavior is that it tremendously overrates the amount of learning that could possibly take place. For example, he cites the case in which a chimney swift was hatched and reared in a dark narrow cavity. It could not open its wings or see anything in focus, since its nearest focal point was farther than any portion of its small nesting site. When it was released at an age when normally reared swifts fly with ease, it was able to evaluate binocular disparities and shifting retinal images, to avoid obstacles in space, and to effect a pinpoint landing. Indeed, the information required to perform such behavior is so tremendous in quantity that superhuman learning powers would have to be credited to the bird if its whole performance constituted a learned skill. Naturally, Lorenz does not exclude the possibility that the bird could have learned to move agonistic and antagonistic muscles in a reciprocal manner. But still it is manifestly clear that the prenatal or early learning hypothesis in such a case requires a huge amount of learning, and calling such behavior innate is relatively inaccurate, since the proportion of learned elements is very small. It is similar to saying houses are made of wood, or of adobe, even though some portions certainly are not made of wood or adobe.

Last, the behaviorists have accused the ethologists of misrepresenting unanalyzable part functions in such a way as to give them the illusory appearance of natural units. This criticism, Lorenz maintains, is a consequence of behavioristic methodology, which attempts to gain an understanding of the total structure and function of an organic system by general observations only, without prior assumptions and through experiments that ask either-or-questions.

In any natural science, Lorenz (1960) maintains, phenomena are found to be grouped into natural units, each of which is characterized by a large number of specific properties. Quite often these phenomena are named before their causal bases are known, just as a medical clinician names syndromes, or complexes of symptoms, before he knows their causes or treatment. Of course, a prematurely given name may contain an erroneous hypothesis, but the natural unit remains intact. Such concept formations are intended simplifications. The fixed pattern, the I.R.M., and so forth are not fictions, but correspond to real physiological mechanisms, as shown by the multitude of ethological evidence about them.

In connection with this, Lorenz has recently (1961) come up with a definite theoretical position regarding the causal origins of adaptation of organic behavior to the environment.

The core of his position is that there are really two, and only two, entirely independent mechanisms effecting the adaptation of behavior. Whenever an organism shows adaptive behavior, this proves that it has been molded so as to fit the environment in a way that will achieve survival. Any process of molding the organism to environmental requirements is so like forming an image of the environment that it can be said that the organism has acquired information. There are only two ways in which this information basic for adaptation of behavior could have been acquired: first, the process of phylogeny, which evolves behavior as well as any other structural and functional organization; and second, the process of adaptive modification of behavior during the individual's life.

Thus it is an entirely different process if a species experiments by mutation or if an individual experiments by trial and error and records the consequences.

There are, however, close analogies between those two processes, even though they are completely independent mechanisms. In the evolutionary process, part of the progeny is risked in the "experiment" of mutation. A single mutation does not have a high probability of achieving better adaptiveness, but when one does, selection preserves it and it is disseminated quickly among the species. In the same way, one trial in trial-and-error learning has a small chance of being adaptive, but when it is, it is repeated and its place in the behavior repertoire solidified. Both learning and the phylogenetic processes have the very important function of creating and/or adaptively changing the structure of the neural apparatus determining behavior.

In fact, Lorenz goes even further and postulates that learning ability is selected in phylogeny and becomes fixated in the genetic constitution of the species. Adaptive evolution has the result of increasing survival value, and the increase of survival value effected by learning is the ultimate proof of its being in itself the product of adaptive evolution. Thus learning is performed by a very special mechanism built into the organism's system during the course of its evolution. Lorenz concludes that the idea that learning could possibly be the function of an unorganized aggregate of neural elements is logically and biologically nonsense.

It is obvious that in evolutionary processes adaptive modifications are preserved through their survival value. But how is it that the learning organism selects the "good" from the "bad" behavior? Learning theorists have proposed various ways in which the learning mechanism can pick out the behavior possibilities having good survival value. Edward L. Thorndike, for example, pointed to the fulfillment of bodily needs as reinforcing the behavior preceding it, and to bodily damage as tending to eliminate such behavior. Clark L. Hull, on the other hand, postulated drive reduction, or relief of physiological tension. Both theories presuppose a built-in mechanism that is able to direct learning toward survival value. Lorenz therefore proposes that the fixed action pattern, or the consummatory act, is this built-in mechanism; it reinforces learning re-afference, or sensory feedback.

Lorenz emphatically contends that learning is a *specific* survival-achieving function of the organism. Therefore, it is incorrect to speak of learning, as do some ethologists such as Tinbergen, as "entering into" all neurophysiological processes determining behavior. Innumerable observations and experiments have tended to show that modifiability, if it occurs at all, exists only at those evolutionarily preformed places where inbuilt learning mechanisms are waiting to perform just that function. These mechanisms, it must be pointed out, are very often unable to modify any but one very circumscribed system of behavior mechanisms. For example, honey bees can use irregular forms such as trees and rocks as landmarks to find their way to the hive. But they are unable to use these forms as signals indicating the presence or absence of food. Forms that bees will learn to use as food signals must be geometrically regular, preferably radially symmetric. No one, Lorenz asserts, has been able to demonstrate diffuse modifiability of any arbitrarily chosen innately determined element of behavior.

 FUTURE PROSPECTS

From what has been described, it is clear that ethology is a young science which has made a real contribution to this cen-

tury's scientific thinking and research. Indeed in only two decades of ethological research, the impact on certain areas of the
behavioral sciences is such that it probably will have a definite
formative influence on research in these areas during the next
several decades, because quite a large number of scientists are
becoming acquainted with ethology. How different this is
from the sterile learning research which flourished from the
twenties to the forties and from which we have inherited
neither facts nor ideas for further study. But in areas of psychology such as "early experience effects" and the genetic
aspects of behavior we can expect to find significant contributions to be made for some time to come by ethologists, particularly when the earlier-mentioned resistance on the part of
behavioristically oriented scientists is overcome.

Ethologists have indeed compiled impressive evidence on the
many mechanisms that determine behavior. They have never
attempted to construct entire behavior systems from a few
behavior elements, but have always sought first to determine
the natural functional units of behavior and *then* to inquire
into their causal bases. Thus it is that they are always open to
the possibility that on the morrow a new behavior-determining
mechanism may be discovered.

Two newly developed areas of ethological research, the genetic and the neurophysiological bases of behavior, are particularly likely to engender profound influences on future behavioral research, as well as in the disciplines of genetics and
neurophysiology themselves. These developments, especially
those arising from the recent work of von Holst, are of major
importance in that they have provided the scientific world with
definite breakthroughs in techniques and theory. For the first
time, it can be seen that a real neurophysiology of behavior is
being formed, an event which is comparable to the linking of
chemistry and physics in the theory of atomic structure.

All in all, these features of ethology augur favorably for
tremendous advances in the formulation and analysis of behavior systems, in the near future and for a long time to come.

⊕ **REFERENCES**

Allen, A. A. Sex rhythm in the ruffed grouse *(Bonasa umbellus)* and other birds. *Auk* 1954, *51*, 180-199.

Andrew, R. J. Normal and irrelevant toilet behaviour in *Emberiza*, Spp. *Brit. J. Anim. Behaviour*, 1956, *4*, 85-96.

Baerends, G. P. Fortpflanzungsverhalten und Orientierung der Grabwespe, *Ammophila campestris* Jur. *Tijdschr. Ent.*, 1941, *84*, 68-275.

Baerends, G. P. Specialization in organs and movements with a releasing function. *Symp. Soc. Exp. Biol.*, 1950, *4*, 337-360.

Baerends, G. P. Egg recognition in the herring gull. *Proc. 14th Int. Congr. Psychol.*, Montreal: 1954, 93-94.

Baerends, G. P. Aufbau des tierischen Verhaltens. *Kukenthal's Hb. Zool.*, 1956, *10*, 1-32.

Baerends, G. P. The ethological concept "releasing mechanism" illustrated by a study of the stimuli eliciting egg-retrieving in the herring gull. *Anat. Record*, 1957, *128*, 518-519.

Baerends, G. P. Comparative methods and the concept of homology in the study of behaviour. *Arch. Néer. Zool.*, 1958, *13*, Suppl. 1. 401-417.

Baerends, G. P. The ethological analysis of incubation behaviour. *Ibis*, 1959, *101*, 357-368.

Baerends, G. P., and J. M. Baerends-van Roon. An introduction to the study of ethology of cichlid fishes. *Behaviour Suppl.*, 1950, *1*, 1-243.

Beach, F. A. Ontogeny and living systems. In *Group processes*, ed., B. Schaffner. New York: Macy Foundation, 1954, 9-74.

Bowlby, J. *Maternal care and mental health*. Geneva, World Health Organization, 1951.

Bridges, K. M. B. Emotional development in early infancy. *Child Developm.*, 1932, *3*, 342-341.

Brückner, G. H. Untersuchungen zur Tiersoziologie, insbesondere der Auflösung der Familie. *Zs. Psychol.*, 1933, *128*, 1-120.

Caspari, E. Genetic and environmental conditions affecting a behavior trait in *Ephestia kuhniella*. *Anat. Rec.*, 1948, *101*, 690.

Cott, H. B. *Adaptive coloration in animals*. London: Methuen, 1940.

Cotter, W. G. B., Jr. The genetic and physiological analyses of the silk-spinning behavior of *Ephestia kuhniella* Zeller. Unpublished thesis. Wesleyan University, 1951.

Craig, W. The voices of pigeons regarded as a means of social control. *Amer. J. Sociol.*, 1908, *14*, 86-100.

Craig, W. Appetites and aversions as constituents of instincts. *Biol. Bull.*, 1918, *34*, 91-107.

Cullen, Esther. Adaptations in the Kittiwake to cliff-nesting. *Ibis*, 1957, *99*, 275-302.

Darling, F. F. *Wild country*. London: Cambridge University Press, 1938.

Darwin, C. *The expression of emotion in man and animals*. London: 1872.

Dilger, W. C. The behavior of lovebirds. *Scientific American* 1962, *206*, No. 1, 88-98.

Eibl-Eibesfeldt, I. Angeborenes und Erworbenes im Nestbauverhalten der Wanderratte. *Naturwiss.*, 1955a, *42*, 633-634.

Eibl-Eibesfeldt, I. Über Symbiosen, Parasitismus, und andere besondere zwischenartliche Beziehungen bei tropischen Meeresfischen. *Zeit. f. Tierpsychol.*, 1955b, *12*, 203-219.

Eibl-Eibesfeldt, I. Angeborenes und Erworbenes in der Technik des Beutetötens (Versuche am Iltis, *Putorious putorius* L.). *Z. Säugetierkunde*, 1956a, *21*, 135-37.

Eibl-Eibesfeldt, I. Über die ontogenetische Entwicklung der Technik des Nüsseöffnens vom Eichhörnchen *(Sciurus vulgaris* L.). *Z. Säugetierkunde*, 1956b, *21*, 132-134.

Eibl-Eibesfeldt, I. Der Fisch *Aspidontus taeniatus* als Nachahmer des Putzers *Labroides dimidiatus*. *Zeit. f. Tierpsychol.*, 1959, *16*, 19-25.

Fabré, J. H. *Souvenirs entomologiques* I bis X. Paris: Delagrave, 1879-1910.

Fabricius, E. Some experiments on imprinting phenomena in ducks. *Proc. 10th Int. Ornith. Kongr.*, 1951a, 375-379.

Fabricius E. Zur Ethologie junger Anatiden. *Acta Zool. Fennica*, 1951b, *68*, 1-178.

Fraenkel, G. S., and Gunn, D. L. *The orientation of animals*. Oxford: Clarendon Press, 1940.

Freedman, D. G., J. A. King, and O. Elliott. Critical period in the social development of dogs. *Science*, 1961, *133*, 1016-1017.

Goldfarb, W. The effects of early institutional care on adolescent personality. *J. exp. Educ.*, 1943, *12*, 106-129.

Grabowski, U. Prägung eines Jungscafs auf den Menschen. *Zeit. f. Tierpsychol.*, 1941, *4*, 326-329.

Gray, P. H. Theory and evidence of imprinting in human infants. *J. Psychol.*, 1958, *46*, 155-166.

Hebb, D. O. Heredity and environment in mammalian behaviour. *Brit. J. Anim. Bahaviour*, 1953, *1*, 43-47.

Hediger, H. *Wild animals in captivity*. London: Butterworth, 1938.

Heinroth, O. Beiträge zur Biologie, namentlich Ethologie und Psychologie der Anatiden. *Verh. 5th Int. Ornith. Kongr.*, 1910, 589-702.

Heinroth, O. Über bestimmte Bewegungsweisen der Wirbeltiere. *Sitzungsb. ges. Naturforsch. Freunde*, 333-342. Berlin: 1930.

Heinroth, O. *Aus dem Leben der Vögel*. Berlin: Springer, 1938.

Heinroth, O., and M. Heinroth. *Die Vögel Mitteleuropas*. Berlin: Lichterfelde, 1924-1933.

Heinz, H.-J. Vergleichende Beobachtungen über die Putzhandlungen bei Dipteren im allgemeinen und bei *Sarcophaga carnaria* L. im besonderen. *Zeit f. Tierpsychol.*, 1949, *6*, 330-371.

Herter, K., and K. Sgonina. Vorzugstemperatur and Hautbeschafftenheit bei Mäusen. *Zeit. vergl. Physiol.*, 1938, *26*, 366-415.

Hess, E. H. Effects of meprobamate on imprinting in waterfowl. *Ann. N. Y. Acad. Sci.*, 1957, *67*, 724-732.

Hess, E. H. Imprinting. *Science*, 1959a, *130*, 133-141.

Hess, E. H. The relationship between imprinting and motivation. In *Nebraska Symposium on Motivation*, M. R. Jones, ed., 1959b. 44-77.

Hess, E. H. Two conditions limiting critical age for imprinting. *J. comp. physiol. Psychol.*, 1559c, *52*, 515-518.

Hess, E. H. Effects of drugs on imprinting behavior. *Drugs and behavior*, editors, L. Uhr, and J. G. Miller. New York: Wiley and Sons, 1960. 268-271.

Hess, E. H., J. M. Polt, and E. Goodwin. Effects of carisoprodol on early experience and learning. In *The pharmacology and clinical usefulness of carisoprodol*, ed., J. G. Miller, Detroit: Wayne State University Press, 1959. 51-85.

Hess, E. H., and H. H. Schaefer. Innate behavior patterns as indicators of the "critical period." *Zeit. f. Tierpsychol.*, 1959, *16*, 155-160.

Hess, W. R. Stammganglien-Reizversuche. *Vortrag Dtsch. Physiol. ges. Bonn*, 1927.

Hess, W. R. *Das Zwischenhirn: Syndrome, Lokalisationen, Funktionen*. Basel: Schwabe, 1949.

Hess, W. R. *Das Zwischenhirn. Syndrome, Lokalisationen, Funktionen*. Mongr. II. Erweiterte aufl. Basel: Schwabe, 1954.

Hess, W. R. *Hypothalamus and Thalamus. Experimental-dokumente*. Stuttgart: Thieme, 1956. (Parallel English and German text.)

Hinde, R. A., W. H. Thorpe, and M. A. Vince. The following response in young coots and moorhens. *Behaviour*, 1956, *9*, 214-242.

Hirsch, J., R. H. Lindley, and E. C. Tolman. An experimental test of an alleged innate sign stimulus. *J. comp. physiol. Psychol.*, 1955, *48*, 278-280.

Hodge, W. H. Camels of the clouds. *The Nat. Geogr. Mag.*, 1946, *89*, 641-656.

Holst, E. v. Untersuchungen über die Funktionen des Zentralnervensystems beim Regenwurm. *Zool. Jb.*, 1932, *51*, 547-588.

Holst, E. v. Weitere Versuche zum nervösen Mechanismus dei Bewegung beim Regenwurm. *Zool. Jb.*, 1933, *53*, 67-100.

Holst, E. v. Über den Prozess der zentralnervösen Koordination. *Pflüg. Arch. ges. Physiol.*, 1935, *236*, 149-158.

Holst, E. v. Versuche zur Theorie der Relativen Koordination. *Pflüg. Arch. ges. Physiol.*, 1936a, *237*, 93-121.

Holst, E. v. Über den "Magnet-Effekt" als koordinationender Prinzip im Rückenmark. *Pflüg. Arch. ges. Physiol.*, 1936b, *237*, 655-682.

Holst, E. v. Bausteine zu einer vergleichende Physiologie der lokomotorischen Reflexe bei Fischen. II Mitteilung. *Z. vergl. Physiol.*, 1937a, *24*, 532-562.

Holst, E. v. Vom Wesen der Ordnung im Zentralnervensystem. *Naturwiss.*, 1937b, *25*, 625-631, 641-647.

Holst, E. v. Die Auslösung von Stimmungen bei Wirbeltieren durch "punktförmige" elektrische Errengung des Stammhirns. *Naturwiss.*, 1957, *44*, 549-551.

Holst, E. v., and U. v. St. Paul. Das Mischen von Trieben (Instinkbewegungen) durch mehrfache Stammhirnreizung beim Huhn. *Naturwiss.*, 1958, *45*, 579.

Holst, E. v., and U. v. St. Paul. Vom Wirkungsgefüge der Triebe. *Naturwiss.*, 1960, *18*, 409-422.

Holst, E. v., and U. v. St. Paul. Electrically controlled behavior. *Sci. Amer.*, 1962, *206*, No. 3, 50-59.

Hörmann-Heck, S. v. Über den Erbang von Verhaltensmerkmalen bei Grillenbastarden. *Naturwiss.*, 1955, *42*, 470-471.

Hörmann-Heck, S. v. Untersuchugen über den Erbang einiger Verhaltensweisen bei Grillenbastarden (*Gryllus campestris* L. x *Gr. Bimaculatus* de Geer). *Zeit. f. Tierpsychol.*, 1957, *14*, 137-183.

Howard, H. E. *An introduction to the study of bird behaviour.* Cambridge: Cambridge University Press, 1929.

Huxley, J. S. The courtship habits of the great crested Grebe (*Podiceps cristatus*); with an addition to the theory of sexual selection. *Proc. Zool. Soc. London*, 1914, 491-562.

Iersel, J. v. and A. C. Bol. Preening of two tern species. A study on displacement activities. *Behaviour*, 1958, *13*, 1-89.

James, H. Flicker: an unconditioned stimulus for imprinting. *Canad. J. Psychol.*, 1959, *13*, 59-67.

Jaynes, J. Imprinting: the interaction of learned and innate behavior. II. The critical period. *J. comp. physiol. Psychol.*, 1957, *50*, 6-10.

Jechorek, W., and Holst. E. v. Fernreizung freibeweglicher Tiere. *Naturwiss.*, 1956, *43*, 455.

Jennings, H. S. *Contributions to the study of the behavior of lower organisms.* Carnegie Institution of Washington Pub. No. 16, 1904.

Jennings, H. S. *Behavior of the lower organisms.* New York: Macmillan, 1906.

Kennedy, J. S. Is modern ethology objective? *Brit. J. Animal Behaviour*, 1954, *2*, 12-19.

Koehler, O., and A. Zagarus. Beiträge zum Brutverhalten des Halsbandregenpfeifers (*Charadrius h. hiaticula* L.). *Beitr. Fortpfl.-Biol. Vögel*, 1937, *13*, 1-9.

Kortlandt, A. Eine Übersicht der angeborenen Verhaltensweisen des mittleleuropäischen Kormorans (*Phalacrocorax Carbosinensis*), ihre Funktion, ontogenetische Entwicklung und phylogenetische Herkunft. *Arch. Néer. Zool.*, 1940a, *4*, 401-442.

Kortlandt, A. Wechselwirkung zwischen Instinkten. *Arch. Néer. Zool.*, 1940b, *4*, 442-520.

Kruijt, J. P. Speckling of herring gull eggs in relation to brood behaviour. *Arch. Néer. Zool.*, 1958, *12*, 565-567.

Krumbiegel, I. Die Persistenz Physiologischer Eigenschaften in der Stammesgeschichte. *Zeit. f. Tierpsychol.*, 1940, *4*, 249-258.

Kuo, Z. Y. Ontogeny of embryonic behavior in *Aves*. I. The chronology and general nature of the behavior of the chick embryo. *J. exp. Zool.*, 1932a, *61*, 395-430.

Kuo, Z. Y. Ontogeny of embryonic behavior in *Aves*. II. The mechanical factors in the various stages leading to hatching. *J. exp. Zool.*, 1932b, *62*, 453-489.

Kuo, Z. Y. Ontogeny of embryonic behavior in *Aves*. III. The structures and environmental factors in embryonic behavior. *J. comp. Psychol.*, 1932c, *13*, 245-272.

Kuo, Z. Y. Ontogeny of embryonic behavior in *Aves*. IV. The influence of embryonic movements upon the behavior after hatching. *J. comp. Psychol.*, 1932d, *14*, 109-122.

Lack, D. The behavior of the robin. II. *Proc. Zool. Soc. London*, 1939, *109*, 200-219.

Lehrman, D. S. A critique of Konrad Lorenz's theory of instinctive behavior. *Quart. Rev. Biol.*, 1953, *28*, 337-363.

Lehrman, D. S. On the organization of maternal behavior and the problem of instinct. In *L'instinct dans le comportement des animaux et de l'homme*, ed., P. P. Grassé. Paris: Masson et Cie, 1956, 475-520.

Leyhausen, P. Verhaltensstudien an Katzen. Beiheft 2 zur *Zeit. f. Tierpsychologie*, 1956.

Loeb, J. Beiträge zur Physiologie des Grosshirns. *Arch. ges. Physiol.*, 1886, *39*, 265-346.

Loeb, J. Die Orientierung der Tiere gegen das Licht (tierischer Heliotropismus). *Sitzungsb. Würzb. Physik-Med. ges.*, 1888a.

Loeb, J. Die Orientierung der Tiere gegen die Schwerkraft der Erde (tierischer Geotropismus). *Sitzungsb. Würzb. Physik-Med. ges.*, 1888b.

Loeb, J. *Der Heliotropismus der Tiere und seine Uebereinstimmung mit dem Heliotropismus der Pflanzen*. Würzburg: 1889.

Loeb, J. *Forced movements, tropisms, and animal conduct*. Philadelphia: Lippincott, 1918.

Lorenz, K. Z. Beiträge zur Ethologie sozialer Corviden. *J. f. Ornith.*, 1931, *79*, 67-120.

Lorenz, K. Z. Der Kumpan in der Umwelt des Vogels. *J. f. Ornith.*, 1935, *83*, 137-213, 289-413.

Lorenz, K. Z. Über die Bildung des Instinktbegriffes. *Naturwiss.*, 1937, *25*, 289-300, 307-318, 324-331.

Lorenz, K. Z. Vergleichende Bewegungsstudien an Anatiden. *J. f. Ornith.*, 1941, *89*, 194-294.

Lorenz, K. Z. Die angeborenen Formen möglicher Erfahrung. *Zeit. f. Tierpsychol.*, 1943, *5*, 335-409.

Lorenz, K. Z. The comparative method in studying innate behaviour patterns. *Symp. Soc. Exp. Biol.*, 1950, *4*, 221-268.

Lorenz, K. Z. Die Entwicklung der vergleichenden Verhaltensforschung in den letzten 12 Jahren. *Verh. Dtsch. Zool. ges. Freiburg, 1952*, 36-58. Leipzig: Akad. Verlag. 1953.

Lorenz, K. Z. The deprivation experiment: its limitations and its value as a means to separate learned and unlearned elements of behavior. Paper presented at the Downing Hospital, Illinois, 1958a.

Lorenz, K. Z. The evolution of behavior. *Sci. Amer.*, 1958b, *199*, No. 6, 67-78.

Lorenz, K. Z. Prinzipien der vergleichenden Verhaltensforschung, *Fortschr. Zool.*, 1960, *12*, 265-294.

Lorenz, K. Z. Phylogenetische Anpassung und adaptive Modifikation des Verhaltens. *Zeit. f. Tierpsychol.*, 1961, *18*, 139-187.

Lorenz, K. Z., and N. Tinbergen. Taxis und Instinkthandlung in der Eirollbewegung der Graugans. *Zeit. f. Tierpsychol.*, 1938, *2*, 1-29.

Magnus, D. Experimentelle Untersuchungen zur Bionomie und Ethologie des Kaisermantels *Argynnis paphia* L. (Lep. Nymph). I. Über optische Auslöser von Angliegereaktionen und ihre Bedeutung für das Sichfinden der Geschechter. *Zeit. f. Tierpsychol.*, 1958, *15*, 397-426.

Makkink, G. F. Die Kopulation der Brandente (*Tadorna tadorna* L.). *Ardea*, 1931, *20*, 18-22.

Makkink, G. F. An attempt at an ethogram of the European Avocet (*Recurvirostra avosetta* L.) with ethological and psychological remarks. *Ardea*, 1936, *25*, 1-62.

Marler, P. Specific distinctiveness in the communication signals of birds. *Behaviour*, 1957, *9*, 13-39.

McClearn, J. The genetics of mouse behavior in novel situations, *J. comp. physiol. Psychol.*, 1959, *52*, 62-67.

Moltz, Howard. Imprinting: empirical basis and theoretical significance. *Psychol. Bull.*, 1960, *57*, 291-314.

Moltz, H., L. A. Rosenblum, and N. Halikas. Imprinting and level of anxiety. *J. comp. physiol. Psychol.*, 1959, *52*, 240-244.

Morgan, C. L. *Animal life and intelligence.* London: Arnold, 1891.

Morgan, C. L. *Habit and instinct.* London: Arnold, 1896.

Morgan, C. L. *Introduction to comparative psychology.* 1894.

Morris, D. "Typical intensity" and its relation to the problem of ritualisation. *Behaviour*, 1957, *11*, 1-13.

Murie, A. The wolves of Mt. McKinley. *Nat. Park Serv., U.S. Dept. Int. Fauna Series,* No. 5. 1944.

Nice, M. M. Some experiences in imprinting ducklings. *Condor*, 1953, *55*, 33-37.

Oehlert, B. Kampf und Paarbildung bei einigen Cichliden. *Zeit. f. Tierpsychol.*, 1958, *15*, 141-174.

Pernau, F. A. v. Unterricht/ Was mit dem lieblichen Geschöpff, denen Vögeln/ auch ausser dem Fang/ Nur durch die Ergründung Deren Eigenschafften/ und Zahmmachung/ oder anderer Abrichtung/ Man sich vor Lust und Zeit-Vertreib machen können: gestellt. Coburg, 1707. (Printed in 1702 without the author's consent; revised and enlarged edition in Nürnberg, 1716).

Pickwell, G. B. The prairie horned lark. *Trans. Acad. Sci. St. Louis*, 1931, 27, 1-153.

Portielje, A. F. J. Triebleben bzw. intelligente Aeusserungen beim Orang-Utan (*Pongo pigmaeus* Hoppius). *Bijdr. Dierk.*, 1939, *27*, 61-114.

Ramsay, A. O. Familial recognition in domestic birds. *Auk*, 1951, *68*, 1-16.

Ramsay, A. O. Behaviour of some hybrids in the mallard group. *Animal Behaviour*, 1961, *9*, 104-105.

Ramsay, A. O., and E. H. Hess, A laboratory approach to the study of imprinting. *Wilson Bull.*, 1954, *66*, 196-206.

Réaumur, R. A. F. *Mémoires pour servir à l'histoire des insectes.* I-VI. Paris: Impr. Royale, 1734-1742.

Reimarus, H. S. *Allgemeine Betrachtungen über die Triebe der Thiere, hauptsächlich über ihre Kunsttriebe.* Second edition. Hamburg: 1762.

Remane, A. *Die Grundlagen des natürlichen Systems der vergleichenden Anatomie und der Phylogenetik.* Leipzig: Akad. Verlag, 1956.

Riess, B. F. Effect of altered environment and of age on the mother-young relationships among animals. *Ann. N. Y. Acad. Sci.*, 1954, *57*, 606-610.

Roeder, K. D. Spontaneous activity and behavior. *Sci. Mon. Wash.*, 1955, *80*, 362-370.

Schein, M., and E. B. Hale. The effect of early social experience on male sexual behaviour of androgen injected turkeys. *Animal Behaviour*, 1959, 7, 189-200.

Schenckel, R. Zur Deutung der Balzleistungen einiger Phasianiden und Tetraoniden. I. *Ornith. Beob. Bern*, 1956, *53*, 182-201.

Schenckel, R. Zur Deutung der Balzleistungen einiger Phasianiden und Tetraoniden. II *Ornith. Beob. Bern*, 1958, *55*, 65-95.

Schneirla, T. C. Interrelationships of the "innate" and the "acquired" in instinctive behavior. In *L'instinct dans le comportement des animaux et de l'homme*, ed., P. P. Grassé. Paris: Masson et Cie., 1956, 387-452.

Seitz, A. Die Paarbildung bei einigen Cichliden. I. Die Paarbildung bei *Astatotilapia strigigena* (Pfeffer). *Zeit. f. Tierpsychol.*, 1940, *4*, 40-84.

Sevenster, P. A causal analysis of a displacement activity. Unpublished, 1958.

Sherrington, C. S. Notes on the arrangement of some motor fibres in the lumbo-sacral plexus. *J. Physiol.*, 1892, *13*, 621-772.

Spalding, D. A. Instinct, with original observations on young animals. *Macmillan's Magazine*, 1873, *27*, 282-293. Reprinted in *Brit. J. Anim. Behav.*, 1954, *2*, 2-11.

Spitz, R. A., and K. M. Wolf. The smiling response: a contribution to the ontogenesis of social relations. *Genet. Psychol. Monogr.*, 1946, *34*, 57-125.

Thorpe, W. H. Some problems of animal learning. *Proc. Linn. Soc. Lond.*, 1944, *156* part 2, 70-83.

Thorpe, W. H. *Learning and instinct in animals.* London: Methuen, 1956.

Tinbergen, N. On the analysis of social organization among vertebrates, with special reference to birds. *Amer. Midl. Nat.*, 1939, *21*, 210-234.

Tinbergen, N. Die Uebersprungbewegung. *Zeit. f. Tierpsychol.*, 1940, *4*, 1-40.

Tinbergen, N. An objectivistic study of the innate behaviour of animals. *Biblioth. Biother.*, 1942, *1*, 39-98.

Tinbergen, N. Social releasers and the experimental method required for their study. *Wilson Ornith. Bull.*, 1948, *60*, 6-51.

Tinbergen, N. The hierarchical organisation of nervous mechanisms underlying instinctive behaviour. *Symp. Soc. Exp. Biol.*, 1950, *4*, 305-312.

Tinbergen, N. *The study of instinct.* London: Oxford University Press, 1951.

Tinbergen, N. "Derived" activities; their causation, biologicial significance, origin, and emancipation during evolution. *Quar. Rev. Biol.*, 1952, 27, 1-32.

Tinbergen, N., and J. van Iersel. "Displacement reactions" in the three-spined stickleback. *Behaviour*, 1947, *1*, 56-63.

Tinbergen, N., and D. J. Kuenen. Über die auslösenden und richtungsgebenden Reizsituationen der Sperrbewegung von jungen *Drosseln (Turdus m. merula* und *T. e. ericetorum* Turton). *Zeit. f. Tierpsychol.*, 1939, *3*, 37-60.

Uexküll, J. v. *Umwelt und Innenwelt der Tiere.* Jena: 1909. Second edition, Berlin, 1921.

Verwey, J. Die Paarungbiologie des Fischreihers. *Zool. Jb. Physiol.*, 1930, *48*, 1-120.

Weidmann, U. Verhaltensstudien an der Stockente, II. Versuche zur Auslösung und Prägung der Nachfolge- und Anschlussreaktion. *Zeit. f. Tierpsychol.*, 1958, *15*, 277-300.

Weidmann, R., and U. Weidmann. An analysis of the stimulus situation releasing food-begging in the black-headed gull. *Brit. J. Anim. Behaviour*, 1958, *6*, 114.

Weiss, P. Autonomous versus reflexogenous activity of the central nervous system. *Proc. Amer. Phil. Soc.*, 1941a, *84*, 53-64.

Weiss, P. Self-differentiation of the basic patterns of co-ordination. *Comp. Psychol. Monogr.*, 1941b, *17*, 1-96.

Whitman, C. O. Animal behavior. *Biol. Lect. Marine Biol. Lab. Wood's Hole, Mass., 1898*. Boston: 1899. 285-338.

◈ SELECTED READINGS

Lorenz, K. Z. *King Solomon's ring*. New York: Crowell, 1952.

Lorenz, K. Z. *Man meets dog*. Boston: Houghton, 1955.

Both of Lorenz's books are popular accounts of animal behavior, intended for the layman.

Schiller, C. H. *Instinctive behavior*. New York: International Universities Press, 1957.

Contains many important papers translated into English.

Symposia of the Society for Experimental Biology, number 4. Psychological Mechanisms in Animal Behavior. Cambridge: University Press, 1950.

Contains original English and German papers.

Tinbergen, N. *The study of instinct*. Oxford: Clarendon Press, 1951.

The first general survey of ethology.

Thorpe, W. H. *Learning and instinct in animals*. London: Methuen, 1956.

Also a general survey of ethology.

4 ✦ EMOTION

GEORGE MANDLER
UNIVERSITY OF CALIFORNIA, SAN DIEGO, CALIFORNIA

THE PREPARATION OF THIS CHAPTER WAS SUPPORTED IN PART BY GRANT M-4852 FROM THE NATIONAL INSTITUTE OF MENTAL HEALTH, UNITED STATES PUBLIC HEALTH SERVICE. I AM INDEBTED TO DR. STANLEY SCHACHTER FOR MAKING PREPUBLICATION COPIES OF HIS RECENT STUDIES AVAILABLE TO ME. JEAN M. MANDLER'S CRITICAL AND SUBSTANTIVE CONTRIBUTIONS APPEAR THROUGHOUT THE CHAPTER, AND COMMENTS BY R. W. BROWN, W. KESSEN, T. M. NEWCOMB AND S. SCHACHTER ON AN EARLIER DRAFT WERE MOST HELPFUL.

There are probably few topics in psychology that rival emotion in their appeal to the layman, and only too frequently the neophyte will assume that problems of emotional behavior are the major if not the only concern of psychological science. While a cursory acquaintance with contemporary psychology is sufficient to dispel any such misconceptions, the desire to explain emotional phenomena has gripped layman and professional alike throughout the history of our discipline. In light of the intrinsic interest that the topic arouses, it seems strange that the analysis of emotion has lagged behind other apparently less appealing topics. We know more today about verbal learning, psychophysical scaling, and discrimination in the rat, for example, than about the determinants of emotional behavior. As a body of theory and knowledge psychoanalysis probably stands alone in presuming to give a consistent and extensive account of human emotion. Curiously enough, however, the problems that the psychoanalytically oriented psychologist considers to be central to the topic show little overlap with the problems of emotion that have fascinated the experimental and physiological psychologist. One major reason for this disjunction is the concern of psychoanalytic theory with major chunks of behavior, organized over lifetimes and stressing individual differences, contrasted with the fine-grained analysis of immediate determinants of emotional behavior found in the laboratory. The past few years have produced such a wealth of new material in the latter tradition that we can make another attempt to organize the work on human emotion, classically conceived and experimentally attacked. The overriding question is and has been, What is emotion and what determines its occurrence and character?

Since antiquity, students of man have emphasized two facets which, in conjunction, appear to differentiate emotion from other human experiences: First, emotion involves action which is strongly influenced by certain environmental goals and events, and second, it usually presupposes bodily, visceral, or physiological reactions.

Philosophers' tales about "what emotion is" differ little from the accounts of intelligent laymen. The layman will talk about feelings and experiences and often end up by listing such states as joy, anger, happiness, disgust, yearning, anxiety, and many others. Common sense tells us that these various emotions can easily be told apart, that they just feel very different. Mere reflection confirms our view that anger and joy, for example, are basically different and disparate feelings. We also tend to agree that these feelings are caused by other people and by situations, and that they are associated with more or less vague internal physical reactions.

It has been only during the past eighty years that these views have been subjected to critical scrutiny and, as is the case with so many common-sense truths, either modified or abandoned. How far this modification has gone will be our theme in later pages. First, we shall take a brief look at the history of psychological interest in emotion, in conclusion asking whether it is reasonable to expect an answer to the question, What is emotion? We shall then describe in some detail some recent experiments by Dr. Stanley Schachter and his associates. These studies—a major advance in the experimental attack on emotion—will form the background for a detailed discussion of the content of emotional behavior, of the occasions (the stimuli) for its occurrence, and of the role of those elusive physiological reactions.

⟐ SOME HISTORY—PAST AND PRESENT

The major theme for theories of emotion—essentially unchallenged and unexplored for about two thousand years—was set by Aristotle. In his *De Anima* Aristotle distinguished between the matter—the visceral component—of emotion, and its form or idea—what we might call the psychological experience of emotion. How these two components interact or summate is not made quite clear. Much later, Descartes' distinction between the physiological body and the psychological soul and his discussion of their interaction failed to advance the problem significantly. In general, though, experience—the mind and the soul—were given pre-eminence over bodily functions as determiners of emotional experience and expression. As a curtainraiser to modern empirical psychology Darwin's investigation of emotion (1872) was the first to emphasize emotional *behavior* and *expression* rather than felt experience. However, even Darwin let the behavioral, habitual, and physiological aspects of emotion stand side by side as separate principles, inquiring into their development and appearance but only tangentially into their interaction.

The major break in the history of the psychology of emotion must be assigned to William James' speculations published in 1884. James' contribution reached beyond the area of emotion; his was the first important and influential suggestion that the central stuff of psychology—ideas, sensations, feelings, and emotions—was not primary but secondary in the sequence of behavior. Prior to James these essentially cognitive aspects carried the main burden of controlling or causal function. Organisms were thought to act because of certain ideas, to react to the evaluation of sensations, and to emote subsequent to cognitive emotional states. James turned this sequence upside down—though in this he tended to restrict himself to the field of emotion—and suggested that felt experience is subsequent to visceral discharge, that we feel bad because we have been crying, not that we cry because we feel bad. In modern terminology, we say he assigned controlling effects to the visceral discharge, stating that "our feeling of the (bodily) changes *is* the emotion" (James, 1884).

Till James' revolution, conventional wisdom asserted that visceral arousal *followed* some sort of appreciation of the object as good or bad, frightening or pleasing, pleasurable or unpleasurable. James abandoned the priority of these judgmental functions and relied on sheer association of the object or goal with past danger to provide a mechanism for visceral arousal. The perception of the visceral arousal would then lend emotional tone or feeling to the experience. Parenthetically we might note the theoretical notions developed by the Danish scientist Lange at the same time as James presented his theory, and which have been linked with James by reference to the James-Lange theory of emotion. Strictly speaking, however, Lange did not present a psychological theory about emotion. He suggested that "vasomotor disturbances . . . are the real, primary effects of the affections, whereas . . . motor abnormalities, sensation paralysis, subjective sensations, disturbances of secretion, and intelligence—are only secondary disturbances, which have their cause in anomalies of vascular innervation . . ." (Lange, 1885). We will argue that these behavioral "secondary disturbances"—secondary to visceral arousal—are what a *psychology* of emotion is primarily about. Thus a theory of emotion which restricts the term "emotion" to patterns of visceral discharge (Dunlap, 1928; Wenger, 1950), or more generally to bodily states which are not directly observable and which do not operate directly on the environment, is not of immediate concern to us.

We cannot and should not attempt to defend James' position as a satisfactory theory of emotion, but we can suggest that James was the first to state quite clearly that visceral processes do in fact exercise some control over the behavior called emotional.

The most telling attack on James' theory of emotion was

mounted by Cannon, and it seems likely that subsequent research in the area was dominated not so much by Cannon's own neurophysiological theory (the Cannon-Bard theory of the textbooks) as by his five major criticisms of the James theory.

In attacking James' view that the viscera control emotional behavior, Cannon (1929) pointed out the following:

1. Emotional behavior is still present when the viscera are separated from the central nervous system, that is, in cases of sympathectomy or vagotomy when no visceral response can occur.

2. Visceral changes do not seem to differ from emotion to emotion. Rather sharp differences would have to be found if James' position were entirely correct.

3. The viscera are insensitive, that is, feedback from visceral response (and its perception) is diffuse and indistinct at best and could not serve as the basis for differentiating emotion.

4. Visceral changes are relatively slow and their speed would predict that emotion could not occur in less than one to two seconds following stimulation. Introspective evidence seemed to contradict such long latencies.

5. Production of visceral changes by artificial means—for example, by drugs—does not seem to produce emotion.

In the light of modern evidence it seems that all of Cannon's points are valid if it were only James' theory at issue; they can be disputed if we are more interested in describing the conditions which control emotional behavior. We shall discuss in subsequent pages the view that visceral discharge in general, rather than in specific patterns, is the important determinant of emotional behavior, thus taking account of Cannon's points number 2 and 3; that visceral changes are necessary to establish emotional behavior but are not by themselves sufficient, and that they are only operative in combination with environmental conditions, thus accounting for point number 5; and that although visceral changes are essential for the initial establishment of emotional behavior, on later occasions the emotional behavior may prove to have been conditioned to external stimuli, and may occur both without visceral support and—in some form—prior to it, thus accounting for points number 1 and 4.

In defense of Lange's (and thereby partly of James') position, Wenger offered similar arguments which illustrate how a particular theoretical position may be buttressed by later research coming from quite independent sources. Wenger was speaking of patients who had undergone sympathectomies (severance of the sympathetic nervous system from the central nervous system) yet still experienced emotions (in our terms, showed emotional behavior). He asked, "Would such feeling and expression be possible without prior conditioning in the presence of an intact and functioning autonomic nervous system? I doubt it, but I know of little evidence that bears directly on the question" (Wenger, 1950, p. 7). Since 1950, animal experiments have shown that an intact sympathetic nervous system is apparently necessary for the *acquisition* of an avoidance response (presumably based on fear or anxiety), but that the *maintenance* of such a response is not dependent upon autonomic functioning (Wynne and Solomon, 1955). Similarly it has been shown that the acquisition of avoidance responding is correlated with changes in autonomic response (heart rate) but that the maintenance of avoidance responding is not so correlated (Black, 1959). Thus Wenger has been answered affirmatively in this case; prior conditioning does seem to depend on autonomic activity.

Most of the theories of emotion starting with and subsequent to Cannon's criticisms of James fall into the category of neurophysiological theories and are only tangentially concerned with questions of psychological control of emotional behavior. From Cannon's thalamic theory to Hebb's recourse to cell assemblies, much emphasis is put on possible neural mechanisms that mediate emotional behavior from external inputs, but they shed little additional light on the psychological conditions for that behavior. Hebb, though, makes the important contribution of adding the interruption of well-developed behavioral and perceptual sequences as one of the antecedent conditions for emotional behavior.

Discussion of the emotions, no matter how brief, cannot be complete without reference to the major theorist and taxonomist of human behavior and emotion—Sigmund Freud. While few of the determinants of emotional behavior escaped him—he sounds like Pavlov when describing the development of object cathexis and how objects tend to become occasions for instinctual discharge, and he sounds like James when talking about bodily discharge and its perception in anxiety—his major contribution was not so much to the detailed analysis of emotional behavior which concerns us here as to the specification of broad categories of motives and emotions and their emergence in human development. Only in the case of anxiety did he entertain a detailed analysis of the kinds of variables discussed here. Yet his contribution to psychology has been so pervasive that much of our present discussion would be impossible without the stage set by Freud in relation to such topics as consciousness (awareness), the classification of verbal emotional behavior, the energy sources (activation) of emotion, and individual differences.

Our very brief excursion into history has served the purpose of pointing up the major topics that have fascinated psychologists and physiologists of emotion. We might come to one tentative conclusion: There has been a search for a reasonable and consistent theory of emotions, parallel to the theories of learning and perception. The basis for such a search has been the prior belief that it should be possible to arrive at a definition of the word "emotion" in a way that will be plausible and reasonable for all concerned. The most ambitious recent attempt to develop such a theory hinges on agreement to the definition of emotion as a *felt tendency* toward and away from things intuitively appraised as good or bad and accompanied by patterned physiological discharges that differ from emotion to emotion (Arnold, 1960). Modern psychology must come to grips with the use of such terms as "felt tendency" and "intuitively appraised" and we shall see that the specification of how the organism can be said to have a felt tendency and how objects and situations get to be appraised as "good" or "bad" sits at the core of a psychology of emotion—if not of all of psychology.

We shall be concerned with the psychology and not the neurophysiology—or even the physiology—of emotion, without detracting from the important work of physiologists or neuroanatomists, and we shall attempt to specify the conditions of emotional behavior without saying that there is such a thing as emotion and without suggesting that emotion is really something else. But first we must examine what kind of an answer modern psychology can give to the question, What is emotion?

WHAT IS EMOTION?

Psychologists and philosophers are often seduced into an attempt to answer questions such as *What is an emotion? What is perception?* and so forth. The past seventy years in particular, partly as a result of William James' taunt that such definitions "give one nowhere a central point of view," have produced a plethora of definitions of emotion. The modern resolution of this dilemma probably lies in a distinction between two kinds of theoretical terms (among many others). We shall call them *chapter-heading terms* and *theoretical terms*. Chapter-heading terms—and *emotion* is one of them—do no more than collect under one rubric what are believed to be related phenomena, experiments, and observations. What is the basis of this belief? The collection of these instances has no clearly definable boundaries; it arises historically and empirically, with the structure of the boundaries rarely spelled out and, most frequently, appreciated intuitively. In our common everyday language we somehow know in general what emotions are, in the same sense that we appreciate words like *morality, the farm problem, bad weather, culture,* and even *animal.* When pressed we can, in the common language, give some boundary conditions for the use of these words, but we cannot find a definition with which we feel quite comfortable. At best we can supply a list of characteristics, relevant behavior, and so forth.

The second basis for the belief in the unity of emotion stems from an attempt to reduce phenomena to an explanation in terms of previously known processes. This approach leads to definitions of emotion as "nothing but" the operation of drives, activation level, perceptions, physiological processes, or response strengths. Invariably such attempts are judged inadequate by competing reductionists—who prefer some other "basic" process. These processes or concepts, which emotion is "nothing but," constitute in the main our second class of psychological terms—the theoretical terms. They do not—or should not—appeal to a purely intuitive appreciation, but are useful concepts in the business of psychological theorizing, and have been—or should have been—rather rigorously defined in psychological theory.

The fact that so many varied explanatory notions have been invoked in order to make emotion more comprehensible and respectable suggests the solution to our dilemma. Assume for the moment that emotions are not "nothing but," that all these theoretical processes are relevant, that the material under that chapter heading is, among other things, amenable to interpretations which talk about drive strength, activation level, perceptual laws, visceral events, and reports of private experiences. Is it not reasonable, then, to make the further assumption that these various explanations have focused on selected phenomena, all collected under the heading of emotion? Although all these concepts are relevant, none by itself exhausts the problems amassed in that chapter of psychology. And why should it? The term *emotion* represents a collection of observations, bounded intuitively and historically, and many basic psychological processes will be relevant to that collection. What we can do is to try to abstract some boundary conditions for a chapter name, a short list of the classes of observations which appear to be relevant.

There are three interrelated classes of events which are of interest to psychologists of emotion: (a) environmental or stimulus events; (b) physiological, specifically visceral, events; and (c) verbal and motor behavior. It might be noted that there is a fourth, overriding class concerned with individual differences or prior experience, but this class of observations is theoretically relevant to all areas of behavior and need not be treated specifically when we are dealing with general statements.

How does this definition of emotion set it apart from other phenomena that psychologists study? Probably not at all, in the specification of the kinds of variables which operate within each of these classes. Thus, a psychology of learning might consider observation in all three categories, as might a psychology of motivation or of aesthetics. The peculiar concatenation of events which we tend to call emotional indicates, as a first approximation, several characteristics which should be considered in our study.

The psychology of emotion deals with environmental events which control visceral events, either innately or as a result of learning and experience. The relevant visceral or physiological events seem to be those that are discriminable by the organism. Other environmental conditions of interest are those that occasion verbal and nonverbal behavior considered to be emotional. The kinds of behavior that we call emotional are best defined by simply listing them, though we do assume that at least some of them are under the control of the visceral as well as environmental events. And finally, there is a presumption of private feelings, the occurrence of which is inferred from certain kinds of introspective reports.

How these various events interact and exert controlling influences on one another is, then, the problem of emotion in contemporary psychology. James' bold assertions set the stage for this approach, and it is his and Cannon's influence that leads us to examine the research literature and evaluate it in the light of their questions.

We can now look at a series of experiments which attempt to show what kind of manipulations affect the intensity and appearance of emotional behavior. Is it possible to manipulate emotions by changing the physiological state of a person? Do these physiological events have different effects depending on what else is going on in the environment? Are different kinds of internal, visceral states necessary to produce different emotions?

It was questions of this order that Dr. Schachter and his co-workers attempted to ask in the laboratory, and we shall arrive at some answers by following the course of their experiments.

✥ THE SCHACHTER EXPERIMENTS

In a large Midwestern university two students, Harold Heartbeat and Peter Placid, volunteered to take part in a psychological experiment on vision. They were told to appear at the Psychological Laboratories at different times.

Harold's appointment occurred first. He was greeted by a member of the psychology department who asked him if he minded being subjected to a painless injection of a substance whose effects on vision were being studied. He agreed, and was then informed that the injection might have some transitory side effects lasting no more than twenty minutes and consisting of hand tremor, increased heart rate, and a warm and flushed feeling in the face. Since he was assured that these effects would be mild and harmless, he agreed to participate in the experiment. A physician then gave him the injection, and Harold was asked to join another student, who also was taking part in the experiment, in a waiting room, in order to let the drug take effect before the start of the visual tests. Soon after, the other student began to behave in a rather mad and peculiar fashion. He played basketball with some scrap paper and a wastepaper basket, went hula-hooping with a piece of equipment left in the room, made and flew paper airplanes, and even invited Harold to participate in his tomfoolery. But Harold was above such nonsense and did not join in the raucous goings on. Soon thereafter the experimenter came into the waiting room—and at this point we leave Harold to report what happened to Peter Placid a few days later.

Peter's experiences on arriving at the Laboratories were quite similar to Harold's, except for one curious difference. He was told that the substance to be injected would have side effects, but the effects described were numbness in his feet, itching sensations, and a slight headache—quite different from what Harold was told. When he entered the waiting room he also was greeted by another student, and had he known Harold and compared notes with him, he would have found that his colleague-in-waiting was the same student who behaved so extraordinarily with Harold. He would have been surprised to learn that this young man went through almost the identical nonsense that Harold had witnessed earlier. In contrast, Peter found himself unable to resist the blandishments of his raucous comrade and soon was shooting airplanes, hula-hooping, and throwing spitballs at a great rate, far outdoing the excesses of the mysterious stranger. And if he had been asked how he felt about it all, he would have admitted to a rather pleasant feeling of madness, happiness, and euphoria. We leave Peter, too, at the end of his twenty minutes of excess, and ask what all this Midwestern nonsense has to do with our chapter heading—emotion.

Harold and Peter were, obviously, subjects in a psychological experiment which had little to do with vision, but was concerned rather with investigating some of the variables which affect emotional states, such as euphoria. And our account of the two fictional characters describes typical results with two groups of subjects who differed in only one respect: the instructions they had been given about the expected effects of the injection. In both groups the injection consisted of the hormone adrenalin, which typically has the effects described to Harold: flushing, heartbeat, and tremor. The experimental group that Peter was in had been misinformed about the effects of the injections, and its members gaily joined in the events in the waiting room, initiated by a co-worker, or stooge, of the experimenter's. Members of Harold's group, having been correctly informed about the effects of the injection, did not, on the average, exhibit euphoric behavior, and also reported much less of a feeling of happiness or euphoria.

What has happened in these experiments is rather simple, but also startling in light of common-sense notions about emotion. Two groups of subjects have been given identical injections of a drug that produces increased heart rate, tremor, and flushing. The members of one group (Harold's) are told what the effects of the drug would be, and they are relatively unaffected by the euphoric behavior of the stooge; the members of the other group (Peter's) are given wrong information about the effects of the drug, and they are strongly affected by the stooge's behavior and exhibit active emotional involvement. The same physiological background produced by the drug, combined with identical behavior on the part of the stooge, resulted in quite different behavior in the two groups, apparently entirely as a function of what they had been told about the effects of adrenalin.

There were several other groups of subjects in this experiment by Schachter and Singer. Two other groups were also exposed to the euphoric stooge; one group was told nothing at all about any possible side effects of the injection, and another was given a completely ineffective injection of saline (salt water), known technically as a placebo, thus administering a treatment identical with the experimental treatment except for the omission of the active drug. In another series of experiments, a stooge of the experimenter's did not behave madly and euphorically, but rather engaged in angry, aggressive behavior with all the subjects. With this kind of stooge there were three experimental conditions: one group was correctly informed about the effects of the injection (as was Harold's group), another group was told nothing about the injection, and the third group was given a saline injection—forming another placebo group.

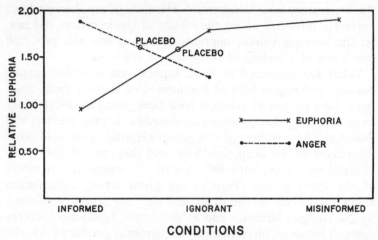

Fig. 1.   Relative euphoria as a function of experimental conditions (explanations) in the Schachter and Singer experiments. The ordinate shows relative euphoria determined by subtracting degree of reported irritation (anger) from degree of reported happiness (euphoria). The figure shows that in the euphoria groups relative "happiness" increases with increasing discrepancy between "explanation" and the visceral arousal, for the anger groups relative "happiness" decreases, in other words, relative "irritation" increases. The position of the two placebo groups is indicated on the graphs.

Following the waiting-room experience, regardless of whether the atmosphere was euphoric or angry, the experimenter—still pretending that this was an experiment on vision —told all the participants that he wanted some measure of their mood before proceeding with the actual experiments; and all subjects filled out a self-report questionnaire asking them how irritated or happy they felt. Furthermore, all the time that the students were in the waiting room they were watched through one-way mirrors, and the degree of their euphoric or angry behavior was recorded. Once they had filled out the questionnaire, the experiment was concluded and they were fully informed about the deception and the purposes of the study.

We can now take a brief look at the results of this series of experiments. Consider first the results of the subjects' reports on happiness and irritation following the waiting-room experience. The measure of self-report was the difference of the happiness (euphoria) ratings minus the irritation (anger) ratings—in other words, a relative degree of happiness or euphoria; the larger this value, the happier the subjects were feeling at the conclusion of the experiment. We note in Figure 1 an increase in this self-report rating for the euphoria group as we go from the Informed to the Ignorant to the Misinformed group. The three groups have been arranged in decreasing order of appropriateness of the information they were given about the injection. They were correctly informed in the first group, given no information in the Ignorant group, and misinformed in the last one. Apart from the increase in relative happiness for the three groups, we find the placebo group (who cannot reasonably be ranked with the other three in terms of appropriateness of information given) placed between the Informed and the Ignorant group. For the Anger experiments, we note a corresponding decrease in relative happiness (or increase in relative irritation) as we go from Informed to Ignorant, with the Placebo group again falling between the two.

It is useful to talk here, as Schachter does, about a discrepancy between the effects of the injection and the explanations given to the subjects. This discrepancy is minimal or nonexistent in the Informed groups, who were told more or less exactly what the effects of the injection would be. For the Misinformed groups, however, there is maximal discrepancy; the injection presumably had one kind of effect, while the explanation prepared the subjects for quite another—in some ways, opposite—effect. The Ignorant subjects fall somewhere between these two extremes; while they were not exposed to

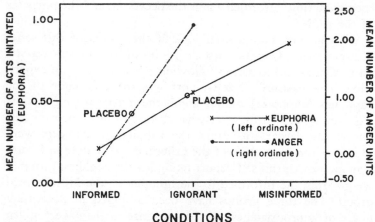

CONDITIONS

Fig. 2. Behavior in the experimental situations as a function of conditions in the Schachter and Singer experiments. The left ordinate shows the mean number or euphoric acts initiated by the subjects in the euphoria groups, the right ordinate shows mean number of agreements with the stooge's angry comments for the anger groups (negative values indicate disagreement with the stooge). The figure shows that for both euphoria and anger the number of relevant acts increases as a function of the discrepancy dimension in the "explanation" conditions.

the minimal discrepancy of the Informed subjects, neither were they subjected to the extreme discrepancy of the Misinformed ones. We can therefore talk about a dimension which extends from high (Misinformed) to low (Informed) discrepancy. Thus, Figure 1 suggests that as discrepancy increases so does the likelihood that the subjects will report emotional experiences similar to the behavior exhibited by the stooge. With high discrepancy (Misinformed) they tend to report the same kinds of feelings that are presumably exhibited by the stooge; with low discrepancy (Informed) their reports do not tend to conform to the stooge's behavior.

Similar findings were reported for the observed behavior of the subjects. In Figure 2, the findings for the euphoria

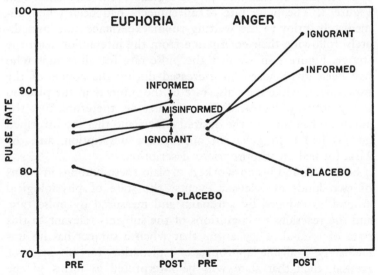

Fig. 3. Changes in pulse rate from a *pre*-experimental to a *post*-experimental measurement. Note that pulse rate increases in all groups that were given adrenalin and decreases in the two placebo groups that were not given adrenalin.

experiments are expressed in terms of euphoric acts initiated by the subjects (indicated on the left ordinate), and the data for the anger group are shown in terms of angry comments by the subjects (right ordinate). Again we find that as the discrepancy dimension (on the abcissa) increases, subjects in the euphoria experiments tend to initiate more euphoric behavior, and subjects in the anger experiments increase the number of angry comments.

Till now we have ignored the question whether there was in fact some increasing discrepancy between what the subjects had been told about the physiological effects of the injection and the effect that the adrenalin actually produced. The only data available to substantiate some congruity or incongruity between instructions and physiological events are shown in Figure 3. The pulse rate of all subjects had been taken immediately prior to the waiting-room experience and immediately following their emergence from the interaction with the stooge. Figure 3 shows that the pulse rate for all groups who had been given adrenalin increased during the course of the experiment, while the pulse rate of the subjects in the placebo group actually decreased. We can assume, therefore, that the adrenalin had some of the desired effects and that the Informed groups had been given an appropriate description, and the Misinformed an inappropriate description.

Schachter and his co-workers explain these findings in terms of two kinds of relevant events: the state of physiological arousal, as induced by adrenalin and measured by pulse rate, and the reactions or cognitions of the subjects relevant to this state of arousal. They argue that when a subject has no immediately available appropriate explanation for his state of arousal, then that state will be interpreted in terms of the particular situation in which he finds himself, that is in terms of reactions appropriate to the situation. We have illustrated this theory in Figure 4 in terms of the present experiments. It was predicted that when subjects were given an injection of adrenalin which produced a state of physiological arousal, but

Fig. 4. The Schachter experiments.

were *not* given an appropriate explanation (as in the Ignorant and, even more so, in the Misinformed group), their reactions would be determined by the environmental situation, that is, by the behavior of the stooge. On the other hand, when a completely appropriate explanation was available, as in the Informed group, no such dependence on the environmental events was expected, and less behavior like the stooge's was anticipated. Finally, given identical explanations and environmental conditions, subjects would describe their feelings as emotional only to the extent that they experienced a state of physiological arousal. This latter prediction suggests that in the Ignorant and Placebo conditions, which were identical as to explanations and environment, a greater degree of emotionality would be found in the Ignorant group that had been given the adrenalin, that is, the physiological arousal.

While the first two predictions tend to be confirmed, the last, especially in reference to the euphoria conditions, apparently fails to be confirmed. However, further analyses of the data were carried out on the basis of the following reasoning. In the Ignorant condition, some of the subjects might have attributed their state of physiological arousal, which all subjects reported, to the injection, even though the experimenter did not mention that possibility. This information was available from the interviews conducted following the experiment, and the subjects in the Ignorant condition who attributed their state of arousal to the injection did in fact turn out to have been significantly less active and angry than those subjects who did not attribute their state of arousal to the injection. Thus when subjects themselves supplied the appropriate explanation, they were self-Informed and in a similar position to the Informed groups, and their behavior also tended to go in the direction of the Informed groups. Not only that, but once the self-Informed subjects had been removed from the analysis of the Ignorant groups, the difference between the Ignorant and the Placebo groups became more marked, and the Ignorant subjects were significantly more active and angry than the Placebo subjects.

A second supplementary analysis concerned the subjects in the Placebo conditions. Here it was argued that just because subjects were not given an injection of adrenalin did not mean that they did not experience some physiological arousal induced by the experimental situation itself. When the subjects in the Placebo condition were divided into two groups, those who showed an increase or no change in pulse rate as against those who showed a decrease in pulse rate, the expected differences in activity and anger again appeared. The Placebo subjects who showed an increase in pulse rate (that is, some degree of physiological arousal) were significantly more active in the euphoria situation and significantly more angry in the anger condition. These findings suggest that the last hypothesis, that emotional behavior is primarily a function of physiological arousal when knowledge and explanation are held constant, is tenable.

Quite apart from the startling effects of the different explanations, a summary of these experiments within the context of the questions we asked on page 279 would read as follows: We do not have to produce different visceral states in order to induce emotions as different as anger and happiness; these different emotions can arise out of the same physiological background. And the deliberate creation of visceral reactions does affect the sheer occurrence of emotional experiences and behavior.

In terms of the James-Cannon controversy, we can say briefly that while it would be difficult to find evidence in these experiments to sustain the belief that emotions are nothing but the perceptions of visceral reactions, James' position that visceral events are a necessary condition for emotional experience or expression finds substantial support. By themselves they do not seem to be sufficient, nor does it appear that different emotions result from different patterns of visceral arousal. However, one other finding is now added to these more historical questions: What a subject is told about his visceral reactions is another apparent determinant of emotional behavior. With the Schachter experiments on hand we can now outline the major variables that are responsible for the production of emotional behavior.

◈ HOW EMOTION IS PRODUCED

We could call this analysis the *juke box theory*, because of certain parallels in the way a juke box operates and the way the human organism apparently produces emotional behavior. We shall begin and end by saying that this juke box model is not supposed to suggest either that people are glorified juke boxes or that the operation of a juke box exhaustively describes the conduct of people in emotional states. The similarity between the two resides in the fact that the operation of a juke box involves two major operations—the insertion of a dime and the selection of a record. Once the dime is inserted, any one of the records stored within the box can be played, but no record is available until the dime is inserted, and furthermore the insertion of the coin does not presuppose the selection of one tune in preference to another. We view the production of emotional behavior as a two-stage process, with the activation of the viscera (possibly the sympathetic nervous system) being similar to the insertion of the dime into the juke box. However, the selection of the record (that is, the kind of emotional behavior that will be produced) is not predetermined by the activation of the physiological responses; it depends, rather, on the pushing of the proper button, which, in the Schachter experiments, is accomplished either by the stooge's behavior or by the explanation. In other words, once the visceral reaction has been activated either the stooge or the experimenter can push the appropriate button to produce the desired emotional behavior. We must immediately deviate from the juke box model to point out that activation (coin insertion) and selection of the emotion (tune selection) are not necessarily independent processes, since the same situation can produce both activation and selection of a particular emotional state, as in Schachter's Placebo groups. The activation need not be produced by adrenalin injected into the subject; emotional situations can also produce the same effect. Having deviated from the juke box model this far, we can say it has served its illustrative purposes and we can return it to the nearest drugstore—where it can serve as a model for dancing behavior. People are not juke boxes.

The notion that visceral arousal serves to activate all possible types of emotional behavior, without selecting any one of them, points to the rather tenuous link between verbal behavior and the private events, such as visceral ones, that control it. Internal visceral cues have some control over verbal behavior— at least to the extent that they are the occasions for people saying that something is going on inside. The degree of specific correspondence between these cues and the verbal behavior is presumably a function of prior learning. Just as we learn that "mansion" is a proper name for a large house and "cottage" an appropriate name for a small house, so we must learn to distinguish between hunger pangs and ulcerative rumblings, between regular and fast heart rates, and possibly even to determine the location of pains. It is self-evident that we learn to use words primarily in social contexts, that parents, teachers, and peers instruct us in the proper use of words. Whenever these words or labels are appropriate to objects and events in the environment, our teachers find it relatively easy to tell us when we are right or wrong. But when the words we are learning are not given in response to objects and events available to everybody else's inspection, that is, when they are given in response to private events known only to each individual user, the task of learning and teaching proper words and labels becomes much more difficult. B. F. Skinner (1945) has discussed the problem of learning words in response to private events, and it is sufficient here to restate and to emphasize the impression all of us carry from common experience: that we are much surer about the proper words, expressions for, and even locations of things such as people and houses than we are about the proper expression, reliability, and clarity of our words for feelings, aches, and pains. The expression, "Something is going on but I don't know what it is," is heard much more frequently in the doctor's office than during an inspection of a new house.

While this analysis is ostensibly concerned with overt verbal behavior—about talking out loud—we shall assume that it applies in the same way to implicit verbal behavior—talking to yourself. Without confusing the discussion of what emotion really is with a discussion of what thinking really is, we shall assume that a large part of thinking is concerned with covert, implicit verbal behavior, with people talking to themselves. Thus, in the Schachter experiments, for example, covert verbal behavior of the order of "My heart is racing," and "I feel hot," can apparently be manipulated by the explanation of the experimenter which either reinforces such behavior ("You will feel hot") or counteracts it ("You will feel numb").

In reference to Schachter's three major independent variables—visceral arousal, stooge behavior, and explanation—the following juke-box-like exposition can be advanced. Whenever there is visceral arousal, all the different verbal and nonverbal responses or behavioral units that have ever been associated with it will be activated or will become available. There are very many of these responses, some of them incompatible, but the most potent seems to be to say that something is going on. At the same time, all the verbal responses about internal private events, and all the emotional responses, such as "My heart is racing" and "I feel angry," are activated to some degree. The visceral arousal is such that no one of these responses is completely determined by it, and, as we shall see on page 326, visceral arousal occurring by itself leads people to say that they feel "as if" they were in an emotional state. The other two independent variables—the occurrence of emotional behavior in the environment and the explanation—determine which of all these many possible responses to the visceral state will become dominant. When the explanation arouses responses congruent with or similar to some of these viscerally determined responses (as in the Informed group), those which are simply descriptive of the visceral state will become dominant. When the explanation is not only incongruous, but actually incompatible with the responses aroused by the internal state (as in the Misinformed group) not only will no response class become dominant, but the descriptive responses(which are incompatible with the explantion) will tend to become less probable. Once the subject finds himself in the presence of the stooge, those responses which are congruent with the stooge's actions will become dominant. Thus, in the Informed group, the explanation has already selected one of the classes of responses activated by the visceral arousal, and the stooge's behavior is ineffective. In the Misinformed group, not only is no response class dominant, but one class—the appropriate explanation—has been reduced in power, and the stooge's behavior becomes the most powerful selector of the remaining responses activated by the visceral arousal.

But why does the subject make a decision at all? Why does he seem to stop considering the possibility that he is in fact euphoric in the presence of the stooge once he has been given the appropriate instructions? We need to invoke some kind of stop rule, some way of explaining why behavior does not continue in an endless running through of all the possible responses that the organism could make in that particular situation. Why does a behavior sequence continue up to a point and then appear—in intuitive terms—to have reached a decision and to terminate in one particular response class?

In searching for stop rules that will explain this phenomenon, we must note first of all that the most frequently observed way of stopping behavior is by reinforcing operations. A description of trial-and-error behavior suggests that the organism engages in behavior which terminates with reinforcement—or, to express it more radically, that an organism under a drive state will engage in behavior until some event reduces that drive state. But, rather than restrict these stop rules to reinforcement operations, we leave the door open to other kinds of events, in our case the occurrences of verbal behavior with maximal or dominant strength. By this we mean that in a situation which is the occasion for a variety of different and generally incompatible responses, the stop rule will be reached when some behavior or response becomes stronger or more probable than all other potential responses. Take the example of a fairly naive observer viewing an abstract painting and being told that it has a title suggesting a common object. He will probably vacillate, maybe somewhat in this fashion: "Looks like nothing in particular, maybe some kind of . . . something moving perhaps—no, that could be low house, and TV antennas—no, looks like horns, could be an electric train— there is movement, maybe an animal, or a car—but those things sticking out could be horns. I guess the closest I can come is a cow." In this case, the final response *cow* was apparently reached after several responses (*movement, horns, movement* again, *animal, horns* again) reinforce the response *cow*, while the other responses do not focus on any particular kind of object or response. Some stop rule was reached when *cow* had become most dominant.

Similarly, in the Schachter studies, when the experimenter suggests that the subject will feel something, he increases the probability that the subject will use the same verbal behavior in response to the internal, visceral cues. The sort of things the Informed subjects are encouraged to tell themselves are responses that have previously occurred in that state. When the sympathetic nervous system has been activated in the past, such responses as "My heart is racing" and "I am sweating," whether correlated with the particular events they refer to or whether in response to a general state of activation, have occurred, and are now made more probable by the instructions of the experimenter. These responses presumably become dominant (much more probable than any other response activated by the visceral reaction), and the stop rule goes into effect; no further trial-and-error behavior, no further explanation will be attempted. In the other groups, however, the explanation does not reinforce any responses previously paired with sympathetic arousal, and no stop rule is invoked until the subject observes the behavior of the stooge. That behavior instructs him that this is a funny (or irritating) situation. Such an instruction has in the past also been associated with the internal cues; it reinforces his euphoric (or angry) behavior, and again the stop rule applies. Thus, given a particular internal state, the personal, private response to it will be a function of the instructions, which include the fact that an injection has taken place, that the experimenter has said something about the effect of the injections, and that the stooge behaves in a certain way.

For further illustration of these factors we can look at another experiment from Schachter's laboratory (Schachter and

Wheeler, 1962). In this study subjects viewed a slapstick movie and were ranked on their degree of obvious amusement while viewing the film and on their subsequent evaluation of the movie. Three groups of subjects were used. On group was given an injection of adrenalin prior to viewing the film, another group was given an injection of saline (placebo), and a third group was given an injection of a tranquilizer (chlorpromazine). The tranquilizer has physiological effects which in general depress sympathetic activity, that is, it acts to some extent in a fashion opposed to that of adrenalin. All of the subjects were given misleading instructions about the purpose of the experiment and none knew what the content of the injection was. As expected, degree of amusement and evaluation of the film varied with degree of physiological (sympathetic) arousal. The adrenalin subjects seemed most amused during the showing of the movie and rated it as funniest, followed by the placebo subjects, with the chlorpromazine subjects in last place. Here again we assume that sympathetic arousal and the instruction, "This is funny" (induced by the presence of a slapstick movie generally considered to be so), have been paired in the past, while sympathetic depression and "funny" verbal behavior have infrequently, if at all, occurred together in the past. Thus the most powerful condition was that in which both sympathetic discharge and the funny movie determined the response, "This is funny"; on the other hand, the internal state in the chlorpromazine group gave no support to that response and it therefore occurred less frequently.

To summarize the different kinds of events that seem to be involved in the production of emotional behavior, we can look at the various antecedent-consequent relations that exist in the emotional complex. In Figure 5 we have used arrows to indicate the direction from some of the antecedent conditions to the consequently produced behavior or reactions.

In the first place we have Environmental conditions—events that are capable of being recorded and transmitted by visual, auditory, and other receptors. For our purposes it is most convenient to think of environmental conditions as including verbal instructions. Environmental variables constitute the main bulk of the psychologist's independent variables, the events that he manipulates to observe their effect on behavior. We shall see shortly that the specification of these events—broadly speaking, the definition of the stimulus—is one of the major problems dividing psychological opinion and demanding our attention. The next class of events of interest are internal visceral reactions, usually related to the arousal of the autonomic nervous system, but including also such skeletal and striped muscle responses as breathing and muscle tension. We assume that the antecedent conditions for this class of events reside in the environmental domain to the extent that certain stimulus conditions lead, innately or through learning, to autonomic or visceral discharge. However, we must also include the possibility that some of the conditions for autonomic arousal may derive from activities of the organism: one can become frightened by one's own actions and thoughts, and certainly some of our own behavior is the occasion for the arousal of the full emotional complex. It is in this sense that emotional behavior has often been spoken of as reverbatory in character, as in the case of the student who goes into an examination in a state of terror, and as a result of the interference of his emotional state finds himself unable to write any coherent answers to the examination questions. The observation of his own incompetence in turn leads to further emotional behavior, and so forth in a rising flood of panic.

We deal, finally, with what could be called the major dependent variables in the emotional complex, so-called emotional behavior, both verbal and nonverbal. In the nonverbal category we can distinguish two kinds of events, none of which are necessarily emotional. On the one hand there is behavior which is merely symptomatic of visceral discharge, such as blushing, blanching, tremor, rapid breathing, crying and—in the case of lower animals and very young children at least—urination and defecation. The other kind of nonverbal emotional behavior runs the gamut from aggressive action, flight, and immobility to rather discrete responses such as facial tics, hand-rubbing, and other signs of nervousness. The most widely studied and intensively discussed emotional behavior is, of course, verbal. This category varies from gross activity such as screaming and whimpering to the fine-grained analysis of introspective reports. In Figure 5 antecedent and consequent variables in everyday

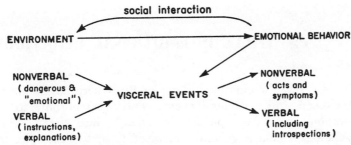

Fig. 5. Some of the variables involved in the emotional complex. Arrows indicate possible antecedent-consequent relations.

emotions are indicated. Apart from the sequence leading from environmental to visceral to behavioral events, there is an important sequence leading from environmental events directly to behavior—and incidentally demonstrated quite clearly in the Schachter experiments. But in addition there is the effect of behavior on visceral events, and finally the effect—at least in the life situation—of emotional behavior on the environment and particularly on the behavior of other people.

Since even this simplified picture of the emotional complex leads to complicated interactions in everyday life, it would be no more reasonable to try to untangle a real life situation in terms of scientific variables than it is reasonable to attempt to analyze the behavior of a single ocean wave in physical variables or the behavior of beef stew in terms of chemical variables. We must, as always in scientific attempts to under-

stand and explain our environment, resort to the laboratory and
the rather esoteric and refined study of a limited number of
variables under limited and controlled conditions. In examining the various events that belong to the emotional complex,
we shall proceed one by one and explore their operation and
definition within three broad areas—environmental, visceral,
and behavioral.

✥ WHAT IS EMOTIONAL BEHAVIOR?

To say that the emotional complex deals with environmental, visceral, and behavioral events contributes nothing to its
definition, apart from putting it squarely into the field of
psychology. Such a general statement fails, for example, to
differentiate emotion from hunger and its relief, which involve
deprivation, stomach contractions, and eating. What we can
do, is to specify the kind of behavior which we want to explore and explain.

For the layman the definition of emotional behavior may
seem to be fairly simple and uncomplicated. We all "know,"
in some sense, what we mean when we say that John is reacting emotionally, that Joan is an actress capable of expressing great emotions, that anger, fear, love, grief and compassion
are emotions. And in light of our inability and reluctance to
define emotion in the preceding pages, we shall let the chapter-
heading category stand, and try to list the sort of behaviors
which we want to call emotional, assuming that we are talking about the same sort of thing that people in general do
when they talk about emotion.

Before going into details of the two major categories of
verbal and nonverbal emotional behavior, we shall point out
two more general aspects of emotional behavior. In the first
place, we are interested in *behavior*—in those activities and
actions of the organism that are observable without the use

of special instruments and that potentially have some effect on the environment. For instance, this limitation excludes heart rate from the behavioral category, because it does not operate directly on the environment. Secondly, emotional behavior seems to have something to do with approach and withdrawal, which makes up a good part of the intuitive "good and bad" dichotomy (cf. Schneirla, 1959).

VERBAL EMOTIONAL BEHAVIOR

There is one kind of verbal behavior that is of particular interest to a psychology of emotion. We often consider a statement emotional if it begins with "I feel" and then makes some reference to unobservable, private events or states. Of particular interest are those phrases that ostensibly make reference to an internal somatic state, and we shall call this referential behavior.

Examples of referential verbal behavior are the usual introspective reports, "My heart is pounding," "I have a heavy feeling in my stomach," "I can feel it in my guts," "I am all raw inside," and so forth—ranging from highly specific reference to analogic and even allegoric talk about one's insides. The extent to which these utterances are actually under internal control will concern us later, but for the time being we can say that this sort of statement is under the control of at least two kinds of events—internal events and environmental nonorganismic events (things that happen outside of our skins, though possibly inside somebody else's). The complexity of this kind of verbal behavior has been barely touched upon by Skinner's discussion (1945) of the kinds of ways in which somebody may, for example, learn to say that his tooth aches. In brief, the problem is that in learning this kind of private-event talk the child—and even adult—is left with relatively little or confusing information as to the appropriate times when such reference is "properly" made. The crux of the matter lies in the behavior of the teacher, the "reinforcing community," in Skinner's terms.

We may teach a child to say that his tooth aches following his pointing to his jaw, or that he should say "I have a stomach ache" when we observe a contingency between large amounts of hot dogs and ice cream consumed and a miserable, feverish-looking boy. Any parent who has observed his child struggle through the distinction between headache and stomach ache or between saying "I am angry" and "I am afraid" is aware of the tenuous connection between specific events and this kind of verbal behavior.

Verbal emotional behavior that is not referential includes a vast array of utterances, primarily used to infer emotional states or reactions from one or another theoretical viewpoint. Thus, "I am definitely never angry" is, for the psychoanalyst, a most important emotional response classified under the rubric of Negation, and possibly used as an index of conflict about hostility or aggression. This kind of classificatory analysis underlies identification of conflict or threat areas by the use of word associations and the analysis of associations in the wider sense. In this connection, verbal behavior is frequently used to infer the stress or threat content of social situations. The appearance of conflict indicators in the associations or speech of a patient in relation to a particular topic, for example, sex or hostility or food, is used to infer an emotional reaction to sexual, hostile, or edible stimuli. We must distinguish, of course, between a subject's emotional response to a particular set of environmental conditions and the appearance of conflict or emotion when talking about a particular topic. For example, it may be the subject matter that is conflict-arousing—that is, it may be unpleasant to talk *about* aggression —but the subject may not necessarily react emotionally to an aggressive situation.

At the present time much work is being done on the analysis of verbal behavior in one particular emotional situation—psychotherapy. Mahl has shown that speech disturbances such as repetition, stuttering, slips of the tongue, and omissions provide a reliable measure of a patient's degree of conflict. When the patient comes near to or touches upon a conflictful topic these indices increase and the manner in which he talks about it may be used as an index of his degree of emotionality about such a topic. Other psychologists and psychiatrists (for example, Dollard and Auld, 1959) have used varieties of different ways of classifying verbal behavior and disturbances of speech to infer emotional upset or anxiety.

Unfortunately, most of the work done in this area is of an inferential character, but this important first step in the classification of verbal behavior should eventually lead to its study under controlled conditions. In this way we will be more readily able to answer questions about the contingencies, prior experiences, and conditions under which this emotional verbal behavior occurs.

Before we proceed with a discussion of nonverbal emotional behavior, we shall consider a persistent challenge confronting psychology and apparently left out of our discussion of emotion—the appeal to private emotional experience. It is implicitly included in our class of verbal behavior, and is discussed here not because it represents a major theoretical position, but rather because of its apparent intuitive appeal and its opposition to an objective psychology.

THE PRIVATE EXPERIENCE OF EMOTION

Philosophy and psychology have always been concerned with one of the most puzzling problems confronting the student of man: how to deal with private experiences, with daily phenomena available only to the individual and quite refractory to analysis or adequate communication. This concern has given rise, among others, to the phenomenological point of view which insists that all knowledge and science are essentially based on private phenomena and experiences. Somewhat simplified, this position asserts that only through the analysis of private experiences can we ever achieve an understanding of the world around us, particularly that only introspection and the examination of private phenomena can lead to a reasonable and useful psychology.

If it were not for the rather extravagant recent claims of some psychologists and psychiatrists influenced by modern existentialism (cf. May *et al.*, 1958), one might have thought that psychology had outgrown the hoary arguments about the "essentials" of "real" experience. The history of psychology since Wundt has been a history of a more and more successful divorce from philosophically posed and dialectically argued pseudo-problems about experience (cf. Mandler and Kessen, 1959). At least two developments have obscured this progress: on the one hand phenomenologically oriented, existentialist philosophies have suggested a relevance of their speculations to modern psychology; on the other hand a general and rather aimless movement has criticized contemporary psychology for its adherence to physicalistic methods presumable irrelevant to its subject matter. We need not be concerned whether there is anything wrong with modern psychology—there well may be—but rather whether the knights in nineteenth-century armor have a viable alternative to offer. It is of particular interest to us here, because it is the psychology of emotion that they have often considered to be their particular bailiwick (cf. Sartre, 1948).

Briefly, modern phenomenologists and existentialists are concerned with the definition—for each individual—of the essential, basic, meaningful, and almost palpable nature of his private experiences. This is to be made possible by such techniques as "the unbiased contemplation of phenomena, putting aside any intellectual consideration" (May *et al*, 1958). We must stress that nobody in modern psychology denies the facts of private experiences (cf. Skinner, 1945)—this is a frequent accusation—and also that the relevance of these speculations about private experiences to psychology is most obscure. Let it be noted that Husserl, one of the patron saints of the movement, took care to say in the second edition of his major work that his phenomenology should not be classified with psychology in its traditional meaning (Welch, 1941). More to the point, the claims of the modern phenomenologist and existentialist *for psychology* can be disposed of in terms of two general arguments.

First, it is unreasonable to expect that private experience can ever be anything but that. It becomes public, that is, comprehensible to others, only after it has been put into some sort of communicable symbolism, namely language. A psychology based upon an ineffable phenomenology is not only not psychology, but it is and must remain private property and therefore inexpressible either by or to a psychiatrist or psychologist. Is private experience inexpressible? Some philosophers and most intelligent laymen will agree that it is. I cannot possible use the rather crude instrument of language to express the myriad impressions, feelings, ideas, notions, and emotions that flood my private screen. I can attempt to approach it, but will forever feel frustrated in trying to do these feelings full justice. If private experience can only be communicated through language, then the events that a phenomenologist contemplates are no different from those that a psychologist investigates—the verbal behavior of his subjects, patients, and friends. Our data are identical; therefore the difference must lie in what we do with them.

What inferences can we draw from the mutterings of our subjects? For the objective psychologist they are manifold and depend upon his particular theoretical predilections. For most phenomenologists, however, they are to be used to infer the essence of the private experience. The existentialist psychiatrist implies, for example, that by empathy and experience he can infer somebody else's private experience, particularly by reference to his own. And here lies the second fallacy of the position. I can only make inferences about your private world if I can be fairly certain that its qualities and nuances are similar—nay, identical—to mine under the same circumstances. If this assumption is true a phenomenological psychology is still possible. But common sense argues against it, and

Titchener's vain attempts to find the elements common to all human experience (even in rather limited and simple experimental situations) seem to doom it.

The remainder is words. Words spoken by our subjects and theoretical words spoken by those trying to understand them. Different psychologists have different notions about the structure underlying these observable behaviors; the phenomenologists defend the primacy of only one of these explanations.

NONVERBAL EMOTIONAL BEHAVIOR

In talking about nonverbal behavior a distinction needs to be made which was not relevant to the problem of verbal behavior; that between respondent and operant behavior. Respondent behavior is occasioned by known stimuli; typical examples are cases of Pavlovian or classical conditioning—salivation in response to meat powder, the eyeblink in response to a puff of air, the knee jerk in response to a tap below the knee, and a whole variety of visceral (autonomic) responses to painful, stressful stimuli. Operant or instrumental behavior, on the other hand, does not necessarily have any known antecedent stimuli and is affected primarily by reinforcement operations following its occurrence. Operant behavior includes of course verbal behavior and is most typical of human behavior in general, its major characteristic being that it acts upon the environment and is modified by it (Skinner, 1938). Emotional behavior typically includes both respondent and operant classes, and the distinction becomes somewhat blurred at times when respondents are affected in appearance and rate of production by environmental events (reinforcement operations).

In any case, we can talk abut operant or instrumental emotional behavior which includes responses we usually call *aggresive, seductive, hostile, fearful,* and so forth. The major difficulty in classifying this kind of behavior is that there is little we can say about it beyond the rather intuitive enumeration indicated in the previous sentence. There are few super-

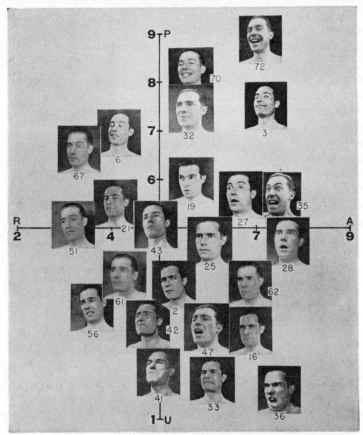

Fig. 6. The location of typical pictures from Schlosberg's study (1952) along the U–P (Unpleasantness-Pleasantness) and A–R (Attention-Rejection) dimensions. For example. picture 36 is rated high on both Unpleasantness and Attention, picture 51 is high on Rejection but neutral in reference to U–P, and picture 72 is high on Pleasantness and fairly high on Attention.

ordinate theories that allow us to construct a rigorous taxonomy of behavior. Even within psychoanalytic theory and the analysis of verbal emotional behavior, the categories tend to be enumerative rather than theoretical. What we mean by enumerative is that categories are listed and established by example; for instance, *aggressive* includes any behavior that tends to hurt other people, or keeps them from behaving in a certain way, or is designed to punish something they did, and so forth. But there is seldom reference to the relations among the things listed. While some personality theories, psychoanalytic theory in particular, have taken steps to bring this classificatory behavior into some kind of theoretical frame, relatively little agreement can be found across theories and among different psychologists on the definition of classes of behavior called emotional. What agreement there is appeals to an intuitive understanding of the common language, and there is of course a good deal of agreement in the way we use some of these emotional words, if for no other reason than that we learn these terms rather uniformly within our language culture. A perusal of the Schachter studies, for example, persuades us that people can generally agree about what kind of behavior to categorize as euphoric or as angry.

Respondent emotional behavior appears to be quite another kettle of fish. Take expressive behavior as an example, and we find that facial expressions can reliably be classified into categories of different emotional words and even into major superordinate dimensions. The extensive work done by Schlosberg and his associates (cf. Woodworth and Schlosberg, 1954) indicates that subjects can classify facial expressions quite reliably and that two major dimensions emerge from this classification. Schlosberg (1952) has called these dimensions Pleasantness-Unpleasantness and Attention-Rejection. Judgments of pictures of facial expressions can be usefully assigned to points defined by these two dimensions. In Figure 6 we have shown a by now classical arrangement of pictures within this dual dimension. It may be useful to the reader to examine a few of these pictures and evaluate his own judgments of their position in relation to the two major axes. The names given the two axes are in a sense quite arbitrary. "Pleasant-unpleasant" and "attending-rejecting" make some intuitive sense, but Schlosberg could just as well have called them Factor A and Factor B. The important conclusion is that most emotional expressions can be classified by the use of these two factors. It is worthy of note that facial expressions of emotion appear to be unlearned. "There are certain basic unlearned patterns of facial expression and they show up in 'real' emotional situations" (Woodworth and Schlosberg, 1954, p. 131). This conclusion is based on the observation of facial expression in blind children, who could not have learned them on an imitative basis. There is still the possibility, unchecked at present, that certain facial expressions are learned by sheer reinforcement in the appropriate situations. As long as this possibility is not eliminated, we can merely say tentatively that some aspects of the facial expression of emotion seem to be unconditioned responses in the respondent or classical sense, while other aspects fall into the operant category.

Given the encouraging results on the judgment of facial expression, it is rather surprising that facial expression has rarely been used in controlled studies of emotion, that is, as a dependent variable in conjunction with some of the other emotional variables. While judgments of facial expression have been made under different conditions, such judgments are usually made by naive subjects in order to investigate some aspect of emotional or social perception. But if people can make such reliable judgments, then psychologists also should be able to do so and to use expressive behaviors more consistently in the laboratory. We might then have a reliable and useful dependent variable for the study of the whole emotional complex.

The last and quite clearly respondent category of nonverbal behavior comprises symptomatic behavior correlated with respondent visceral events. It includes some obvious responses such as blushing, incontinence, and the eyeblink. Of particular interest is the startle response, usually evoked by strong and unexpected stimulation. It has a very typical pattern for most people, and beyond that seems to be typical of all mammals. The most extensive study of the startle response, by Landis and Hunt (1939), suggests that the eyeblink is one of the most diagnostic of its components, and it also persists the longest beyond adaptation to the startling situation. The rest of the very stable startle pattern includes widening of the mouth, head movements, and muscle contractions. It is a miniature representation of much of emotional behavior, ". . . in a single brief episode . . . [it] presents most of the features one finds in the more protracted emotional states; it shows an increased general level of activation and a pattern of response, involving very nearly all parts of the body" (Woodworth and Schlosberg, 1954, p. 185).

Much of our discussion of emotional behavior has assumed the antecedent presence or operation of environmental or visceral conditions. We shall note presently that the process is quite circular—the definition and enumeration of environmental events that are said to be emotional usually depend upon the diagnosis of emotional behavior.

 # THE EMOTIONAL STIMULI

How do we know that a particular environmental situation is emotional? Perhaps the best we can do is to say that someone, or even everyone, reacts emotionally in the presence of this or that stimulus. However, even when we can assert that a particular situation invariably elicits emotional reactions from all organisms (or, to be somewhat cautious, from a particular species) we are still only asserting the character of the stimulus situation on the basis of organismic response. At the present time there is no classification of emotional stimuli independent of an organism's response. Thus, while a concept formation task, or a maze, or a ratio schedule, or a projective test may be defined somewhat independently of the response of the organism to be studied, no such distinction is possible in the field of emotion. Even though psychologists and others have tried to define stress stimuli, for example, they always assume some invariance in the subject's response to it. To say that an electric shock is a stress stimulus is to say that it elicits stress reactions; if, for a particular subject, it should perchance not show such reactions, we would say that for that subject electric shock is not stressful—it is not an emotional stress condition.

We can, however, make the distinction between unconditioned or unlearned stress stimuli which are correlated with emotional or stress reactions from all members of the group of organisms we are studying, and conditioned or learned stimuli which not only show variability in emotional response, but also apparently produce different kinds of reactions from different subjects.

The first class of stimuli, the unlearned conditions—better called the invariant conditions—include the ubiquitous painful stimuli as well as a wide variety of species-specific fear stimuli. For example, we know that signs of distress may appear in many kinds of animals at the appearance of a predator, for example, hawks for ducklings, owls for chaffinches, and so forth. Some of the more tender emotions—such as sexual behavior or smiling—also seem to be under the control of unlearned stimulus conditions. Contemporary ethological research (see also Professor Hess's contribution in this volume) has only scratched the surface of specifying the wide variety of emotional behavior evoked in a variety of organisms under conditions that are fairly independent of previous experience.

What has probably influenced modern conceptions of invariant physiological response more than anything else is W. B. Cannon's notion of the emergency reaction, primarily a response determined by the release of adrenalin into the blood-

stream (Cannon, 1932). The subsequent—primarily sympathetic—effects and the rather vague antecedent conditions
often referred to as tissue injury have given psychologists their
primary vocabulary about stress (the response) and stressors
(the invariant conditions). Dominant among these stressors has
been the stimulation of pain receptor or free nerve endings,
which usually elicits the emergency reaction. However, other
stimulus conditions, such as loss of support and sudden intense
stimulation (the startle stimulus), also seem to elicit this discharge from the autonomic nervous system. All in all, physiologists and neurologists have provided us with some enumeration
and even categorization of the kinds of events that are responsible for the visceral actions that are apparently part of our
emotional complex.

When we come to the problem of variable stimuli—of conditions that vary from subject to subject and from situation
to situation in their ability to elicit either overt emotional
behavior or visceral response—we find ourselves with both
feet firmly planted in the mid-air of ignorance. Essentially, we
are concerned with the variables that are responsible for "good"
and "bad" judgments in a vague sense, with "approach" and
"withdrawal" in a more servicable language, and with the
major relations between environment and response in general.
While it can be said with great facility that we are concerned
here with simple conditioning, that anything that has been
paired with the invariant stressor will, under the proper conditions, produce a conditioned emotional response (behavioral
or visceral), such statements are little more than affirmations of
belief with little solid basis of experimental prediction and verification. It is a problem which long ago concerned Cannon, and
which is touched upon by the Schachter experiments. The question is this: How can the same environmental input produce
different kinds of emotional reactions depending on the presence or absence of other environmental conditions? Or: How
can the index of stress (for example, visceral), which tells us
whether the preceding stimulus has been a stressor or not, be

apparently identical and yet produce different kinds of emotional behavior? Why does a bear represent a potent stressor, yet lose that function when a simple cage is put around him (or us)? Why does loss of support and the subsequent autonomic reaction often lead to panic yet apparently induce euphoria (at least in some people) when it is experienced on a roller coaster? The caged bear and roller coaster effects are only partially answered by Schachter's expirements, which suggest the double controlling action of environmental and visceral events. In the "caged bear" situation, however, the bear serves two functions: he may be the signal for emotional behavior and also serve as an adequate stimulus for visceral response, but neither of these response clusters appears in any great force when the cage is introduced. The roller coaster phenomenon is probably closer to the Schachter situation, in that the same kind of visceral response will lead to different felt or observed emotion under different conditions. On the basis of past experience it might be assumed that roller coasters in fair grounds just do not lead to fearful emotional behavior. We are not very close to being able to say why this is so, any more than Schachter is able to say specifically why the euphoric situation is euphoric—except by demonstration and intuitive agreement.

What does seem to be the case—and this does not answer any questions but merely poses the problem—is that some categorization takes place immediately following the registration of external events (cf. Bruner, 1957). Such categorization of input, which assigns "bear in the open" to a different category from "bear in cage," is a long way from simple stimulus generalization and conditioning theory; it requires a rather important psychological effort yet to come—the determination of the laws under which such categorization develops, and how such categorization can be predicted from the knowledge of the past history of the organism. To say that there is such categorization or coding asserts the problem area, just as saying that people appraise situations as "good" or "bad" raises the same question. A proper answer is a theory about the mechanism that does the coding or appraising. That we do not have as yet.

We do have one solution for predicting the categorization of emotional situations. This purely operational solution lies in the area of social induction. There is good reason to believe that the most powerful environment for the induction of certain kinds of behavior is to have that behavior exhibited by others. The Schachter experiments show quite clearly that people tend to be euphoric in the presence of a euphoric stooge, that they are angry in the presence of an angry stooge. Recent experiments by Nowlis on mood demonstrate the general point that the mood represented by the majority of a social group influences the mood of all of its members.

The three major categories available to the psychologists for the production of emotional behavior thus are tissue injury or painful stimulation, social induction, and a vast category of presumptive stressors or emotional situations, mostly social in nature.

 # PHYSIOLOGY AND THE PSYCHOLOGY OF EMOTION

We stated earlier, perhaps somewhat brashly, that the physiological or visceral events relevant to a *psychology* of emotion are those that a subject can discriminate. We can now elaborate on this statement.

Physiology and physiological psychology have long been concerned with their own chapter-heading problems in the field of emotion. More than in many other fields, the borderlines between the physiology and the psychology of emotion are blurred, and even the most intrepid philosophical surveyor shrinks from drawing exact boundaries between these two areas of theory and research. In order to evaluate the role of physiological variables in a psychology of emotion, a distinction will be useful between physiological variables *per se* and psychologically functional physiological variables.

Physiological variables as such cover the whole spectrum of events which physiologists and physiological psychologists consider their proper area of interest. They include, for example, recordings of the electrical activity of the brain (electroencephalography), the effects of the ablation of certain parts of the cortex, the measurement of pulse rate as a result of adrenalin injections, and the conduction of impulses from receptors. In short, whatever the chapter heading of physiology in the book of science subsumes—and again the boundaries are not too clear—is proper to this pigeonhole.

Psychologically functional physiological variables are, of course, subsumed under the above heading, but they form a much smaller collection. They refer only to those physiological variations which have demonstrable causal effects on behavior, the chapter heading reserved for the psychologist. As psychologists, concerned with the necessary and sufficient antecedents of behavior, we may restrict our curiosity about physiological variables to those events that make a difference, that in fact affect behavioral events. Thus, for example, variations in cholesterol level in the blood is of great interest to some physiologists; however, at the present time there is no evidence that such variations have any behavioral effects. Curiously, this particular variable may be a function of certain behavioral events such as choice of diet, but here we are talking about the reverse of the topic of interest, namely a physiologically functional psychological variable.

Briefly then, a psychology of emotion must pay attention to physiological variables to the extent that they affect our dependent variables—certain verbal and nonverbal behaviors classified as emotional. On the other hand all of psychology can be enriched by a better knowledge of the neurophysiological processes that mediate between input and output.

Before we investigate what some of the functional physiological variables might be, a word about correlated and controlling variables. By correlated variables we mean those events that may appear together, but about which no statements can be made as to which one controls or affects the other. By controlling variables we mean those observable events for which it can be shown that the presence of one or more of them is either necessary or sufficient for variation in some behavior to occur. We may call this correlational as against causal analysis, but for the present purposes correlation and control will adequately convey the sense of our distinction. In the case of physiological variables this distinction has frequently been overlooked. For example, it has been demonstrated that subjects who are more disturbed by sexual stimuli show greater *increases* in body temperature than subjects who are less disturbed by such material, and that subjects who are disturbed by aggressive material similarly show greater *decreases* in body temperature (Mandler *et al.*, 1961). We are not able to say at present which variable is controlling the other. All we know is that they seem to occur together, and it is quite possible that one or more other variables may singly or in conjunction be responsible for the correlations between disturbance and body temperature. Similarly, we may show that under experimental conditions designed to produce anger a group of subjects exhibits a different pattern of physiological reaction from the pattern exhibited under conditions designed to produce fear (Ax, 1953). However, this permits us only to say that the experimental conditions are *physiologically* functional variables. In the absence of showing how these different conditions produce different behavior in subjects—differences in report and other behavioral indices of fear and anger—we cannot assume that the *physiological* variations function as controlling variables over angry and fearful behavior. Such a demonstration would require the production of the physiological changes under environmentally identical conditions. What a correlational physiological variable may permit us to do—in the absence of showing controlling properties—is to use it as an index. For example, subjects may always show a certain correlation between heart rate and fear; in that case we may use the physiological event—epiphenomenal though it might be— as an additional index of the emotion *fear* without assuming any controlling or causal relations between the two sets of events. Unfortunately the evidence for specific physiological variables that control behavior is rather meager. We have already seen that this was one of the major issues on which Cannon attacked James' theory of emotion. In order for emotion to be satisfactorily reduced to "nothing but" the perception of visceral and muscular changes, we would have to demonstrate specific differences in the physiological conditions prior to the occurrence of various emotional behavior. Thirty-five years after Cannon's statement that all emotions seem to have similar, if not identical, visceral antecedents, no serious argument can be produced to challenge him, though data available from some very few studies have shown different physiological patterns *correlated* with different emotional behaviors.

One of these studies is the experiment by Ax, described above, on the differentiation of fear and anger. And even this correlational study has not yet been replicated—one study even showing the absence of the kinds of patterns that would be predicted from Ax's data (Kahn, 1960). In another study Wolf and Wolff were able to show that a patient whose stomach wall was exposed by a fistula showed different visceral reactions (observed on the stomach lining) under conditions of anger and fear. However, the fact that these authors could not differentiate any other reactions and that they too fail to establish any controlling connection weakens the specific Jamesian argument even further. And while other experimenters have been able to demonstrate some physiological differentiation associated with such emotions as disgust (Brunswick, 1924) and startle (Landis and Hunt, 1939), the question about the control of emotional behavior by physiological variables remains open.

If we restrict ourselves to the correlation question—to what

extent emotional behavior (verbal and otherwise) and physiological indices are correlated—the results are more encouraging, even though our conclusions need to be tempered with
caution. Apart from the studies which have investigated the
pattern of physiological activity correlated with different emotional states, the most intensive work in this area has been concerned with the relationship between verbal response and the
psychogalvanic response (PGR) which is complexly related to
activities of the sweat glands. In these studies the physiological
response, the PGR, has frequently been used as an index of
emotional response. This index function actually resulted in
psychologists putting more faith in the appearance of the PGR
as an index of emotional behavior than they were willing to put
in subjects' verbal behavior, be it in the form of rating the
emotionality of environmental events such as emotionally-
loaded words or in the form of the content of free associations
to such events. This development was particularly apparent
in the so-called studies of learning without awareness in which
the PGR response to stimuli presented at or near the apparent
visual threshold appeared to be a more sensitive measure of a
subject's response than was his verbal reaction. However, more
recent evidence suggests that, whereas the two measures are
correlated, "there is no convincing evidence that the human
organism can ... differentially respond [with the PGR] to
external stimuli that are at an intensity level too low to elicit
a discriminated verbal report . . . [A] verbal report is as sensitive an indicator of perception as any other response that has
been studied" (Eriksen, 1960).

If we ask not about relative sensitivity of the two indices,
but rather about the relation between them, the evidence for
such a correlation is fairly clear. Hsü showed that subjects'
ratings or evaluations of words were correlated with their
PGR reaction to these words, and recently Traxel demonstrated a highly reliable linear relation between emotional
judgments and the accompanying PGR.

We have already indicated that there is presumptive evidence that referential behavior is under the control of visceral events. We might then assume that the investigation of the relation between actual physiological events and the verbal behavior which makes reference to it will more directly substantiate a relation between controlling physiological variables and subsequent behavior. In other words, are not statements like "I have a tense feeling in my chest" or "I feel my heart racing" under the control of events in the chest and the heart? Actually, we are not able to assume any more control—without relevant research—than in the previous cases. For example, someone may learn to make statements about his internal private events under the control of environmental stimuli or irrelevant internal stimuli. Thus, I could say, "I am blushing," in an embarrassing situation without showing any signs of peripheral vasodilation. Or I may have learned to talk about tenseness in my stomach in a stress situation without stomach events exerting any influence on such a remark. However, the investigation of these relations falls properly within the area of emotion as we have defined it.

It is possible to obtain fairly reliable estimates as to what extent people notice or discriminate their internal visceral events. Such ratings show remarkable individual differences, varying from people who rarely if ever notice their guts acting up to others who report that their insides appear to be in a constant state of turmoil. When these reports about habitual perceptions of visceral events are compared with actual levels of physiological reaction in a stress situation, we find that at the extreme ends (that is, people who report very little or very much of such goings-on) there are rather striking differences in over-all physiological activity. However, when the full range of individual differences is taken into account the relation between report and measured activity is positive but of rather small magnitude (Mandler, Mandler, and Uviller, 1958; Mandler and Kremen, 1958).

It is noteworthy that in these and other studies a composite measure of several physiological indices (such as heart rate, blood flow, sweating, and finger temperature) is usually a better index of a subject's report of visceral activity than is any single such measure, or even the relation between a single measure such as heart rate and the rating of heart activity. Thus there is presumptive evidence that if people react to anything referentially in their visceral upheaval, it is likely to be a rather global, general condition of arousal. It is exactly such general sympathetic arousal that Schachter and his group produced by the injection of adrenalin, and that had the striking effects discussed earlier.

It seems reasonable to say that at the present state of knowledge the apparent controlling visceral events are rather diffuse and global in character and that little, if any, evidence is available that more detailed or discrete internal events actually control behavior. In one small study in which an attempt was made to make behavior contingent upon small changes in heart rate, no evidence of a subject's ability to make such a discrimination was found (Mandler and Kahn, 1960). In this study a subject was asked to guess which of two lights in front of him would be lighted in any one trial. Unknown to the subject one of the lights went on when his heart rate increased at least two beats per minute, the other when it decreased by the same amount. After 5,000 such trials there was no evidence that the subject was able to make such a discrimination. We suggest that if such a lack of discrimination should hold for all or most people, then no referential response could be made to small changes in visceral activity.

We have now returned to the problem posed by our initial assertion that for physiological events to control behavior effectively they must be discriminable. How do we go from a subject's inability to make a discrimination between two lights that are under the control of his heart rate to the sweeping statement that he therefore could not make referential verbal statements about changes in heart rate of the order of two beats per minute?

The assumption underlying this assertion is rather simple.

If any response can be brought under the control of a particular stimulus condition of input, then all responses in the organism's repertory can be brought under the control of such conditions. The only reservation that needs to be made is that no incompatible responses should be involved in such an operation. If this assumption sounds rather sweeping, some reflection on generally accepted phenomena leads us to the conclusion that it has lurked in the background of psychology for quite some time.

In experiments on operant conditioning or instrumental learning, animals of various phyletic levels have been required to perform responses ranging fairly widely across their repertory. The white rat alone has had to swim, jump, run, push, stand still, raise a paw, crouch, scratch, fight, and copulate, and the pigeon has had to peck, turn, dance, and play ping pong, in order to earn their meager pittance. The things people have had to do, in and out of the laboratory, in order to be reinforced staggers the imagination. But failure to obtain satisfactory learning has usually been blamed on the discriminability of the stimulus. While psychologists have occasionally concerned themselves with the ease of elicitation or learning of a response—the problem of "how to do it" rather than "when to do it" (Mandler, 1954)—these cases are more concerned with the availability of the response pattern than with a negation of our general statement above. Such a negation would involve the assertion that there are some responses which cannot be brought under the control of certain stimuli. In the absence of such specific assertions in the psychological literature, we may assume that our generalization—that any response may be brought under the control of a previously discriminated stimulus—not only is not startling, but rather underlies much of current psychological research. The only restriction that needs to be placed on this suggestion is concerned with the conditions under which a response can be brought under control. It is quite obvious that all discriminated stimuli do not control all possible behavior, and that such control is only possible when an experimenter can produce the appropriate reinforcement contingencies; in other words, the control has to be taught. Such teaching involves the necessary discrimination by the experimenter or observer of the controlling conditions. Assuming that he has this, we can amend our initial statement to read: If an observer can discriminate the conditions that control one kind of behavior, then those conditions can control any other kind of behavior of the subject.

The next step is simple. If any stimulus—internal or external—controls any emotional behavior, such as laughter, hyperactivity, aggression, or crying, then it could *in principle* also control verbal behavior. We can therefore assume that all stimuli that control emotional behavior are in principle capable of controlling referential verbal behavior. What is more important is the corollary that if any stimulus controls emotional behavior it must be discriminable—with discriminability always defined by the differential occurrence of behavior —verbal or other.

The major problem with which we are faced is the identification of these psychologically functioning internal stimuli. To say that they are in principle discriminable does not tell us— as experimenters and explainers—what they are, where they are located (in terms of receptor stimulation) or how we can experimentally isolate them. To say that it is in principle possible to have a subject make referential verbal responses to the kind of internal events that control grief, humor, euphoria, and anger brings us no closer to the experimental production of these events. For the time being, we can only say that these events are at least consequent to the activation of the sympathetic nervous system (as in the Schachter studies). Technological advances in the externalization of these events by modern physiological techniques may bring the day closer when we can specify more exactly the internal events that are not only discriminable by the organism but also are necessary or sufficient conditions for the occurrence of emotional behavior.

One final word on the possible controlling physiological events. While it is quite clear that the only events that could possibly control emotional behavior are those which activate receptors, it is not at all certain whether we know what classes of visceral activity actually have consequences on the receptors of the organism. Thus, it is fairly certain that changes in stomach peristalsis are discriminable and that gross changes in heart rate are also discriminable; it is not at all clear whether the PGR can be discriminated, or for that matter small changes in blood pressure or peripheral blood flow. This problem becomes fairly serious in connection with the PGR and the measurement of activation. There is no present evidence that changes in the PGR can be discriminated by human subjects. The measures of electrical resistance of the skin (PGR) may therefore be adequate additional indices of activation, but we cannot infer that they represent any causal influence on human behavior.

ACTIVATION AND EMOTION

The mention of the PGR and activation brings us to a general concept of activation which has become fashionable in psychophysiological circles in recent years. Some of the early discussions of activation have much of the flavor of the "nothing but" approaches to emotion. Duffy, as early as 1932, suggested the replacement of the term *emotion* by *arousal*, and Lindsley in the *Handbook of Experimental Psychology* in 1951 comes close to a similar suggestion. Woodworth and Schlosberg (1954) tend to evade the issue by suggesting that we talk about activation rather than emotion without necessarily insisting that one word replace the other. We have already seen that such attempts at "nothing but" explanations are still tied up in the search for a theory of emotion, whereas we should be trying to specify the variables that apply to emotional behavior.

The activation concept has of course a very respectable place in a psychology of emotion. Activation is usually defined as a continuum involving activity of the cerebral cortex (measured by the EEG), degree of muscle tension, and, at the behavioral level, stretching from sleep to violent motion. In modern activation theory, level of activation is usually related neurologically to the activity of the ascending reticular activating system (for an extended discussion of these concepts the reader is referred to Lindsley [1951], Woodworth and Schlosberg [1954], and Malmo [1959]). For our present purposes it is generally accepted that so-called emotional behavior occurs concomitantly with high levels of activation, and that different emotions, for example, happiness, anger, and rage, may be assigned various positions on the continuum. To the extent that activation involves recruitment and arousal of the sympathetic nervous system, such a position is quite reasonable, but it does not do the major job for us—it does not exhaustively explain the events that control emotional behavior. We may say that one of the necessary conditions is an activated organism, and we may even take one step further and assume some correspondence (though not identity) between the activation concept and the drive concept in modern learning theory and thus make contact between our problem area and motivational theory and problems. But the statement that emotion usually involves activation does not of course imply that activation usually involves emotion. Thus, a man trying to lift a two-hundred-pound weight is quite activated, but it would stretch our chapter heading quite a bit to say that he is necessarily in an emotional state. The general notion that activation is necessary for all organized behavior has recently been questioned by the demonstration that discriminative operant behavior can occur during sleep, that is, under very low levels of activation (Granda and Hammack, 1961).

Finally, there are still many problems involved in the measurement and definition of activation. While EEG and muscle tension indices seems to be fairly reliable, it is rather difficult to specify any single index of visceral activation which is our major interest. Not only is the PGR unreliable—adrenalin even seems to inhibit it (Darrow, 1936)—but any other single measure of autonomic activation has to be considered with caution on two grounds. First, there is now clear evidence that people differ in their patterns of physiological activity (Lacey and Lacey, 1958). One person may typically show his greatest degree of activation in heart rate, while another may be consistently low in heart rate, but reliably activated in surface body temperature. Lacey has even suggested that the best measure of arousal for any one person would be the relative strength of his single most active index of physiological activity. Second, we have already indicated that different situations may have different physiological effects, as in the Ax study, and thus any single measure of sympathetic activation would be inadequate to rank different emotional states. We shall have occasion to return to the problem of activation briefly in our discussion of individual differences.

THE PSYCHOLOGY OF THE PHYSIOLOGY OF EMOTION

We now enter a rather tricky area of discussion: the specification of the variables that produce the physiological events which in turn control emotional behavior. Having concluded in the previous sections that we know very little about the physiological events themselves, it is difficult, to say the least, to discuss the processes which control these unknown events; we know much in general and little in particular about these processes. In general it is quite clear that classical Pavlovian or respondent conditioning can adequately handle the problem of visceral arousal. From the beginnings of research on conditioning, the visceral responses of the organism have been a favorite target of experimentation. Recent Russian research (for example, Bykov, 1957) has indicated that a host of different physiological reactions ranging from kidney reactions to insulin secretion, and covering most of the physiological events which we have mentioned heretofore, can be brought under the control of environmental stimuli by pairing these with the unconditioned stimuli for the visceral events. As a matter of fact, the evidence is by now so clear and overwhelming, that the process whereby situations arouse visceral emotional responses, whether it be through first, second, or even higher order conditioning, need not be debated any longer. Important details about the parameters of such processes are still in doubt, but the basic psychological—if not the physiological—mechanisms linking environment and visceral response are fairly well known.

Our question, however, about the conditioning of the psychologically *functional* visceral events awaits the identification of those events. We might speculate that the conditioning of any single physiological response or organ is unlikely to be basic to our interest in a psychology of emotion. We have already seen that different situations may arouse different visceral activities, but we have been unable to establish that those activities are the specific controlling events of emotional behavior. On the other hand, we have suggested that the internal visceral activity of interest is likely to be a rather diffuse general activation of the sympathetic nervous system. Little is known about the spread of conditioning from one organ to the other, about which organ is involved in such a process, or about the conditioning of large blocks or areas of visceral activity at one time.

There is one general condition under which such pervasive conditioning might take place, and that is during infancy. The autonomic nervous system of the young child during the first few weeks of life is extremely labile and shows rather extreme swings in a variety of organ systems. Respiration varies from very fast to very slow rates; the heart rate, even under slight stimulation, varies from 50 to 200 beats per minute; and other organ systems show similar variability. Under these conditions, pairing of stimuli in the environment with such a labile and variable state of the organism may well be the basis of the kind of conditioning that is necessary to produce diffuse visceral discharge.

Another set of conditions appropriate to our requirements are those situations which innately discharge adrenalin into the blood stream. During early infancy these appear to be the stimulation of free nerve endings (pain), loss of support, and some high levels of stimulation (for example, noise). There are also various species-specific events, such as a hawk-like figure for young ducklings, that produce the sort of distress that may be associated with the release of adrenalin into the blood stream. Once the release of adrenalin has been conditioned to environmental events, we have a situation similar to the Schachter studies where adrenalin was injected directly into the blood stream.

While the effect of conditioned stimuli on visceral reaction, often subsumed under the topics of conditioned pain, fear, and anxiety, has been studied extensively, such studies have, with minor exceptions, been restricted to single organ systems, particularly the PGR. However, until we know the effective internal events for emotional behavior, even more general studies can be only suggestive. The only advantage of thus putting the cart before the horse is that we may get a general idea what characteristics of the physiological cart must be hitched to the behavioral horse.

 # JAMES AND CANNON RECONSIDERED: A RECAPITULATION

Let us now look back at a persisting problem: To what extent are visceral events necessary for the production of emotional states? Assuming that we know what the psychologically functional physiological variables are, must they be present for emotional behavior to occur? The assertion that they must was of course James's major point. And if we look back at Cannon's major criticisms presented on page 273 and at our discussion of the juke box theory on page 289, we may reach the following conclusions. Cannon's criticism about the insensitivity of the viscera is relatively unimportant given the additional assumption that changes occurring in different parts of the autonomic nervous system may summate to produce emotional effects. Cannon's point that different emotions seem to be characterized by the same or similar visceral changes is well taken, and in conjunction with Schachter's experiment probably correct, but it does not deny the viscera an important controlling role over emotional behavior, even though they have been deprived of James' "nothing but" character. General discharge of the autonomic nervous system is one of the variables controlling most emotional behavior.

Cannon's argument that emotional behavior may be present in the absence of visceral activity will probably have to be restricted to saying that it will only be present when intact visceral structures and responses have previously mediated the link between environmental conditions and emotional behavior. Emotional behavior is probably absent or minimal when visceral discharge is absent during the acquisition of the behavior. Visceral response is important for the establishment, but not for the maintenance, of emotional behavior.

In the light of the evidence presented here, particularly in Schachter's experiments, there is no doubt that Cannon's statement that visceral changes alone, produced by artificial means, do not produce emotions (as James should have argued), is close to the truth. However, the data that have been accumulated in this connection, primarily by Marañon as early as 1924 and subsequently by other investigators, support our general conclusion that visceral changes of a rather diffuse character do partially control emotional behavior. Marañon and his successors found that people injected with adrenalin reported "as if" emotions. These subjects say that they feel as if they were afraid or as if they were awaiting some joyous events. We can properly call these partial emotions; the verbal statements are forthcoming, but the subject himself assigns rather low probabilities to them. As soon as the appropriate situational or instructional variables are provided—as in the Schachter experiments or by Marañon's talking to them about some emotional events—then the emotional behavior appears full blown and without the "as if" reservation.

We are left with one final criticism of Cannon's—that emotional reactions appear much more quickly than the visceral responses that, according to James, were supposed to have produced them. This criticism does of course apply to Schachter's experiments and our exposition as well. If the visceral response, whatever its character, is necessary for the production of emotional behavior, that behavior should not appear in full-blown form until the visceral response has been initiated. Introspective evidence at least seems to argue that emotional states do occur with much shorter latencies than could be predicted from such a position.

There are three possible solutions to this particular problem. One is that the introspective reports of emotional response are not too reliable. When they do seem to indicate emotional responses of rather short latencies they are simply reflections of a generalized startle response to emotional stimuli, and the response does not become complete until the visceral discharge 1-2 seconds later. Another possibility is that in adult subjects we are always dealing with experienced organisms whose reaction to emotional stimuli is already conditioned; the link between environment and emotional response has been provided prior to the particular situation that the psychologist happens to be investigating. In other words, familiar emotional stimuli immediately produce some aspect of the emotional response. Finally, we can suggest that frequent perception of visceral response leads to its symbolic representation. This means, in nontechnical terms, that after we have had much and varied experience with the visceral component of emotions, we can think about this kind of stimulation, about the internal upset that represents this kind of emotional experience, and we can do this with rather short latencies. Such a suggestion (Kessen

and Mandler, 1961) would require a slow process of development of emotional response from childhood to adulthood; as
we have more emotional experiences we are more likely to have
such cognitive emotions, just as after increased experience with
other kinds of stimuli we can eventually think about them and
manipulate them symbolically.

Both the second and third positions require a somewhat different emotional response in infancy from that of adulthood.
The evidence indicates that such is in fact the case and that we
can talk (as Schneirla has suggested) about a shift from a
Jamesian to a Cannonic position as the organism develops.
Particularly in the case of fear and the response to pain, the
evidence suggests that young children—especially during the
first year of life—have the kinds of long latencies of emotional
response to painful stimulation that a dependence upon the
occurrence of visceral discharge would demand. With experience—whether it is a simple conditioning of the emotional
response to environmental stimuli or whether it is a symbolic
representation of the visceral experience—emotional response
of long latency then shifts to the more immediate response
which presumably takes place in the adult.

 INDIVIDUAL DIFFERENCES

Even though we have discussed the various mechanisms involved in emotional behavior as if all people were not only
created but also preserved equal, and even though we dis-
avowed an interest in individual difference variables, the problem of individual variation in response to emotional stimuli
and in the expression of emotional behavior has intruded into
our discussion at several points. Obviously it is impossible to
discuss the psychology of a field as vast and varied as the
human emotions without some reference to one of the most

obvious facts of life—that in everyday experience people differ widely in their emotional behavior.

Psychologists have tended to treat the problem of individual differences from two extreme points of view. They have either suggested that individual differences are a nasty problem that keeps the devoted scientist from doing his research properly, and therefore require him to use large numbers of subjects so that statistical manipulation may wash out these differences, or they have implied that there really is nothing much *beyond* individual differences in the study of man and that once we have accounted for these we have accounted for all the really important variables in psychological investigations. The conjunction of the two positions is slowly coming to be the meeting point of psychological research. On the one hand we believe that important psychological laws or principles must be of such a nature that they apply to all people, and that therefore the "typical" demonstration of these principles is what we must pursue in the laboratory. On the other hand, the operation of these principles under the vast combination of circumstances of daily life and experience produces people who do in fact differ from one another—to the point where it is reasonable to say that no two of the two and one-half billion members of the species are alike or have been exposed to the same genetic and environmental influences. There are nothing but unique individuals, but there are no laws unique to individuals. Given this position, one can agree that in experiments on emotion, and particularly stress, the effects of experimental stress conditions "are dwarfed in significance by individual differences in response to stress conditions" and that "proper understanding of the effects of stress conditions requires knowledge of the characteristics of the individuals who are exposed to these conditions" (Lazarus and Baker, 1956).

What are the major points of influence of individual differences on the types of variables which we have discussed here? It will suffice to point out where and how these differences may affect emotional behavior without going into the vast area of theory and research that attempts to say how people come to differ in these ways, an area that would take in much of the contemporary psychology of personality.

We have already indicated that whether a particular environmental situation is perceived as emotional depends on the classificatory or coding behavior of the organism. The difference between the "bear in the open" and the "bear in the cage" depends on the prior experience of the person exposed to the two bears, as do reactions to mustachioed men or masculine women or St. Bernards or Chihuahuas. Whether various environmental conditions will control emotional behavior or visceral response depends on the prior experience of the person exposed to them.

At the visceral level, we have already mentioned Lacey's findings that different people show different, stable patterns of visceral response. Whether different patterns imply different visceral tonus and whether they are affected by experience are questions which we cannot definitely answer at the present time. The whole question of differential response of the autonomic nervous system, even disregarding patterns of response, is subject to further investigation.

Even assuming differential visceral response as a result of congenital or experiential factors, we do not know whether the same degree of visceral discharge has the same behavioral results in different people. Indications are that people perceive the actions of their viscera in different ways, so that some of us apparently overreact to such events, or pay more attention to them than others (Mandler and Kremen, 1958).

And, finally, we know that emotional expression, the consequent emotional behavior we are interested in, varies widely from person to person. We know that people have habitual ways of responding to so-called emotional or stressful situations, that some are cautious and unexpressive in the face of emotional stress, that others are impetuous and express their feelings easily, that some people tend to be aggressive, others dependent, that some attack the challenge, others withdraw from it. The whole question of people's control over their emotions, of defense mechanisms, of handling of impulses, falls under this rubric, and all these variables are naturally pertinent to the investigation of emotion.

These variables have not only concerned the clinical psychologist, the psychiatrist, and the personality theorist, but during the past fifteen years they have been successfully brought into the laboratory. The extensive literature on the measurement of individual differences in anxiety (Taylor, 1953; Mandler and Cowen, 1958; Sarason *et al.*, 1960) has opened up the whole problem of the measurement of individual differences in one emotional complex—anxiety. This line of approach suggests that people may differ in their level of anxiety, drive, or activation (Spence, 1956; Malmo, 1959) and in their susceptibility to interference from visceral activity and anxiety symptoms (Mandler and Sarason, 1952). The possibility that emotional stimuli, by activation of the autonomic nervous system, may lead to higher drive or activation levels is of course quite consistent with our discussion (cf. also Malmo, 1959; and Taylor, 1956). On the other hand such *activation*—indexed by the PGR and improved performance under some conditions—may be quite different from *emotionality* which may interfere with ongoing behavior, and is accompanied by increased visceral response and the usual signs of emotional upset (Mandler *et al.*, 1961).

The problem of the effect of emotion on other kinds of behavior such as simple or complex learning, examination efficiency, and social interaction is of course tied up with the problem of individual differences. We need not make any value judgments about emotions being good or bad, organizing or disorganizing, as long as we keep in mind that a veritable galaxy of variables is operating in the emotional complex, and that with the experienced human organism their effect will depend to a large extent on his previous history and constitutional make-up.

✦ THE PROBLEM OF ANXIETY

Our discussion of the emotional complex has veered more and more away from problems of euphoria and anger to problems of stress and anxiety. The reasons for this emphasis are two-fold: first, psychologists have probably spent more time and energy on problems of anxiety than on all the other emotional complexes taken together, and second, anxiety and fear are often considered to be examples of emotion *par excellence.* This position is somewhat paradoxical, since theoretically anxiety and fear have often been put into a category separate from the other emotions. This is particularly true in Freud's writings, where anxiety is primarily an ego function and not a derivative of the id and associated impulses. Modern learning theorists, also, have demonstrated that anxiety is a secondary drive without being able, generally, to demonstrate a similar role for other emotions.

In the framework of our present discussion, however, anxiety and fear seem to fit rather well. External stimuli (which elicit visceral responses and escape behavior) eventually are the occasions for avoidance behavior which is apparently mediated by visceral response. This latter interpretation—that the visceral response mediates avoidance behavior—is common to both modern learning theorists and the psychoanalytic school. Thus, Mowrer suggests that anxiety is based on an unpleasurable (to be escaped from) conditioned autonomic reaction, while Freud says that the three attributes of anxiety are its unpleasurable quality, discharge phenomena, and their perception (shades of William James!). He suggests later on that the increase in excitation (presumably including visceral excitation) "is responsible for [anxiety's] unpleasurable character" (Freud, 1936, p.70).

While all these positions seem to be consistent with our analysis of emotional behavior under the control of external and visceral events, they do include a new component which we shall have to consider, namely the unpleasurable quality of the visceral or autonomic discharge.

It is quite obvious that sympathetic discharge *per se*, even when artificially induced as in the Schachter experiments, does not produce reactions from human subjects that indicate any unpleasurable quality. And for the time being we can define as unpleasurable any event which produces escape or avoidance behavior. Certainly Schachter's euphoric or humorous conditions, which produced, if anything, pleasurable behavior from his subjects, would strongly argue against such a position. Furthermore, animal experiments indicate that the injection of adrenalin (and the production of sympathetic reactions) does not have any negative reinforcing properties, that is, the injection of adrenalin following a response does not lower its probability of occurrence. In a T-maze rats reacted to the injection of adrenalin indifferently (just as they did to an injection of dextrose); adrenalin had no effect on their choice behavior, whereas shock and histamine did have negative reinforcing effects (Sharpless, 1961).

The observation that sympathetic discharge has no obvious negative or unpleasurable effects must be contrasted with the finding that visceral responses and the acquisition of avoidance behavior are correlated (Black, 1959; Wynne and Solomon, 1955), and that small doses of adrenalin significantly increase the avoidance of shock in rats (Latané and Schachter, 1962). At the same time we cannot dismiss the possibility that massive autonomic discharge does have noxious effects. Particularly in the infant there does seem to be a correlation between distress and the presence of high degrees of visceral activity. Similarly, some visceral events, such as reverse peristalsis, do have unpleasurable qualities. The jury is still out as to the degree to which massive visceral activity *per se* may, particularly in the inexperienced organism, have noxious effects. It seems quite clear, however, that within rather wide ranges autonomic, particular sympathetic, activity does not have such effects.

One possible resolution in the present state of knowledge is to assume that while visceral activity does control activity and is not by itself noxious or unpleasurable, the direction of that control into avoidance or escape or even approach depends on other variables. This is, of course, the position of Schachter and of the juke box theory. Furthermore, even apparently similar stimuli and visceral reactions can have different emotional effects. The roller coaster effect discussed on page 311 is one such example. A more important one is the recently accumulated evidence (Barber, 1959; Melzack, 1961) that even conditions that have usually been accepted as obviously noxious, namely, painful stimuli acting on pain receptors or free nerve endings, may have quite varying effects depending on a multiplicity of experiential and situational factors. "Pain... refers to a category of complex experiences, not to a single sensation produced by a specific stimulus" (Melzack, 1961). It appears, therefore, that we must look elsewhere for the "noxious" control of escape or avoidance behavior and also for the source of unpleasure in anxiety and fear. None of this denies the role of visceral events in the control of emotional behavior; it does say that what kinds of behavior a particular visceral discharge will evoke depends on other variables.

It is quite beyond our present purpose to explore the kinds of mechanisms that may fullfill this "noxious" function. We might suggest that visceral responses, to the degree that they have been paired with noxious events, will also tend to have noxious effects. In other words, it is possible that when autonomic discharge has been paired with shock it will then mediate avoidance behavior. Another possibility, found throughout the personality and psychoanalytic literature, is that control over the onset and termination of the discharge is what determines its noxious aspects. Thus, in a roller coaster the rider determines whether to initiate the visceral discharge or not, and he may also have some control over or knowledge of its termination; at any rate, he can control the onset and predict the end of the loss of support. Similarly, Mowrer and Viek (1948) have shown that "fear is much greater in rats which cannot terminate . . . shock than in rats which can do so." The term "feeling of helplessness" has been used to refer to this particular variable, though control of onset and termination by the subject may be a more useful experimental device and probably covers the same ground as the more vague term "helplessness." But whatever combination of events turns out to be the important determiner of anxiety, we can now put it into the same grab-bag as the other emotions and at least assign environment and viscera joint responsibility for controlling this particular kind of emotional behavior.

Our trek through the wilderness of emotions has taken us from poor duped Harold Heartbeat to the problem of anxiety. All through our travels conventional psychological mechanisms have stood us in good stead—mainly the notions that behavior starts when something is presented to the organism, internally or externally, and that it stops when the conditions that have got it going are removed or changed. This kind of conventional wisdom is, of course, particularly applicable to problems of fear and anxiety. Before we close, we shall examine briefly an addendum to these assumptions—the notion that anxiety or distress sometimes occurs when behavior is interrupted and, more important, that some of the conditions that control or terminate distress may not necessarily involve flight from the evoking conditions.

The basic phenomena to be considered are twofold—first, the observation that young children, newborns in particular, often exhibit distress when there are no obvious antecedent conditions that seem to be controlling it. We have already referred to the immature nervous system of the newborn, and indicated that the variability and immaturity of the autonomic nervous system may be responsible for the squalling, obviously distressed infant who has just recently been fed and changed. We note further that children around the first six to twelve months often show signs of distress when their mother is absent for any appreciable length of time or when an unusual or previously unencountered adult enters their world. These two phenomena are usually referred to as separation and stranger anxiety. Secondly, we note what every mother knows, that distress, even when the controlling stimulus is not known, can be controlled by activities such as sucking and rocking.

In discussions of these most interesting characteristics of the emotional life of the newborn it has recently been suggested (Kessen and Mandler, 1961) that, apart from the flight-from-trauma interpretation of anxiety and fear, we might entertain the additional hypothesis that some events such as sucking and rocking have inhibitory powers over states of distress. In other

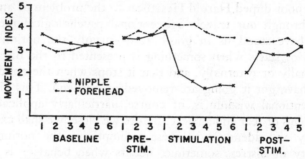

Fig. 7. Effect of nonnutritive sucking on movement in the human newborn. The units on the abcissa represent five seconds each comprising a 30-second baseline period, a 15-second period immediately preceding stimulation, a 30-second stimulation period, and a 25-second period following the cessation of stimulation. The ordinate shows an objective measure of movement of the infants obtained from continuous motion picture photography. The infants in the "nipple" group were given a nipple stuffed with cloth, the "forehead" control group were stimulated by slight rubbing on the forehead. The figure shows quite clearly a dramatic reduction in movement within five seconds of the insertion of the nipple and the onset of sucking.

words, even in the presence of hunger and cold, the sucking response is followed rather rapidly and effectively by quieting and a cessation of all the signs of distress. Thus, sucking and some other events are classed as inhibitors—simply to indicate that their onset is followed by the cessation or inhibition of distress or anxiety. One such dramatic example of the effects of nonnutritive sucking is shown in Figure 7, where the average activity of a group of newborns (four days old) drops drastically following the onset of the sucking response (Kessen and Leutzendorff, 1962). While we are only at the beginning of the exploration of these mechanisms and have little notion how far they apply to the adult, we can entertain the notion of mechanisms other than flight or removal of a noxious stimulus as reducing anxiety and distress. It has also been suggested that the absence of the mother (separation anxiety) can be viewed as the absence of a person who has been consistently paired with inhibition (sucking and rocking in particular) and that these manifestations of anxiety might be disinhibition phenomena. In other words, anxiety (and possibly some other emotions) occur not always because a traumatic event has taken place but sometimes because events that have served to inhibit and suppress distressful feelings and states have ceased to be present.

We have presented this last suggestion primarily to indicate that psychology is far from saying any final words on the topic of emotion. Much is yet to be discovered about the combination of events and behavior that determine the human activities classed as emotions.

THE PSYCHOLOGY OF EMOTION AND COMMON SENSE

In our introduction we suggested a common-sense definition of emotion that mentioned feelings and experiences, vague physical (visceral) sensations, and the things and people that make a person emotional, and we ended with a list of easily discernible and most certainly different emotions. How does the account given in the preceding pages square with this common-sense description?

In the first place, it appears that the prevalent notion that emotions are highly specific mental events, that they are *sui generis*, is not only typical of common-sense descriptions, but may also have ensnared the psychologist of emotion. Emotion is less a mental act than a chapter heading which summarizes many different aspects of behavior collected under the name emotional behavior. The particular combination of environmental events, physiological response, and prior experience that determines emotional behavior is often specific to that behavior, but it is unlikely that any special laws will have to be invoked for a peculiarly "emotional" explanation. At the same time it is too early to specify the laws that operate within the confines of emotional behavior. The major laws governing behavior—and thus emotional behavior—are still to be pronounced to the satisfaction of most psychologists. But the layman will be disappointed if he expects to find any special emotional "things" in those laws.

As far as the physical background of emotion is concerned, we can agree with common sense that some sort of internal, visceral response accompanies the production of emotional behavior. However, the notion that different kinds of visceral events—highly specific to each emotion—control this production is likely to be false, except for some very few special states such as disgust. The major *content* of our emotions is determined by the sort of things that go on around us, particularly the things people do and say to us.

We might speculate that the reason why people have for centuries tended to lump the different emotional states together may be found in the common visceral background of most emotions. The experience that holds these states together is the general visceral arousal—the state of physiological activity. We have seen that psychologists too have tended to use this phenomenon as a means of grouping emotional behavior. In everyday life we probably know that we are emotional because of some slight awareness of or response to the state of our guts; but how we feel specifically is controlled by external events and past experience.

Much is still to be learned about the determinants of emotional behavior. For the time being we know about some of the events that might push Harold Heartbeat or Peter Placid into one or another emotional crisis. The Schachter experiments and other current discoveries in the area indicate some of the variables and directions which are likely to be followed during the next few years, even though no definite goal or resolution may be in sight.

⊕ REFERENCES

Arnold, Magda B. *Emotion and personality.* (Vols. I and II) New York: Columbia Univ. Press, 1960.

Ax, A. The physiological differentiation between fear and anger in humans. *Psychosom. Med.* 1953, *15*, 433-442.

Barber, T. X. Toward a theory of pain: Relief of chronic pain by prefrontal leucotomy, opiates, placebos, and hypnosis. *Psychol. Bull.*, 1959, *56*, 430-460.

Black, A. H. Heart rate changes during avoidance learning in dogs. *Canad. J. Psychol.*, 1959, *13*, 229-242.

Bruner, J. S. On perceptual readiness. *Psychol. Rev.*, 1957, *64*, 123-152.

Brunswick, D. The effects of emotional stimuli on the gastro-intestinal tone. *J comp. Physiol.*, 1924, *4*, 19-79, 225-287.

Bykov, K. M. *The cerebral cortex and the internal organs.* New York: Chemical, 1957.

Cannon, W. B. *Bodily changes in pain, hunger, fear and rage.* (2nd edition) New York: Appleton-Century-Crofts, 1929.

Cannon, W. B. *The wisdom of the body*. New York: Norton, 1932.

Darrow, C. W. The galvanic skin reflex (sweating) and blood-pressure as preparatory and facilitative functions. *Psychol. Bull.*, 1936, *33*, 73-94.

Darwin, C. *The expression of the emotions in man and animals*. London: Murray, 1872.

Dollard, J., and F. Auld. *Scoring human motives*. New Haven: Yale Univ. Press, 1959.

Dollard, J., and N. E. Miller. *Personality and psychotherapy*. New York: McGraw-Hill, 1950.

Duffy, Elizabeth. The measurement of muscular tension as a technique for the study of emotional tendencies. *Amer. J. Psychol.*, 1932, *44*, 146-162.

Dunlap, K. Emotion as dynamic background. In M. L. Reymert (Ed.) *Feelings and emotion: The Wittenberg symposium*. Worcester: Clark Univ. Press, 1928.

Eriksen, C. W. Discrimination and learning without awareness: A methodological survey and evaluation. *Psychol. Rev.*, 1960, *67*, 279-300.

Freud, S. *The problem of anxiety*. New York: Norton, 1936.

Granda, A. M., and J. T. Hammack. Operant behavior during sleep. *Science*, 1961, *133*, 1485-1486.

Hebb, D. O. *The organization of behavior*. New York: Wiley, 1949.

Hsü, E. H. Comparative study of factor patterns, physiologically and psychologically determined. *J. gen. Psychol.*, 1952, *47*, 105-128.

James. W. What is an emotion? *Mind*, 1884, *9*, 188-205.

Kahn, M. A polygraph study of the catharsis of aggression. Unpublished doctoral dissertation, Harvard Univ. 1960.

Kessen, W., and Anne-Marie Leutzendorff. The effect of non-nutritive sucking on the movement of the human newborn. In preparation, 1962.

Kessen, W., and G. Mandler. Anxiety, pain, and the inhibition of distress. *Psychol. Rev.*, 1961, *68*, 396-404.

Lacey, J. I., and Beatrice C. Lacey. Verification and extension of the principle of autonomic response-stereotypy. *Amer. J. Psychol.*, 1958, 71, 50-73.

Landis, C., and W. A. Hunt. *The startle pattern.* New York: Farrar, 1939.

Lange, C. G., *Ueber Gemüthsbewegungen.* Leipzig: Theodor Thomas, 1887. (original Danish publication 1885; English translation in Lange, C. G., and W. James. *The emotions.* Baltimore: Williams & Wilkins, 1922).

Latané, B., and S. Schachter. Adrenalin and anticipatory avoidance. *J. comp. physiol. Psychol.*, 1962, in press.

Lazarus, R. S., and R. W. Baker. Personality and psychological stress—A theoretical and methodological framework. *Psychol. Newsletter*, 1956, 8, 21-32.

Lindsley, D. B. Emotion. In S.S. Smith (Ed.) *Handbook of experimental psychology.* New York: Wiley, 1951.

Mahl, G. F. Exploring emotional states by content analysis. In I. Pool (Ed.) *Trends in content analysis.* Urbana: Univ. of Illinois Press, 1959.

Malmo, R. B. Activation: A neuropsychological dimension. *Psychol. Rev.*, 1959, 66, 367-386.

Mandler, G. Response factors in human learning. *Psychol. Rev.*, 1954, 61, 235-244.

Mandler, G., and Judith E. Cowen. Test anxiety questionnaires. *J. consult. Psychol.*, 1958, 22, 228-229.

Mandler, G., and M. Kahn. Discrimination of changes in heart rate: Two unsuccessful attempts. *J. exp. Anal. Behav.*, 1960, 3, 21-25.

Mandler, G., and W. Kessen. *The language of psychology.* New York: Wiley, 1959.

Mandler, G., and I. Kremen. Autonomic feedback: A correlational study. *J. Pers.*, 1958, 26, 388-399; 1960, 28, 545.

Mandler, G., Jean M. Mandler, I. Kremen, and R.D. Sholiton. The response to threat: Relations among verbal and physiological indices. *Psychol. Monogr.*, 1961, 75, No. 9 (Whole No. 513).

Mandler, G., Jean M. Mandler, and Ellen T. Uviller. Autonomic feedback: The perception of autonomic activity. *J. abnorm. soc. Psychol.*, 1958, *56*, 367-373.

Mandler, G., and S. B. Sarason. A study of anxiety and learning. *J. abnorm. soc. Psychol.*, 1952, *47*, 166-173.

Marañon, G. Contribution a l'étude de l'action émotive de l'adrenalin. *Rev. Franc. D'endocrinol.*, 1924, *2*, 301-325.

May, R., E. Angel, and H. F. Ellenberger (Eds.). *Existence: A new dimension in psychiatry and psychology.* New York: Basic Books, 1958.

Melzack, R. The perception of pain. *Scient. Amer.*, 1961, *204*, 41-49.

Mowrer, O. H. On the dual nature of learning: A reinterpretation of "conditioning" and "problem solving." *Harv. educ. Rev.*, 1947, *17*, 102-148.

Mowrer, O. H., and P. Viek. An experimental analogue of fear from a sense of helplessness. *J. abnorm. soc. Psychol.*, 1948, *43*, 193-200.

Nowlis, V. On the use of drugs in the analysis of complex human behavior with emphasis on the study of mood. In R. A. Patton (Ed.) *Current trends in the description and analysis of behavior.* Pittsburgh: Univ. Pittsburgh, 1958.

Sarason, S. B., K. S. Davidson, F. F. Lighthall, R. R. Waite, and B. K. Ruebush. *Anxiety in elementary school children.* New York: Wiley, 1960.

Sartre, J. P. *The emotions: Outline of a theory.* New York: Philosophical Library, 1948.

Schachter, S., and J. E. Singer. Cognitive, social and physiological determinants of emotional state. *Psychol. Rev.*, 1962, in press.

Schachter, S., and L. Wheeler. Epinephrine, chlorpromazine and amusement. *J. abnorm. soc. Psychol.*, 1962, in press.

Schlosberg, H. The description of facial expressions in terms of two dimensions. *J. exp. Psychol.*, 1952, *44*, 229-237.

Schneirla, T. R. An evolutionary and developmental theory of biphasic processes underlying approach and withdrawal. In

M. R. Jones (Ed.) *Nebraska symposium on motivation: 1959.* Lincoln: Univ. of Nebraska Press, 1959.

Sharpless, S. K. Effects of intravenous injections of epinephrine and norepinephrine in a choice situation. *J. comp. physiol. Psychol.,* 1961, *54,* 103-108.

Skinner, B. F. *The behavior of organisms.* New York: Appleton-Century-Crofts, 1938.

Skinner, B. F. The operational analysis of psychological terms. *Psychol. Rev.,* 1945, *52,* 270-277.

Spence, K. W. *Behavior theory and conditioning.* New Haven: Yale Univ. Press, 1956.

Taylor, Janet A. A personality scale of manifest anxiety. *J. abnorm. soc. Psychol.,* 1953, *48,* 285-290.

Taylor, Janet A. Drive theory and manifest anxiety. *Psychol. Bull.,* 1956, *53,* 303-320.

Traxel, W. Die Möglichkeit einer objektiven Messung der Stärke von Gefühlen. *Psychol. Forsch.,* 1960, *26,* 75-90.

Welch, E. P. *The philosophy of Edmund Husserl.* New York: Columbia Univ. Press, 1941.

Wenger, M. A. Emotion as visceral action: An extension of Lange's theory. In M. L. Reymert (Ed.) *Feelings and emotions.* New York: McGraw-Hill, 1950.

Woodworth, R. S., and H. Schlosberg. *Experimental psychology.* (Rev. ed.) New York: Holt, 1954.

Wolf, S., and H. G. Wolff. *Human gastric function.* New York: Oxford Univ. Press, 1943.

Wynne, L. C., and R. L. Solomon. Traumatic avoidance learning: Acquisition and extinction in dogs deprived of normal peripheral autonomic functioning. *Genet. Psychol. Monogr.,* 1955, *52,* 241-284.

✦ INDEX